Microwave Handbook

VOLUME 1

COMPONENTS AND OPERATING

Edited by M. W. Dixon, G3PFR

Radio Society of Great Britain

Published by the Radio Society of Great Britain, Cranborne Road, Potters Bar, Herts EN6 3JE.

First published 1989
Reprinted 1991

Figures 4.60 and 4.74 are the copyright of Pitman Publishing, from Williams' *Antenna Theory & Design*, Vol 2, and permission for their use has been granted.

ISBN 0 900612 88 6 (set of three volumes)
      0 900612 89 4 (volume one)

ERRATA

The following corrections should be noted:

1. Page 2.19, column 1, paragraph following 13. The latitude for Edinburgh Castle should read "55°56.5′N" (shown as "50°56.5′N").

2. Page 2.24, column 2, Program 3. The line numbered 880 should read:

    M=FNA(6)*2.5+1.25

    (It is shown as   M=FNA(6)*2.5*1.25)

3. Page 5.5, column 1. The two equations obscured during printing should read:

$$\lambda = \frac{2\pi}{w\sqrt{LC}}$$

$$V = \frac{1}{\sqrt{LC}}$$

Cover design by Linda Penny, Radio Society of Great Britain.
Printed in Great Britain by Bath Press Ltd, Lower Bristol Road, Bath BA2 3BL.

Acknowledgements

The principal contributors to Volume 1 were as follows:

Chapter 1 (Introduction) – M Dixon, G3PFR, and J N Gannaway, G3YGF.

Chapter 2 (Operating techniques) – M Dixon, G3PFR, and J N Gannaway, G3YGF.

Chapter 3 (System analysis and propagation) – B Chambers, G8AGN.

Chapter 4 (Microwave antennas) – M H Walters, G3JVL.

Chapter 5 (Transmission lines and components) – S J Davies, G4KNZ/ZL2AZQ, and J N Gannaway, G3YGF.

Chapter 6 (Microwave semiconductors and valves) – S J Davies, G4KNZ/ZL2AZQ, and J N Gannaway, G3YGF.

Acknowledgement is also made to other members of the RSGB Microwave Committee and many others who have helped in the writing and compilation of this book, in particular to:

Committee or past-committee members: G4DDK, G4FRE, G4CNV, G3WDG, G4KGC, G4FSG, G3RPE, G3PHO, G3HWR, G4KNZ.

Non-committee members: G4MBS, G8MWR, G3SEK, OE9PMJ, DC8UG, G3BNL, Mr S Page, GW3XYW, G3LQR, G3JHM, OZ9CR, G4PMK, G4HUP, G8TIR, G4COM, G8DEK, G4DDN, G6WWM, HB9MIN, N W Kent Beacon Group.

We would also like to acknowledge material and assistance from the following book, journals and companies: Donald C. Livingston, *The Physics of Microwave Propagation*, © 1970, pp 15, 16, 109, 110, 111, 113. Reprinted by permission of Prentice-Hall, Inc, Englewood Cliffs, N. J. *Radio Communication, Wireless World, Microwaves, Microwave system News, Microwave Journal, DUBUS-Info, VHF Communications*, Andrew Corporation, Hewlett-Packard, Mitsubishi Electric UK and Omni-Spectra.

The typesetting of the book was undertaken by S J Davies, G4KNZ/ZL2AZQ.

Contents

Preface

Since the last edition of the well-known *RSGB VHF/UHF Manual* in 1983 there has been an almost explosive growth in amateur microwave techniques, designs and devices available, some of them so new that amateur exploitation has barely caught up with the technology available! All this has led to increased band occupancy and to some quite startling practical results. The last two editions of the *VHF/UHF Manual* were the first such publications to contain a significant chapter on microwaves. This chapter was widely accepted as a terse but informative guide to amateur microwave practices.

The need for a microwave handbook was recognised as long ago as the second half of the 'seventies by the late Dain Evans, G3RPE, then chairman of the RSGB Microwave Committee. Work on the book and its contents started around 1981-2, and continued fairly spasmodically until mid-1985 when the committee made determined efforts to complete the work. This was at a time when many new devices and techniques, arising largely from the consumer electronics industry, started to become available, and many were attractive to the microwave enthusiast.

This is our first attempt to collect the information and experience available and to collate it into a handbook. In such a rapidly changing field it is difficult to produce a comprehensive book which is also up-to-date. We have tried to achieve this by involving a large number of authors and by giving each the responsibility for a chapter or part chapter, as appropriate.

This may have resulted in differing styles but was felt to be the best way of obtaining up-to-date information. One aspect of microwave operation which we have not attempted to cover in an integrated chapter is space and eme. This is because it was felt that it would be difficult, costly and time consuming for the average amateur to build and operate a station with this capability, without first gaining some terrestrial communications experience at microwave frequencies. It was thus felt more appropriate, at this stage, to introduce the basic concepts in more detail than was previously possible in the *VHF/UHF Manual*. For this reason also, it is hoped that the mixture of theoretical and practical topics presented will be of direct interest and use to readers, and will form a firm foundation on which to build their experience.

This book's compilation has consumed a large part of the effort of the Microwave Committee for the past few years and we hope that the outcome will encourage more design, constructional and operating activity, and result in further articles for *Radio Communication* and the *Microwave Newsletter*.

Mike Dixon, G3PFR
Chairman (1989–90) Microwave Committee

Dain Evans, G3RPE, who was instrumental in conceiving this handbook, died just before publication of the first volume. As a mark of respect this handbook is dedicated to his memory.

RSGB Microwave Committee

RSGB microwave support

In common with all national societies, RSGB fulfils many roles in amateur radio. The hobby is unique in that it is governed by international legislation which is interpreted at national level to conform to the particular needs of each country. These individual needs cannot be considered in isolation, for radio communication transcends national boundaries. Microwave activities are now no exception. Thus the Society's interests and work have at least two major facets: national and international. Furthermore it has to represent the interests of the hobby against a background of widely ranging frequency allocations and fierce competition for this spectrum space. As amateurs, therefore, we have to be "professional" in this competitive world, a task which is not always easy for "part-timers" and hobbyists!

Again, microwaves are no exception: here our activities are probably under the scrutiny of the most demanding of professional eyes and in a region of the spectrum where competition is currently strongest.

Accordingly, the "governing body" of the Society – its Council – relies increasingly upon the specialist input in this area from its spectrum committees (the HF, VHF/UHF and Microwave Committees) and the Licensing Advisory Committee concerning licensing matters, as well as support from other committees on such matters as the planning and standards of beacons and repeaters, operating modes and standards, propagation, education and many other aspects of this exceedingly diverse hobby.

What has all this got to do with introducing this microwave handbook? Simply that people will not be made aware of what goes on "behind the scenes" by reading the technical content of the book! In the next few paragraphs there follows a brief sketch of some of the seen and unseen activities which support our enjoyment of the facilities available in the microwave spectrum.

Communicating information

The UK is somewhat unique in that most microwave information has, until recently, been communicated via the Society's journal: this is in quite stark contrast to Germany, for instance, where there are several internationally circulated, independent, commercial publications directed specifically to vhf and above. Two notable publications are *VHF Communications* and *DUBUS Informationen*, both of which have made very significant contributions to the microwave scene, often with commercial backing in the form of self-build kits. As will be seen, there are now parallels within the UK, with better information communication taking place than in earlier years: this handbook is part of it, as is the *Microwave Newsletter* mentioned later.

Radio Communication

Apart from an occasional article of microwave interest in the Society's journal, the needs of the microwave enthusiast were rather neglected until Dain Evans, G3RPE, started a regular special-interest column entitled "1,000MHz and up" (now simply "Microwaves") in 1970. He compiled and wrote the column until 1978. The purpose of the column was to present a mixture of operating news, views and achievements, short technical articles and, from time to time, to try to summarise the international microwave scene. It was, indeed, the first regular feature column to carry proven technical content in addition to the news and views of members.

Charles Suckling, G3WDG, took over writing the column in 1978 and continued until 1984, maintaining the now traditional mixture of contents.

From 1984 to the present date, the task was taken over by Mike Dixon, G3PFR, who continues to provide topical news and views. The content of the column has changed slightly over the past three years, with a little less accent on the technical, and more on operating and licensing/planning and policy matters. The reasons for this are that, first, the regular *Microwave Newsletter*, compiled and edited by Microwave Committee members, had made its appearance and become firmly established. Second, the space available in *Radio Communication* was no longer sufficient to contain many of the technical items generated by either committee members or other microwave enthusiasts. Third, pressure on this part of the spectrum has meant much time spent in planning to accommodate both professional and new amateur needs.

The Microwave Newsletter

The *Microwave Newsletter* was started as a news sheet in early 1980 by Julian Gannaway, G3YGF, Steve Davies,

G4KNZ, and Hugh Griffiths, G4CNV, originally as a means for co-ordinating nationwide activity for the then fairly new 10GHz Cumulative Contests. It was started as a private venture concentrating on operating news, but soon expanded to include more technical material, initially on the practical aspects of operating techniques such as portable operation, beam setting, path calculations and like subjects. It grew to include both speculative and reproducible equipment designs. As a result of continuing growth, production and distribution became such a large task that it was taken over by RSGB HQ staff in 1981. The original authors, members of the Microwave Committee, continued to compile and edit it, thus confirming the committee's responsibility for the *Newsletter*.

As a result of many requests for back numbers, the technical content of the newsletters was gathered together to form the somewhat impromptu *Microwave Newsletter Technical Collection* which was published in 1983. This publication was, in many ways, the forerunner of this handbook, just as the *Microwave Newsletter* was the forerunner of the other specialist newsletters now published by RSGB. It was the response to both the *Newsletter* and the *Technical Collection* which brought home the need for a more comprehensive microwave manual and at the same time provided the impetus for its completion.

In 1985, the compiling and editing of the *Newsletter* was taken over by other members of the committee – Peter Day, G3PHO, and Barry Chambers, G8AGN – a voluntary task which is still quite demanding on time and resource, despite the main printing and distribution being done by RSGB HQ staff. They rely heavily on topical and technical input from members to maintain quality and interest.

The Microwave Committee Components Service

In parallel with the development of the *Newsletter*, the growth of interest in narrowband working on 10GHz had highlighted the need to make certain critical components for these designs more readily available to the constructor. These were supplied initially in small quantities by the *Newsletter* editors, G3YGF, G4KNZ and G4CNV, as a privately financed service. However, in order to meet the increasing demand and to expand the range of components stocked, in 1983 the committee obtained funding from RSGB in the form of a loan to run the Microwave Committee Components Service. The service has been very successful and additional capital has since been invested to increase the range of components still further.

The stock-holding, packaging and despatch aspects of the service are handled, on a voluntary basis, by committee members. The types and sources of components stocked are chosen by the committee. Bulk ordering, incoming orders, invoicing and accounting are all carried out by RSGB HQ staff. The service is financially controlled so that all administrative and postal costs are covered, and any (very) marginal operating profit made from the advantages of bulk purchasing are put back into slowly expanding the service.

The quality and nature of the service, as with the *Newsletter*, is very dependent upon input from its users: the stocklist is published periodically in the *Newsletter* and users of the service are asked for their opinions as to what new components should be considered for introduction. The service does not aim to either compete with existing suppliers or to carry stocks of components which are easily accessible to the constructor, but to provide an easy source from which Society members can obtain the more esoteric, hard-to-obtain components.

Latterly, as well as stocking the "traditional" components such as microwave mixers, detectors, multiplier diodes, chip resistors and capacitors, a limited range of newer devices such as GaAsfets, microwave monolithic integrated circuits (mmics), prescaler chips, precision power terminations, 24GHz mixer/oscillator modules and pcb material has been introduced – partly to promote the more widespread use of such components and partly to support many of the newer designs and ideas incorporated into this book.

Exhibitions and "round tables"

The committee believes that exhibitions and "round tables" are an important means of encouraging home construction and activity, particularly on the higher microwave bands. Levels of activity are still fairly low and tend to occur in widely scattered but quite definite areas – usually as the result of the enthusiasm of one or two local "gurus"! Both types of event provide an opportunity for microwave enthusiasts from widely spread geographical areas to meet each other and exchange views, ideas and experiences directly. They also give an opportunity to meet members of the Microwave Committee (and vice versa!).

The exhibitions provide something of a "shop-window" for the microwave fraternity: formal committee displays and specialist lectures/demonstrations are usually arranged. Members of the Microwave Committee and many other RSGB committees are present to assist in answering members' (and non-members') queries and problems.

"Round tables", on the other hand, are very specialist gatherings, usually arranged by kind permission of a large professional organisation, such as a university department or commercial research establishment, who also make available a range of professional testgear to help amateurs align and test their equipment. With increasing complexity and standards of performance expected, access to professional testgear at some stage is becoming more important. The "round tables" also present the opportunity for more-experienced amateurs to provide advice and technical assistance to the less-experienced newcomers: there is obviously a need to develop designs for simple "homebrew" testgear which can be calibrated against professional test equipment – an opportunity which occurs at these meetings.

Details of both exhibitions and "round tables" are periodically announced in both the *Newsletter* and the *Radio Communication* column, as are reports of the meetings.

Other areas of support

Circuit development

At the time of rapid development of narrowband techniques at 10GHz (and below) there was a need for a high-quality uhf local oscillator source suitable for multiplying up to the microwave bands. The task of designing a pcb circuit was undertaken by members of the committee and culminated in a very successful design which was written up for *Radio Communication* in 1981. This still forms the basis for many microwave designs, including many of those found within this book. Other, as yet unpublished, designs will also be found here.

Promotion of design and construction

In trying to encourage new design and thinking, some of the equipment designs in the following pages are quite speculative, although the vast majority are well proven and reproducible. The committee will actively support any *sound* technical developments in the amateur field by:

(a) promoting design and construction contests and awards;

(b) investigating and further developing new designs, as might be necessary;

(c) being prepared to expand and write up any significant new designs for publication in either the *Newsletter* or *Radio Communication*.

However, it must be stressed that the committee and its members cannot, and should not, originate all the ideas and developments. It therefore looks to the general membership who experiment and use the microwave bands to feed back information on their successful designs.

Assessment and "editorial" activity

It has been found that one of the main hindrances to the publication of good technical articles is that, while the experienced or imaginative microwave amateur may spend a great deal of time in designing, building and operating new equipment, he or she is often not prepared to put pen to paper (or fingers to word processors!) in enough detail to produce a comprehensive account of what has been achieved. Thus much valuable amateur work goes unrecorded and unpublished, or may be passed on in the form of hastily scribbled notes and diagrams. It is the committee's intention that any worthwhile design or constructional work which comes to its notice will find a place in the *Newsletter, Radio Communication* or ultimately in later editions of this handbook! It goes without saying that current and topical operating news will find its place in our publications as proof that amateur experimentation on the microwave bands is alive and well and no longer the province of the dedicated few.

Promotion of operating

Microwave operation is encouraged and supported in two main ways. First, by the organisation of operating contests and activity periods, some of which are specifically microwave, such as the microwave and 10GHz Cumulatives, and some of which are part of larger, national events, such as the VHF National Field Day. Further activity is encouraged by coordinating national events, as far as possible, with international (IARU sponsored) events.

Second, by the provision of various awards and certificates to mark many different levels of operating achievement. In addition, some of the more prestigious awards are sponsored by professional organisations operating internationally in the fields of microwave systems and manufacture; their recognition and support of amateur effort, in many ways, is proof enough of the value and credibility of amateur microwave endeavour. Long may this relationship last!

In the past, microwave operation has been largely from portable sites and this has tended to limit the level of activity and restrict operation to the contests or activity periods. We wish to encourage home station operation on all of the bands so that more regular activity is generated – even if the distances worked are not as great. If you have equipment for the bands, *use it!* Seek every opportunity to operate, for only in this way will you get maximum use and enjoyment out of the equipment and maybe achieve what you thought was impossible.

Support from outside the committee

It would be very inward looking if we did not make acknowledgement of the contributions made by the many individual amateurs and organisations who in their turn support the committee and the Society. This mutual support comes by organising local activity days and helping to organise more general events; by creating activity by actually operating in these events; by regular operating and reporting of results; by organising and partaking in local microwave discussion nets (usually on a vhf band); by building, installing, running and maintaining beacons and beacon/repeaters; by organising "round tables" and helping to organise other exhibitions; by organising dxpeditions; by encouraging others to "have a go" and, where necessary, showing them how; and finally to those who sponsor and make awards possible.

It would be impossible to name them all, but the committee would like in particular to acknowledge the support of The Marconi Company, Mullard Ltd, Alpha Industries, Microwave Associates and Plessey Ltd for sponsoring awards or assisting in component supplies; British Telecom and the Martlesham Radio Society, IBA (Crawley Court), Sheffield University Radio Society and YTV Leeds for organising "round tables"; the Department of Trade and Industry (Radio Regulatory Division) for relaxation of the terms of the UK amateur licence to allow unattended and digital modes, and the use of cw by Class B licensees under all operating conditions (especially important in the microwave bands); to clubs and groups of active amateurs all over the country who regularly support the contests and activity periods; to BATC, *Practical Wireless* and G8MWR and his Microwave Society for encouraging many new amateurs into microwave operation using the simpler wideband techniques at 10GHz and latterly at 24GHz.

Mike Dixon, G3PFR, and Julian Gannaway, G3YGF

CHAPTER 1

Introduction

Increasing numbers of amateurs are spending their leisure time in acquiring the knowledge and skills necessary to build and operate the equipment needed in a microwave station. This is the region of the electromagnetic spectrum where the otherwise ubiquitous "black box" has yet to spread, although there are signs of an impending invasion at least on some of the bands! The microwave field is thus still an area where home construction is dominant, either in designing and building from scratch or modifying surplus microwave equipment to suit a particular need. It is also an area of amateur endeavour where there is still considerable scope for originality, improvisation and some compromise.

Much of the enthusiasm expressed in this handbook dates back to exploratory work carried out from the early 'seventies onwards by many of its contributors. Many of their results and developments have been published or summarised in the Society's journal *Radio Communication* over the intervening years, although much has gone unrecorded.

Just as in the very early days of amateur radio, when the question was "What use are radio waves shorter than 200m?", the question today might be "What use are radio waves of frequency above 30HGz?". Why should the amateur be interested in frequencies which have traditionally been associated with line-of-sight are now possible on may of the microwave bands by tropospheric modes, both enhancement and forward scatter, and by the eme path. The current ranges, which may be both marginal and unreliable in professional terms, are likely to be extended on a more reliable basis by means of amateur terrestrial networks and satellites. Indeed, the potential for reliable communication, if developed in the right way, is much higher than at the lower frequencies where worldwide communication depends on the vagaries of the ionosphere.

in contrast to the lower-frequency bands, the results obtained are usually more dependent on the individual amateur's imagination, persistence, dedication and effort, rather than the depth of his or her pocket. It is true that most people will need to acquire and develop special constructional and operating skills, but this is the essence of amateur radio!

The size of the challenge extends from a little over 1GHz to 240GHz, thus presenting the opportunity to exercise many and diverse techniques. To climb the small hill from uhf to lower microwaves is only one fairly easy step, although even this presents its own problems! To progress beyond the "foothills" to the "high peaks" requires both special techniques and special equipment: neither are impossible to attain, as we will show.

This book discusses both theoretical and practical subjects - most of the volume is devoted to a largely non-mathematical explanation of active and passive microwave components, and this is followed in volumes 2 and 3 by much practical information on equipment for all the bands in current use. This volume comprises chapters 1 to 6 inclusive.

Chapter 2 covers practical aspects of microwave operating. The techniques are very different to those on the lower bands, and it is much more difficult to establish contacts due to the fundamental need for high-gain antennas, leading to narrow antenna beamwidths.

Chapter 3 deals with all aspects of systems analysis and propagation. An understanding of these topics will greatly improve the chances of making contacts over previously untried paths.

Chapter 4 discusses antennas and their design. By far the greatest gains or losses are to be had by designing good or bad antenna systems! They are much more important than those at low frequencies. Much practical advice on mast and rigging is included.

Chapter 5 covers transmission lines and passive components, while Chapter 6 covers active components. Successful construction and use is unlikely without a basic understanding of the function of components.

Volume 2 follows on naturally from volume 1 and comprises chapters 7 to 13 inclusive. Chapter 7 deals with constructional techniques. Many professional designs call for expensive, close-tolerance machining or pcb production. Our aim here is to show how good results can be achieved by fairly elementary "workshop" methods translated into "kitchen table" (or garage workbench) techniques, which are much more appropriate for the amateur constructor.

Chapter 8 presents designs for many modules which are common to most bands, for instance local oscillator sources and amplifiers.

Chapter 9 covers beacons and repeaters. Because of relatively low levels of activity (compared with vhf and uhf bands), beacons and beacon/repeaters are essential for indicating conditions and setting up equipment. Some ideas and practical examples of beacon constructions are given, as well as the UK licensing and operational requirements for both beacons and beacon/repeaters, current at the time of going to press. Of course, licensing conditions must always be checked with the appropriate licensing authority before proceeding with beacon or repeater design and building.

Chapter 10 describes simple, home-built test gear which can be used to test and align microwave equipment. Some band-specific equipment and techniques will also be found in Chapters 14 to 19 where appropriate. It is important to try to design equipment so that it can be easily aligned using simple test gear which the amateur can build or own. However, this might mean developing a very different approach to alignment compared with that used by those with regular access to professional test equipment.

Chapter 11 considers safety aspects. Serious microwave operating requires a large effort in engineering a good (and safe) mast/antenna system. Other mechanical aspects of safety must be considered. The operator also needs to be aware of the possible dangers of high rf fields, even though the actual hazards have been greatly exaggerated by the media.

Chapter 12 covers filters, and the remarks earlier regarding Chapters 5 and 6 are also applicable here.

Chapter 13 is a "pot-pourri" of data of all kinds, from several sources. The prime sources of information are indicated so that the reader can seek more information should this prove necessary. It is often possible to gain access to such publications through a public library reference section or by obtaining copies from a national library, such as the British Library. Your public library should be able to advise you how to go about this.

The final volume contains Chapters 14 to 20 inclusive which give designs for all the bands between 1.3 and 24GHz, selecting the best, most reliable and most easily constructed designs at present in use. Some of the practical designs may be regarded as "old" technology. However, state-of-the-art techniques are still largely unproven in terms of feasibility and reliability for the amateur with limited resources, whereas the older technology is known to be feasible with modest resources and gives the maximum probability of success. It is for these reasons that some of these well-proven concepts have been gathered together here.

Chapter 20, dealing with the bands above 24GHz, is largely speculative, since there has been very little practical experience gained on these new bands. It is hoped that this situation will have changed radically before this handbook is due for revision!

In presenting this book, the Society's first microwave handbook, the authors have been aiming at a moving target in several ways: an expanding amateur movement, an increasing awareness of the potential microwave communication (by both amateurs and professionals!), and expanding environment of ideas and novel components and last, but not least, the need for learning and self-education in an increasingly technologically aware society. On the other hand, the basics have changed little: it is hoped that this manual will provide both a firm foundation in fundamentals and at the same time provide some impetus for more amateurs to experience and enjoy the microwave bands.

CHAPTER 2

Operating techniques

2.1 INTRODUCTION

Microwave operation should not be regarded simply as an extension of the operating techniques practised on the lower-frequency bands. Although some similarities do exist, there are many more ways in which practical microwave operation differs from the "norm" and it is the purpose of this chapter to outline these differences.

In general it is possible for the amateur to easily generate high powers only on the two lowest frequency bands, viz 1.3 and 2.3GHz. On 3.4GHz and above, the amateur is often confined to power levels which these days are regarded as "QRP"; that is, output levels of between a few milliwatts and, say, 10W. Feeder losses increase rapidly with frequency (hence the use of waveguide at the higher frequencies). These limitations are offset to some extent by using high-gain antenna systems, short lengths of high-quality feeder, and low-noise receive preamplifiers, usually built around gallium arsenide fets and mounted at or very close to the antenna. Transmit multipliers may also be sited at or close to the antenna.

These facts, coupled with financial and other considerations, may determine whether the majority of the operation is from a fixed-station location or portable from hill-top sites. The advantages of a better site can often outweigh the disadvantages of low powers and other equipment limitations.

One very significant facet of microwave operation which is different to practices on other bands is that under "normal" conditions involving line-of-sight or troposcatter propagation, not only should the equipment capability be quite closely known but also the path losses can be quite accurately assessed (see Chapter 3, "Systems analysis", and later in this chapter).

However, unknown factors such as obstructions or enhanced modes of propagation often provide the amateur with the thrill and excitement of working other stations at unexpected signal strengths and distances.

The contents of this chapter are divided into six main sections which deal with procedures, fixed-station operating, portable operating, awards, certificates and contests, the use of calculation and, finally, simple computing as an aid to operating.

2.2 OPERATING PROCEDURES

2.2.1 Comparison with vhf/uhf

The equipment and some of the operating techniques needed to establish a contact on the microwave bands can be very different to those used at hf and vhf. The antennas used are highly directional and the general level of activity is much lower.

High-gain (and hence highly directional) antennas are an essential feature of most microwave stations because they are necessary to compensate for the much weaker signals which would be received by a dipole, which is physically much smaller at these frequencies. Feeder losses are higher, and transmitters and receivers often less "potent" than on the lower bands.

Although, on some of the shorter line-of-sight paths, signals may be strong enough to be found easily using the techniques common on the hf/vhf bands, many paths will be either obstructed or of such a length that the signals will not be much above noise even when all the antennas and equipment are correctly aligned, and in these cases a systematic approach is almost essential to guarantee success. Operating protocols are discussed in section 2.2.3 but it is probably wise at this point to summarise the main conditions to be met to "guarantee" a contact:

1. *The equipment must be capable of overcoming the path loss*, so it must be reliable and its performance known; this should be established before use. The path losses are often fairly predictable and can be calculated beforehand to give the operator some idea of the likely levels of signal to be expected.

2. *Both stations must have their antennas pointed at each other to within the beamwidths*. Using higher-gain antennas or working at higher frequencies both reduce the antenna beamwidths, so that they have to be pointed more accurately. This requires knowledge of the locations of both stations, calculation of the beam headings and a means of setting them. The beamwidths of some typical antennas are given in Table 2.1.

3. *The receiver must be set to within its bandwidth of the transmit frequency.* Improvements in both receiver and

Table 2.1. Comparison of antenna gains and beamwidths for various bands

Antenna	Band (MHz)	Gain (dB)	Beamwidth (degrees)
16-ele Yagi	144	16	24
17ft dish	144	16	26
20ft dish	432	26	8
25-ele loop Yagi	432	19	18
30ft dish	432	30	5
4 x loop Yagi	1,296	24	10
6ft dish	1,296	25	9
1ft dish	10GHz	28	7
4ft dish	10GHz	40	1.7
1ft dish	24GHz	35	3
4ft dish	24GHz	47	0.7

Table 2.2. Marker frequency accuracies and marker crystal characteristics

Accuracy	Frequency	Fractional accuracy
100Hz	432MHz	2 parts in 10^7
1kHz	1,296MHz	8 parts in 10^7
1kHz	10GHz	1 part in 10^7
100kHz	10GHz	1 part in 10^5
1kHz	24GHz	4 parts in 10^8
100kHz	24GHz	4 parts in 10^6

Typical tolerances of crystals

As built in circuit	±30ppm	3 parts in 10^5
Variation with temp (0-60°)	±30ppm	3 parts in 10^5
Best case (10-30°)		2 parts in 10^6
Ovened crystal		1 part in 10^8
Off-air standard		1 part in 10^{10} to 10^{11}

transmitter stability have resulted in the use of narrower bandwidths at higher frequencies, so that frequencies need to be measured more accurately. Both stations should have a reference available with which frequencies can be set to a fraction of the receiver bandwidth. Table 2.2 gives the accuracies required for some of the typical modes and frequencies and a means of achieving them.

4. *The transmitter must be on when the receiving station is listening for it!* Thus a strict protocol should be adopted to ensure this state of affairs.

If all these conditions are followed, then a test should just consist of listening: when the path loss falls to a value which the equipment can overcome, signals will be heard. This may all seem very obvious, but many of the developments which improve the performance of amateur equipment, for instance higher-gain antennas and narrower bandwidths, also make these requirements harder to meet.

If the operator must do something while listening, then tuning the receiver over a *few* bandwidths is acceptable and can help concentration. In practice, most people seem to relax one or two of these conditions considerably, usually by tuning a considerable distance on the receiver, and searching with the antenna heading. One can get away with this if the signals are fairly strong and consistent, but the chances of finding a weak or fading signal are greatly reduced. Consider the number of possible combinations of frequency and beam direction in the following example (on 10GHz):

Receiver bandwidth:	300kHz
Tuning range:	30MHz, giving 100 possible channels
Antenna beamwidth:	3°
Uncertainty in direction:	15°, giving five different headings

Thus there are $5 \times 100 = 500$ possible combinations to try. This searching considerably reduces the time spent listening in the correct place and so greatly reduces the chance of finding the signal, particularly if the equipment is also unreliable!

This has admittedly been a description of an ideal approach, but the closer one can get to it, the more successful the operator will be in the tests. Familiarity with, and successful experience in using, the equipment is the best way to become convinced of the effectiveness of this type of approach. When the equipment can be set up to these standards it will be found that signals which are only just above noise level can be detected, and the operator will then begin to notice the benefits obtainable by squeezing every decibel of performance out of the equipment.

With regard to frequency measurement, most absorption wavemeters are far too inaccurate to set a receiver frequency on their own since the 3dB bandwidth of the wavemeter (for instance on 10GHz) may be between 3 and 100MHz, depending on the Q of the wavemeter. Receiver and transmitter tuning are often uncalibrated at these frequencies, especially when using Gunn oscillators. A very useful target to aim for would be a receiver scale with 100kHz divisions which, if combined with a crystal calibrator generating "pips" every 10 to 100MHz in the band, would be accurate enough for most simple, wideband equipment. An accuracy of 10ppm in the crystal will give 100kHz at 10GHz. Typical accuracies are given in Table 2.2.

For narrowband work, an accuracy of several orders of magnitude better is required. This could be obtained with an "ovened" crystal, but this still has to be set on frequency in the first place using some more accurate reference.

The real solution to the problem of accurate frequency standards is to compare or phase-lock the crystal calibrator to an off-air frequency standard such as Droitwich or Rugby. Many other standard frequency transmissions exist as part of a worldwide service; the two stations quoted are of most use to the UK operator. If both stations do this or even lock their transmitter or receiver local oscillators to this standard, then accuracy is guaranteed. Some of the standard transmissions also carry other useful information such as time signals (Rugby) and weather forecasts (Droitwich). An accurate reference such as this is also useful on the lower-frequency bands, and details of a suitable receiver and harmonic generator are given in [1].

2.2.2 Talkback

Regardless of the technical standard of the equipment, in very few instances (excepting, perhaps, 1.3GHz) is it possible to call "CQ" on a microwave band and expect a reply. It is much more common to arrange a "sked", a series of tests between respective stations, or to use a lower-frequency band (for instance 144 or 432MHz) to establish initial contact and possibly to act as a "talkback" channel. In the UK it has been common practice for some years to use 144.175MHz $\pm$25kHz, (ssb) (or 144.33MHz $\pm$10kHz) as microwave "calling windows", especially during contests and cumulative contests (see later). Due to the very crowded nature of the 144–146MHz band in continental Europe, it has become established practice there to call for microwave contacts on either 432.35MHz $\pm$25kHz (ssb) or on 1,296.2MHz $\pm$25kHz (ssb).

It is therefore desirable that the operator should have multimode facilities available for both 144 and 432MHz, to set up contacts on the higher bands – for instance using 144MHz to set up contacts on 432 and 1,296MHz, or 432MHz to set up contacts on 1.3GHz and higher. Whichever method is used it may pay dividends to put out a call such as "CQ from xxxxx, looking for contacts on a, b, c band and listening on this frequency for any replies".

2.2.3 Procedures

Whether a "sked" or a series of tests is being undertaken it is good and sensible practice to adopt a disciplined, timed sequence of transmitting and receiving on the microwave band similar to that adopted for eme or meteor scatter QSOs. Although the equipment parameters and the basic path loss may have been estimated, there are usually some unknowns remaining, and the adoption of such a procedure is more likely to lead to successful contacts than the rather "slacker" procedures often used on the lower frequencies.

With these points in mind it is suggested that such a procedure and "timetable" be agreed with the other station before moving up in frequency to the band where the attempted contact is to take place. The requirements of such a protocol are these:

1. A clock or wristwatch accurate to within a few seconds of standard time.

2. Regular transmit/receive periods, for example 1min, 5min or any other mutually agreed period, changing on the minute.

3. Agreement as to when to start, who starts, and for how long the sked should continue.

4. If the sked fails, a return to talkback (or telephone!) to fix another sked for some time later.

5. Agreement on a locator system to enable both stations to calculate the bearings and distances, for example latitude/longitude, National Grid References, or derived from them, for example the Maidenhead locator.

6. The use, at least initially, of cw or ssb, but preferably the former.

7. Frequency setting must be sufficiently accurate at both ends of the path to allow each operator to find the other's signals.

2.2.4 Forecasting conditions

With regard to "lifts" or "openings", much can be learned and anticipated by a combination of tactics, many of which should already be familiar to the more experienced users of vhf and uhf. Regular viewing and interpretation of the synoptic (weather) charts either on television or in daily newspapers, looking for co-channel interference on uhf tv, abnormal reception of distant uhf repeaters or, more recently, by the direct acquisition of weather satellite data, should enable the operator to predict potential "lifts". Much confirmatory (or otherwise) evidence can be gleaned from regular monitoring of beacons or repeaters, particularly on 432MHz and higher.

Start to look for lifts when there is stable high-pressure weather over the country, and particularly when this drifts slowly eastwards with a slow decline of pressure. This will usually give good openings to western Europe. These conditions are most common in September–November, but are also common in the late spring. Over the sea, ducts may form almost daily during stable weather in the summer months which are particularly noticeable on the higher microwave bands; they are particularly good around dawn and dusk.

As should be evident from Fig 3.34, Chapter 3, the effectiveness of a "duct" or "layer" enhancement of a given thickness is frequency dependent, and the probability of the formation of shallow layers is much higher than that of the formation of deep ones. It follows, since there is a relationship between the layer thickness and its ability to propagate a particular frequency, that there is a higher probability of enhanced conditions occurring at microwave frequencies than at vhf or uhf.

Depending on the height and thickness of the layers, "regular" signals such as beacons may either exhibit greatly enhanced signal strengths when the transmitting and receiving antennas lie in or close to the layer(s), or greatly diminished strengths if either or both antennas lie significantly above or below the layer(s). This is frequently observed with the UK beacons GB3MLY (432MHz) and GB3MLE (1,296MHz); European dx may be clearly audible on both bands while the beacons are completely inaudible! However, poor conditions on 144 or 432MHz do not necessarily imply poor conditions on the higher bands for the reasons given above.

In contrast, very bad weather can also provide enhanced signals. Very heavy rain or thunder cells can scatter enough energy to bring the signal levels well above the normal troposcatter level. These signals sound similar to auroral signals on vhf.

Nevertheless, regular listening, logging of signals received and the accumulation of meteorological observations should, in the course of time, not only improve the operators' chances of detecting and exploiting enhancements but could also make a significant contribution to the further understanding of microwave propagation. Above all, therefore, the serious microwave operator should be methodical.

2.3 FIXED-STATION OPERATION

2.3.1 Aims of fixed operation

Bearing in mind the constraints of limited power, feeder losses and size/gain of the antenna installation, the microwave operator should consider a number of factors when setting up a fixed station. It is usually not sufficient to approach microwave operation on as casual a basis as might be possible on the lower vhf or the hf bands, where "a few watts to a piece of wire" will always give some sort of results.

The first decision the operator must make is "What are my objectives?" Are they short-to-medium distance general communication, troposcatter, use of tropo-enhancement modes, eme or what? These questions should be answered because, for terrestrial communications, site and antenna/feeder considerations are far more important in determining station effectiveness than at lower frequencies. The answer to such questions will, to a great extent, determine the band(s), power, mode(s) and antenna/feeder system aspirations of the operator. These might vary, for example, from full legal power and a large, fully steerable dish on 1.3 or 2.3GHz for eme down to a few milliwatts of wideband fm to a small dish or horn for semi-local communication on 10GHz.

The next consideration, having decided the objectives, is to see how these will fit into what may be broadly considered to be the "domestic scene". Is the site reasonably "in the clear"? Will there be planning consent problems for a large antenna installation? Is the feeder-run of minimum practicable length? And so on.

Finally must come the question of resourcing – is the time, skill and finance available or does the operator need to start in a modest way and develop the system as fast as these constraints allow? In general it is not too costly, time-consuming or technically demanding to produce a few hundred milliwatts to a few watts on the lower microwave bands, or a few tens of milliwatts on the higher bands. What will be costly, time-consuming and technically demanding is the establishment of a first-class antenna/feeder system, high power and multimode capability which will provide the user with the means to push terrestrial communications potential to its limits (when operated well!) and, possibly, fulfil the stringent requirements of eme work. If the operator is prepared to compromise and sacrifice this "ultimate" performance for a usable, practical and less-demanding system which can be developed as resources permit, then communication will be assured over limited distances (perhaps a few tens to a few hundred km) and with limited modes under "normal" conditions; under "lift" conditions these distances could extend enormously and even the relatively poorly equipped station will give its operator the chance to secure dx contacts.

2.3.2 Antenna systems

On the lower bands (1.3, 2.3 and to some extent 3.4GHz) the choice of antenna will lie in the range from a single conventional or quad-loop Yagi through stacked/bayed multiple Yagis to, typically, a "skeleton" dish of perhaps 1 to 3m in diameter mounted on the station mast and fully rotatable. Larger dishes used for eme are usually mounted at ground level and need to be fully steerable. Details of suitable antennas for these bands are given in Chapter 4. With regard to the feeder, which is effectively an integral part of the design of a microwave antenna system, the principle to follow is the shortest length of the best-quality cable the operator can afford. Figures for feeder losses are given in Chapter 13, and from this and the manufacturer's price list a choice can be made. It is, as far as the amateur is concerned, invariably a cost/effectiveness compromise.

For the higher bands (5.7GHz and up), the choice of antenna is relatively limited; a "skeleton" dish of perhaps 0.5 to 2m diameter or preferably a "fly-swatter" or "periscope" antenna will serve for all bands with the advantage that, with proper planning and installation, it can minimise or eliminate the need for a feeder and its associated losses. Again, some details of this type of antenna and feed assemblies are given in Chapter 4. There seems to be a growing practice (especially in continental Europe) to employ a skeleton dish with a single feeder and multiband feed covering typically 1.3 to 5.7GHz, and this approach should be considered a serious option. Suitable multiband feeds are described in [3], [4] and [5]. It should be realised that such feeds represent a compromise solution and they are not particularly efficient compared with a dedicated, single-band feed. However, they may be acceptable to operators who are unable to accommodate more than a single (dish) antenna on their mast, or afford to duplicate the feeder to more than one antenna.

At 10 and 24GHz a small solid dish of 0.3 to 0.6m diameter or a 20dB horn becomes a practical proposition, and it is desirable for the transceiver to be mounted near the dish to minimise the high feeder losses associated with such frequencies – such a system might even be considered for 3.4 and 5.7GHz where the transmit multipliers and at least the receive preamp could be mast-mounted.

For *all* bands, receive performance is always greatly improved by the use of a low-noise mast-head receive preamplifier connected as close to the antenna as possible. The reader is referred to the appropriate band chapters for ideas regarding preamplifiers, switching relays, feeders and their interconnection.

2.3.3 Summary

To summarise, it is felt that the operator must first decide what he or she wants to achieve on the microwave band(s). Second, the operator must then decide how these objectives are to be attained, and then finally select the designs for equipment and antennas best suited to these needs. At the time of writing relatively little commercially produced equipment for amateur use is available and this will usually mean that the operator will either have to build "from scratch" or adapt existing (often "surplus") equipment for the bands. This may be another very good reason for starting with relatively simple equipment and developing its potential as the need arises. A simple computer program to assist in station design is given in section 2.7. It will give the operator some idea of the equipment potential under normal conditions, either "line-of-sight" or troposcatter, using the different modes which are commonly used in amateur communications.

2.4 PORTABLE OPERATION

2.4.1 Advantages of portable operation

If, as outlined in section 2.3 above, the operator is restricted to using low power, limited modes, small antennas and possibly high feeder losses from an indifferent site, effectiveness of operation can be maximised by adopting the techniques already outlined. Such an operator may still be able to obtain similar results to better-equipped fixed stations by the relatively simple expedient of taking his or her microwave equipment out portable to a better site. Low-powered equipment and smaller antennas can often be quickly loaded into a car and taken to a better site at quite short notice if preparations are made in advance. By using the band and weather observations previously discussed and coupling these with "snap" portable operation it may prove possible to catch many of the quite spectacular enhancements which occur from time to time.

When very-low-loss propagation modes are involved, it matters little whether the signal generated is 100mW, 1W, 10W or more, or whether the antenna/feeder and

transmitter/receiver is highly sophisticated. The main advantage of a clear portable site is that local site obstructions and long feeders with their attendant losses can be largely avoided. Under these circumstances the operator can obtain good results from "barefoot" transverters or transmitter-receiver combinations. The more ambitious portable operator may choose to increase both power and antenna size as experience or needs increase, and in these respects portable operation may follow the same course of development as that outlined for fixed-station operation.

The same advice as for fixed-station operation should be followed with regard to the use of talkback and orderly procedures; again the use of cw, at least initially, is advised as the most potent means of communication, with ssb a close second best.

Whether "snap" or more regular portable operation is undertaken, then certain aspects of this type of operation should be carefully considered beforehand. It is possible to do much effective preparative work before undertaking such operation and this is as desirable as when planning a "full-sized expedition". Although the logistics may be very much simpler, the principles remain the same.

First a "packing list" should be compiled to check that all equipment needed is available, known to be functional and can be loaded systematically (and safely) into the vehicle. Such a list is, to an extent, one of individual preference, but might look something like the one given below, depending on the band(s) involved and the type of site to be used.

Path list	Spare car keys
Licence copy	Microwave transceiver
Logbook	Microwave dish/antenna
Compass	Dish feed/dipole/penny etc
Maps	Fully charged batteries
Spirit level	Binoculars
Notepad and pen	Cassette recorder
Talkback transceiver	Cables (all)
Talkback antenna	Spare clothes
Mast and guys	Thermos flask (full)
Tripod	Tools
Plastic bags	Spares

2.4.2 Choice of site

In choosing a site, reference may be made to detailed maps, first at the 1:625,000 scale to give some indication of the general topography of the terrain out to, say, 100km, and then at the 1:50,000 scale (or larger) which should indicate the local path obstructions which may play a significant part in the success or failure of operation from the site, particularly at the higher frequencies and under "normal" propagation conditions. The quality of the site can be quantified by calculating the extra path losses involved due to the obstructions which

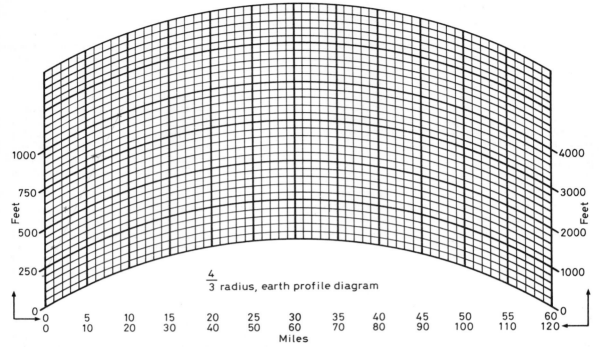

Fig 2.1. Profile plotting sheet (altitude in feet, distance in statute miles – metric measures may, of course, be used if preferred). The home station altitude is entered at the 0 miles point and the distant station altitude at the appropriate distance along either distance scale. Other spot heights at known distances are plotted in a similar manner. Joining the points together will produce a path profile. If a straight line joining the two stations together passes above the highest obstruction, then the path is line-of-sight. If it passes through either an obstruction or through the zero altitude line, then the path contains obstructions

form the horizon in various directions. Details of troposcatter losses are given in [2].

Having decided on a site, check the access; if it is a roadside site served by a public road there will usually be no difficulty in operating. However, the site may be privately owned or be part of an estate or national park, in which case there may be restrictions imposed on the operator. It is thus a good idea to check these points beforehand. Permission will seldom be refused if the landowner is approached in the right manner beforehand and the operator shows a sensible and responsible attitude while on the site. This will usually mean the adoption of some form of "country code", most of which is common sense:

• Avoid climbing over walls and fences, and close gates.
• Do not leave litter.
• Keep to recognised footpaths as far as possible.
• Avoid disturbing livestock.
• Avoid the risk of fire or other damage
• Generally behave as one would expect visitors to behave when in one's own home or garden.

At the end of operation a word of thanks to the site owner is common courtesy and will often assist in the granting of permission to operate on future occasions.

When surveying the potential of a site the operator should work out most of the distances, bearings and path profiles in advance of operation simply by reference to maps. This is particularly appropriate for operation on the higher bands such as 10 and 24GHz, and a few hours spent in doing such work will free the valuable time on site for actually operating the station. By maintaining an up-to-date file of path details, quick reference can be made in the field and the chances of successful contacts greatly improved. Once such a file has been constructed it does not need to be done again, only modified or extended.

In the UK the microwave operator is singularly well provided with detailed maps in the Ordnance Survey (OS) series and has the choice of using the National Grid Reference (NGR) system, latitude and longitude, or the Maidenhead system which is based on latitude and longitude when calculating bearings and distances. These maps contain the information for both systems. NGRs are widely used within the UK, while the latter

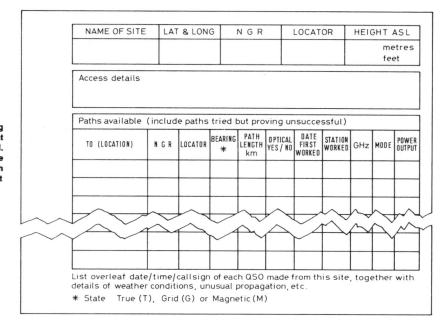

Fig 2.2. Special microwave logging sheet. This is one suggested format which has proved useful in the field. No doubt the operator will devise his or her own layout and fill in useful information before going out portable, as explained in the text

NAME OF SITE	LAT & LONG	N G R	LOCATOR	HEIGHT ASL
				metres feet

Access details

Paths available (include paths tried but proving unsuccessful)

TO (LOCATION)	N G R	LOCATOR	BEARING *	PATH LENGTH km	OPTICAL YES / NO	DATE FIRST WORKED	STATION WORKED	GHz	MODE	POWER OUTPUT

List overleaf date/time/callsign of each QSO made from this site, together with details of weather conditions, unusual propagation, etc.

* State   True (T), Grid (G) or Magnetic (M)

are more commonly used for longer-distance, international contacts. Several simple computer programs are given in section 2.7 which should greatly simplify such calculations. Path profiles can be manually plotted using "earth-profile" plotting paper, an example of which is reproduced in Fig 2.1. Alternatively a simple path-plotting program may be found in section 2.7.

Armed with this information, orderly operating techniques as earlier discussed (and perhaps an element of skill and luck) the chances of successful operation will be controlled mainly by conditions. One additional item of equipment might be a special log sheet such as that shown in Fig 2.2; this is just one of the possibilities designed to assist in the accumulation of useful data in an easily accessible form and which could be used to supplement the main station log or the portable log. No doubt the keen and methodical operator will devise his or her own sheet to suit the particular needs of the station.

2.4.3 Antennas and masts

Both the talkback and the microwave antennas can, unless very large, be supported on a single, well-guyed mast 3.5 to 8m (10 to 25ft) long, constructed of tubing which "plugs" or screws together, each section of which is short enough to fit easily within the available car space. Alternatively on the higher bands, for instance 10 or 24GHz, the most likely type of antenna will be a dish of typically 46cm (18in) to 92cm (36in) diameter. In this case, a lightweight sectional mast might be used to support the talkback antenna (such as an HB9CV or small Yagi), while the microwave antenna and transceiver might be mounted on a tripod or on the car roof. While mounting the equipment on the car roof does restrict the sites which can be accessed, it does provide a simple, stable platform to operate from, with power and shelter conveniently at hand. Both mast and tripod should be sited close together so that both sets of equipment can be operated simultaneously and the tripod should be guyed as well as the mast; the dish will present considerable "windage" and unless adequately guyed is likely to blow over, causing damage to the equipment, perhaps even before the operating session has commenced. The mast should be free enough to rotate easily, but not so free that even a light wind will cause it to blow round like a weather vane.

The microwave antenna mount should be capable of being clamped in place once it is aligned in the right direction. One advantage of using a single mast is that the ground-plate can be fitted with a compass scale which can be aligned while erecting the mast. A pointer can be fitted to the base of the mast, adjacent to this scale, and a reasonably accurate beam bearing obtained from the scale without the need constantly to take compass bearings for each successive contact which might lie in different directions. For very lightweight operation the user might dispense with a mast altogether and rely on a wall, rock, fence post, cairn or survey "trig-point" to support the gear and antenna.

When using high-gain dishes having beamwidths of 5° or less, it is essential that not only does the dish

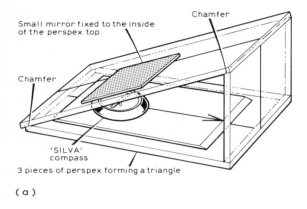

Small mirror fixed to the inside
of the perspex top

Chamfer

Chamfer

'SILVA' compass

3 pieces of perspex forming a triangle

(a)

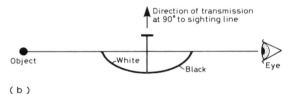

Direction of transmission
at 90° to sighting line

Object

White

Black

Eye

(b)

Fig 2.3. (a) Sighting compass constructed from a map-reading compass. (b) Sighting across the face of a dish antenna

point in the right direction but that it is also aligned in the vertical plane – that is, the mast is truly vertical or the table of the tripod is truly horizontal. A spirit level will allow such alignment with a minimum of complication.

With regard to talkback, the operator should preferably try to use at least 25W on the talkback band; very often, and for a great variety of reasons, the talkback signals may be considerably weaker than those received on the microwave band. Around 5 to 10dB antenna gain on the talkback band should be acceptable. On either the talkback band or the microwave band the modes used should be, in order of preference (effectiveness): cw, ssb, am, nbfm (with limiter) and wbfm. The aim of talkback is to provide a reliable communication link to assist the microwave operation. In some cases, the 432MHz repeater network may prove useful, particularly since it is not very heavily used. The telephone is, if available, also a very useful fallback if all else fails.

2.4.4 Bearings

When taking compass readings the operator should be well away from ferrous metal objects which may affect the accuracy of the readings; cars, metal fences, power lines and even certain types of rock should be avoided; it is often advisable to take a series of readings from different places near the equipment in order to rule out the possibility of such errors. A

suitable sighting compass can be constructed from a map-reading compass as shown in Fig 2.3(a). Sightings may be taken along the boom of a Yagi, along the axis of waveguide or across the face of a dish, not forgetting to add (or subtract) 90° to the compass sighting if this method is used. Sighting across the face of the dish (Fig 2.3(b)) has the advantage that the operator is using an integral part of the antenna structure and that the sighting line can be at any angle of elevation, depending where the operator stands to take the sighting. This could be horizontally at landmarks or up to the sun, moon or stars without having to tilt the dish up at an angle. Sighting is made easier by painting the front and back of the dish in contrasting colours so that a sharp dividing line is seen from the side. At night the edges can be very clearly seen if a torch is shone to illuminate (!) the front of the dish, leaving the back dark. To get good accuracy the operator should stand about 3m (10ft) from the dish, and farther if possible.

Sighting on landmarks can be quite accurate provided a well-defined, visible object can be found. This is more difficult than might be expected, especially in the country as most natural features of the landscape tend to be poorly defined and hard to locate at a distance. Bear in mind that 1° corresponds to a distance of 150m (about 500ft) at a range of 8km (5 miles), in turn corresponding to 0.1in on a 1in map. The feature has to be pinpointed to this degree of accuracy, so that good objects to sight on are water towers, cooling towers, church towers or steeples, radio masts and similar objects. Roads and other "linear" features are not very useful from a distance as it is very difficult to pinpoint any position along their length.

At night (in the northern hemisphere) the Pole Star gives a bearing of true north. By sighting up across the front of the dish at the star, the dish can be set due east or west. Other bearings can then be taken off the calibrated scale previously mentioned.

Microwave beacons or other amateur stations, the position of which is accurately known, might be used for beam heading, although the operator should beware of reflections off hills or large man-made objects or the effects of other unusual propagation.

Using sun position is a very accurate method of beam setting and can serve several purposes. The position of the sun can be calculated from the equations given in an astronomical reference book (such as [6]), using a pocket calculator with reference to an almanac for some of the data. Briefly, the sun's position is defined by two astronomical co-ordinates, its Greenwich hour angle (Gha) and declination (Dec). These are its longitude and latitude in the sky. They cannot be used directly for determining the azimuth of the sun and have to be converted to useful co-ordinates using two equations:

El $=\arcsin(\sin(\text{Lat})\sin(\text{Dec})+\cos(\text{Lat})\cos(\text{Dec})\cos(\text{Lha}))$

Az $=\arccos(\cos(\text{Lat})\sin(\text{Dec})/\cos(\text{El})-\tan(\text{Lat})\tan(\text{El}))$

where El = Elevation of the sun
Az = Azimuth of the sun (its bearing relative to true north)
Lat = Latitude of station (+ve N, –ve S)
Dec = Declination of sun (+ve N, –ve S)
Gha = Greenwich hour angle of sun
Lha = Local hour angle
= Gha + long of station (east)
– long of station (west)

These equations are easily solved using a scientific calculator, but a programmable calculator is to be preferred if a large number of calculations are envisaged. Clearly it is necessary to know the Gha and Dec of the sun and these are tabulated in various almanacs. One recommended almanac is the Nautical Almanac (obtained from HMSO) which tabulates these co-ordinates for both sun and moon (and the equations apply equally to the moon) for every hour of every day of the year. For those who do not wish to invest in such an almanac, it may be possible to obtain the data via a local reference library. A suitable suite of microcomputer programs will be found in [7].

On a bright day, with the sun casting strong shadows, it is easy to see the shadow of the dish feed and simply adjust the dish until the shadow is central in the dish. On a cloudy day just point the dish at the approximate position of the sun; if the receiver is sensitive enough to detect sun noise, optimise the position by maximising the noise by ear or watching the S-meter while adjusting the dish.

If you really must observe the sun with the unaided eye, then the very least eye protection is to look through arc-welders' goggles or through a sheet of didymium glass intended to fit an arc-welder's mask. This glass is the only commonly available material which possesses enough optical density to prevent eye damage, since it absorbs light of all wavelengths from ultraviolet to infrared. *Under no circumstances be tempted to use the naked eye, sunglasses, binoculars or a telescope.* Another caution: especially on a clear sunny day and with a highly polished solid dish, there may be enough concentration of heat at the dish focus to damage the feed! However, that would be of less consequence than eyes permanently damaged through a moment's rashness.

Several kinds of "north" have been referred to indirectly and these are summarised below:

Magnetic north is used mainly when setting bearings with a compass and is about 7.5° west of true north in the UK at the present (1987), decreasing by about 0.5° in six years. The figure of 7.5° also varies with location

by about 3°, being about 9° in Wales and 6° near the east coast. The exact figure should be obtained from a recent map of the area. Aeronautical maps are particularly useful for this, as they have an overprint of lat/long and lines of constant magnetic variation. The heights of ground are clearly marked and they are available in 1:250,000 and 1:500,000 scales (2.5km/cm, 5km/cm) from airport shops or the Civil Aviation Authority.

Grid north also differs from true north. This is the north with respect to which NGRs are calculated, and again the deviation is marked on each map.

True north is that which is obtained from lat/long and any astronomical measurements are referred to it. Ideally all bearings should be converted to true north before use to avoid confusion; in all cases the type of north to which a bearing refers should always be stated.

2.4.5 Powering portable equipment

With relatively simple and low-powered equipment there is little problem in powering it from batteries. If in good condition, the car battery might be used or a spare car battery carried. Alternatively, the smaller, non-spillable motorcycle-sized batteries or gel-acid batteries such as those used as power backup in alarm systems will suffice to run the equipment for quite long periods, especially when most of the operator's time may be spent in receiving rather than transmitting. Since a lead-acid battery may only provide 11.6V when nearly discharged or as much as 13.8V when fully charged, it is a good idea to be certain that the equipment to be used can function at, say, 11.6V. This will enable the incorporation of a low voltage-drop regulator such as that described in Chapter 8, "Common microwave equipment", so that the equipment will function correctly until the voltage falls from its fully charged state to about 12V.

For higher powers it may be necessary to carry a petrol- or diesel-driven generator. The operator should not forget to put batteries on charge as soon as the portable operating session is over, for there is nothing more frustrating than finding the batteries flat when next needed. Similarly, if a generator is used, it should be refuelled and serviced on a regular basis.

2.4.6 Safety in portable operation

General conditions governing safety in amateur operating are comprehensively covered in Chapter 11, "Safety". Needless to say, these should be carefully observed and followed where they are appropriate, either in the fixed-station environment or when portable operation is undertaken.

With regard to mountain-top (lightweight or rucksack) portable operation, several additional points need to be considered, for these arise out of the physical, psychological and physiological stresses imposed on the operator by exposure to weather conditions, especially on high and open sites in maritime or sub-arctic climates.

Sudden deterioration in weather conditions (not uncommon in hilly or mountainous districts, particularly in the late winter/early spring and late autumn/early winter) can lead to fatality through exhaustion following exposure. These conditions can lead to a rapid loss of circulatory capacity, control of body temperature (hypothermia) and consciousness which, if not treated promptly, may lead to death. Exhaustion is caused by exposure to extreme cold, strong winds, driving rain and other adverse conditions, and people who are physically unfit, ill-clad and ill-nourished are more likely to succumb rapidly to the combined effects of exposure and exhaustion than those who are reasonably fit, well-clad and have access to hot drinks and high-calorie foods.

One of the very early signs of impending exhaustion is some loss of coherence in speech (or response to speech) together with a certain degree of loss of co-ordination in movement; these signs are difficult to recognise in oneself but may be obvious to a companion. Hence it is always better and safer to operate with a companion. If this is not possible then the minimum precaution to be taken is to inform others of the exact whereabouts of the site and the expected time of return. This will enable search-and-rescue operations to be initiated should this prove necessary.

It is common sense to carry spare warm, windproof clothing, hot drinks (or the means to make them) and food. These can be kept safe in the car boot if operation takes place from a roadside site, or packed into a rucksack if mountain climbing is involved. An elementary first-aid kit is a sensible addition to the equipment.

Alcoholic drinks are not a good idea – not only do they lead to muddled thinking and operating, but also may have exactly the opposite physiological effects to those popularly ascribed to them. While conferring a feeling of warmth and well-being, alcohol will usually impair circulation and LOWER the body temperature by virtue of an altered circulation pattern. It is much better to rely on hot, sweet drinks or soups for sustenance.

At the other end of the scale, hyperthermia (caused by excessive physical effort particularly in high temperatures) can have similar effects, but the remedy is different – in this case cooling is needed and may be attained by removing excess clothing and taking cool drinks. Rest is also beneficial as this results in the production of less metabolic heat, whereas in hypothermia one of the requirements is to keep the sufferer moving in order to generate such heat. Sunburn, caused by the high ultraviolet content of the sun's rays at high altitude (and often near the sea), can be a problem in conditions which from a comfort aspect might be ideal. Simply be aware of the problem and follow accepted practices in the use of skin protection creams and sunglasses.

This may seem to be a somewhat gloomy list of precautions to attach to activities which should provide the operator with pleasure. However, the effects described are real and can happen with dramatic suddenness. Be prepared!

One point bearing heavily on both portable operating technique and safety is this. The operator should make every effort to become thoroughly familiar with the use of maps and compass. Not only will this allow accurate beam setting but should enable the operator to retreat gracefully, quickly and safely from a mountain top should the need arise – possibly under conditions of fog or darkness as the fickleness of the mountain climate should never be underestimated.

The general points on mountain safety were ably summed up by G3PHO [8] and are as follows:

1. Build up to the occasion by eating heartily before the event. Some 5,000 calories per day are required when mountain walking, even in summer conditions, whereas the average semi-sedentary person may only require 1,500 to 2,500 calories per day.

2. Carry no more than 16kg (35lb) in the rucksack. More than this, and certainly more than a third of the body weight, only serves to use rapidly the store of bodily energy. Spread the load among companions *who should be with you in such conditions.*

3. Acquire suitable clothing for the job, for example strong walking boots, a warm brushed-cotton shirt, one or two thin woollen jumpers and a thicker, outer garment so that the body temperature can be regulated. Do *not* have an "all or nothing" arrangement with one thick sweater. Also included in the clothing list should be a windproof and waterproof cagoule or anorak, together with waterproof over-trousers. *Strong winds are more dangerous than rain* as they rapidly lower the skin temperature to dangerous levels if not guarded against.

4. Carry a survival bag (large polythene type available at camping and mountaineering shops) and also a first-aid kit. Carry a whistle for emergency calls – this might seem superfluous when the operator is carrying radio equipment, but the likelihood of a distress call being picked up on an amateur frequency may be small, whereas members of a rescue team are accustomed to listening for whistle signals while searching for missing or injured persons.

5. Have ample food and hot drinks for the day *plus* emergency rations such as chocolate, dried fruits or mint cake (you might have to stay the night).

6. Inform someone where you are going and stick to the route. Inform them of the expected time of return.

7. Be equipped with good maps of the mountains (1:25000 scale is the best in the UK), carry a good

compass (for instance Silva or Suunto) *and know how to use both in dense fog and darkness.*

8. Learn to spot the first signs of mountain hypothermia (irrational behaviour, shivering, slow response to conversation) and what to do if a member of the party shows them.

While the above remarks are primarily directed to the true "mountain-topper" type of portable operation, some of them might also apply to more conventional portable operation, particularly of the 24h contest type where sleeplessness can contribute to exhaustion. For further information on mountain safety the reader should read and heed the contents of any good book on mountain craft, such as that cited in [9].

2.5 AWARDS, CERTIFICATES AND CONTESTS

2.5.1 Introduction

This section outlines the awards, certificates and contests available to the microwave operator in the UK and gives some detail of contests elsewhere in IARU Region 1.

There exists, within the "portfolio", a number of awards and trophies administered directly by the Council of the RSGB or by recommendation to Council by one of its specialist committees under whose jurisdiction the award falls. In general these awards are made only for work judged to be of outstanding significance or merit and, although many are available on an annual basis, this does necessarily mean that they are always awarded since there may not, at any particular time, be work of sufficient merit to warrant the award. Some of the awards are open only to members of RSGB but some may be awardable to non-members. Similarly some are intended for award only within the UK, while others may be available for award to non-UK operators.

In addition there are a number of certificates available which are awarded to mark various levels of operating achievement. Such certificates are awarded by the Society's VHF/UHF and Microwave Awards Manager and such claims must be accompanied by proof (QSL cards) of the contacts. If the claimant is an overseas resident and it is impracticable to send the necessary cards the claim may instead be accompanied by a written statement of authenticity signed by the vhf/uhf/microwave manager of the society concerned. Valid contacts are those achieved using any mode, power or place of operation (fixed, portable, alternative address or temporary alternative address) allowed under the terms of the claimant's licence, with the only exceptions that contacts via repeaters or artificial satellites are not valid. Thus contacts via eme or during contests are just as valid for claims as those during "ordinary" terrestrial or non-contest operation. It should be noted, however, that eme contacts are not valid for contest scoring. Most are available to both the swl and the transmitting amateur.

An outline of some of the major contests available to operators in the UK and nearer Europe is given and, although details may differ from one national society to another, the general entry rules for those contests involving microwave operation may be taken as a guide to typical entry requirements throughout IARU Region 1. Dates, duration and bands used, for instance, may vary since band allocations vary from one national administration to another. At the time of writing (1988) there is considerable change taking place in band availability and allocation within Europe and it is thus difficult to be definitive as to exactly what band allocations are available in which countries. The format of contests supporting international microwave activity is thus subject to change almost without notice.

2.5.2 Awards

The awards briefly described below are those currently available to microwave operators in the UK. In some cases there will be "competition" for the awards in the sense that hf and vhf/uhf operators will be equally eligible for consideration, whereas other awards are specifically directed to microwave achievement. The awards can be conveniently be divided into two groups: Group A, orientated around innovation, research or development and Group B, centred around operating achievement.

Group A – Awards for innovation, research or development

The Marconi Medal and Premium. This is an award sponsored by the Marconi Company and available on an annual basis for 10 years (1978 to 1988); it is hoped this period will be extended. Its citation states that it is "for microwave development, propagation investigation or other microwave innovation". The award is presented on the recommendation of RSGB Council and has, with the agreement of the Marconi Company, been awarded to non-UK amateurs for outstanding work at microwave frequencies. Recommendations administered by the Microwave Committee.

The RSGB Microwave Award. The citation for this award reads "to further encourage amateur activity on the microwave bands the RSGB will present, on behalf of Microwave Associates, a suitable award for the first amateurs or groups of amateurs to complete a full two-way contact on 10GHz over a path exceeding 1,000km. A second similar award will be made for a full two-way contact on 24GHz exceeding 250km". In fact both of these awards have already been made, and it is hoped that these awards will be extended as follows:

10GHz – for the first contact exceeding 2,000km
24GHz – for the first contact exceeding 500km
47GHz – for the first contact exceeding 100km
Bands above 47GHz – for the first contact exceeding
   25km

Adjudicated by the Microwave Committee.

The Fraser Shepherd Award and Premium. This award is given "for research into microwave applications to radio communications" and is adjudicated by the Society's Microwave Committee.

The Alpha Microwave Award. This cup, sponsored by Alpha Industries, is awarded annually to the winner of the UK section of the 10GHz Cumulative "contests", for more details of which see later. Results adjudicated by the Microwave Committee on behalf of the VHF Contests Committee.

The John Rouse Memorial Trophy. This cup is available for the "best home-constructed equipment at an exhibition" and is adjudicated and awarded on the recommendation of the Microwave Committee. From 1988 the trophy was augmented by a premium and plaque.

The Mullard Award. Sponsored by Mullard Ltd, this award is available to "a member (or group of members) of RSGB who has (have) made significant contributions or innovations which further the art of radio communication". Again this award is made on Council recommendation but is not, like the previous awards, specifically microwave. However, the microwave constructor/operator is in a strong position to fulfil the award requirements.

The Courtney-Price Trophy. Administered by the Technical and Publications Committee of the Society, this trophy is awarded on an annual basis for "the most outstanding technical development in amateur radio in the year ending 30 June". This is again not a specifically microwave award (like the next four), but since the most significant amateur technical advances are probably taking place at microwave frequencies, then the chances of a microwave operator winning this award must be quite high!

The Wortley-Talbot Award. The citation for this award says quite simply "for outstanding experimental work in amateur radio". Adjudicated by Technical and Publications Committee. Remarks as above!

The Norman Keith Adams Prize. Awarded annually for "the most original article published in *Radio Communication* during the year ending 30 June". Administered by Technical and Publications Committee. A possibility for microwave operators!

The Ostermeyer Trophy. Awarded annually for "the most meritorious piece of home-constructed radio or electronic equipment published in *Radio Communication*

during the year ending 30 June". Administered by the Technical and Publications Committee, this trophy could be a target for the microwave constructor!

The 1962 VHF Committee Cup. Awarded annually for the best item of home-constructed equipment entered into an RSGB convention or exhibition. Administered by Technical and Publications Committee. Remarks as above!

Group B – Operating awards

The Louis Varney Cup. Administered by the VHF Committee, this is awarded for "advances in space communications". Increasing use of the microwave bands in space communication in coming years will make this cup an award to be sought by microwave operators.

The VHF European Cup. Administered by the VHF Contests Committee, this cup is awarded to the top-scoring UK station entering the IARU Region 1 VHF contests. Microwave operators should stand a very sporting chance here, since (see later) the IARU VHF contests are multiband and involve many of the currently available microwave allocations.

VHF Contests Committee Cup. Awarded to the winner of the RSGB April 1.3GHz contest.

Further details of any of the awards outlined above can be obtained on application to RSGB Headquarters.

2.5.3 Certificates

Certificates are available in three main categories, recognising operating achievements at vhf, uhf and microwaves. Since the boundary between uhf and microwave operation is not clear and there is a degree of overlap of techniques, some of the longer-established certificates are available for a combination of vhf, uhf and microwave operation, and their availability extends to the lowest of the bands, viz 1.3GHz.

For this reason, details of the achievements needed to gain vhf and uhf certificates are given here and should not be seen as being out of context. All certificate claims described in this section must be accompanied by an approved claim form available from the Society's VHF Awards Manager, whose name and address appears in *Radio Communication*, and be supported by acceptable documentary evidence as described earlier.

RSGB "Four metres and down" certificates

These certificates are available in three categories – Standard, Senior and Supreme – for operation in the 70, 144, 432 and 1,296MHz bands, and are available to both the swl and transmitting amateur. The requirements for each are given in Table 2.3. Operators may use any mode, power or location (fixed or portable) which the licence allows, with the exception that contacts through

Fig 2.4. Four Metres and Down Standard Certificate with Distance Award sticker

repeaters or artificial satellites are not valid. Portable operation must be from a single site for a particular (band) claim.

Requirements for the receiving category are the same as in Table 2.3.

The Supreme Award will be made to claimants holding any three validated Senior certificates OR any two Senior certificates plus a Standard 1,296MHz certificate. Similarly for the receiving category.

Each of the awards uses the same basic certificate, with appropriate stickers, the basic certificate being illustrated in Fig 2.4.

RSGB Microwave Award certificates

There are two forms of this certificate currently available. The "old" format (297 by 420mm) and the "new" (253 by 204mm) which will replace the old certificate: at the moment the claimant has the choice! They are illustrated in Figs 2.5 and 2.6.

The "basic" certificate (in either format) requires the submission of QSL cards for a minimum of five QRA (QTH) locator or international locator (LOC) squares worked (or heard). These may be from a fixed location or a portable location. For the latter, a portable location is defined as a place within a 5km radius of a particular map reference (in NGR or lat/long). This will enable the portable operator to avoid local obstructions, especially when operating on the higher bands, without breaking the "spirit" of the rules. Any mode or power within the terms of the

licence may be used, and again contacts via repeaters or artificial satellites do not count.

Extensions to the basic certificate will be awarded in the form of stickers acknowledging increasing numbers of squares confirmed in multiples of five.

Table 2.3

Band (MHz)	Category	Counties	Countries
70	Standard	30	3
	Senior	60	6
144	Standard	40	9
	Senior	60	15
432	Standard	20	3
	Senior	40	9
1296	Standard	20	3
	Senior	40	6

Table 2.4

Band (GHz)	Minimum distance (km)	
1.3	600	
2.3	500	
3.4	400	
5.7	300	
10	150	
24	25	(beginner)
	75	(intermediate)
	150	(advanced)

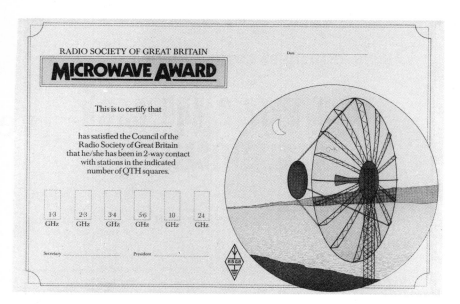

RADIO SOCIETY OF GREAT BRITAIN

MICROWAVE AWARD

This is to certify that

has satisfied the Council of the
Radio Society of Great Britain
that he/she has been in 2-way contact
with stations in the indicated
number of QTH squares.

| 1·3 | 2·3 | 3·4 | 5·6 | 10 | 24 |
| GHz | GHz | GHz | GHz | GHz | GHz |

Secretary _____ President _____

Fig 2.5. Old-format Microwave Certificate

RSGB Microwave Distance certificates

These are available on all the currently used microwave bands. Here the requirement is for a single confirmed contact exceeding the distances given in Table 2.4. The certificate is the Four Metres and Down Certificate,

augmented with a sticker for the band/distance appropriate to the application (see Fig 2.4).

2.5.4. Contests supporting microwave activity

It is not intended to give guidance on contest operating techniques since at microwave frequencies there is

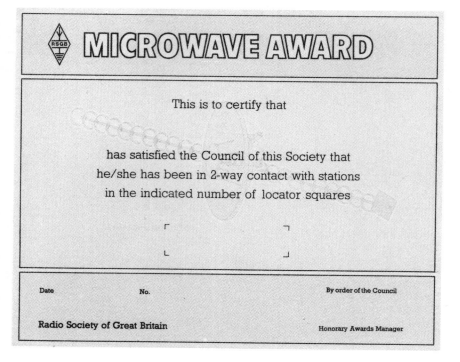

MICROWAVE AWARD

This is to certify that

has satisfied the Council of this Society that
he/she has been in 2-way contact with stations
in the indicated number of locator squares

Date   No.   By order of the Council

Radio Society of Great Britain   Honorary Awards Manager

Fig 2.6. New-format Microwave Certificate

seldom the same degree of "urgency" as pertains at lower frequencies, and the techniques of operating in hf and vhf contests are well known in any case. Use of the general advice given earlier in this chapter should enhance an operator's chances of success. Adherence to band plans, where these exist, is mandatory, for non-compliance may lead to disqualification!

There are a number of contests at both national and international level which provide microwave activity and from which confirmed contacts can be used to support certificate claims. While it is hoped that the list to be given is reasonably comprehensive, there may be some omissions since the format, timing, duration and number of bands in use varies from country to country, and the degree of co-ordination of contests throughout IARU Region 1, though improving, still has some way to go! Written from a UK viewpoint, only those contests likely to be workable from the UK have been included in the absence of detail available from the more distant countries of Region 1.

Each year an "Operating Guide" supplement is published in the January issue of the RSGB magazine *Radio Communication*. This contains the latest general rules for all contests sponsored by the Society and includes IARU rules. As these rules may change from year to year, prospective contestants should note the content of the guide before entering the contests. There may also be variations to these general rules (especially for microwave-only contests) and these are published from time to time in the monthly "Contest News" feature in *Radio Communication*. The prospective operator is advised to study these as they appear.

It can be assumed that most of the contests given here will have European support and some are eligible to receive non-UK entries, even though they be RSGB-sponsored rather than IARU-sponsored. In the same way, entry to those sponsored by individual European societies may be open to UK operators and even if formal entry is not allowed it is still desirable that UK operators should participate and provide activity.

The contest list following is the best available at the time of writing. The actual dates, formats and other details, as already stated, may vary from country to country. The list is given on a month-by-month basis with more detail given after the list in the form of footnotes.

January		(9)
February		(9)
March	VERON 144MHz to 24GHz	(1) (9)
	IARU Region 1 VHF/UHF/SHF	(4)
April	RSGB Microwave Cumulatives	(2)
	RSGB 10GHz Cumulatives	(3)
	RSGB 432MHz to 24GHz	(4)
	RSGB 1,296MHz Trophy Contest	(5)

May	144MHz to 24GHz	(1)
June		
July	RSGB VHF NFD & SWL	(6)
	144MHz to 24GHz	(1)
August	RSGB 1,296/2,320MHz	(7)
September		
October	IARU Region 1 432MHz to	
	24GHz Contest	(4)
	RSGB 1.3/2.3GHz Cumulatives	(8)
November		(9)
December		(9)

Notes:

(1) Held in March, May and July.

(2) Usually six Microwave Cumulatives will take place, one per month from April to September inclusive. In 1986, for instance, the bands eligible for entry alternated between 3.4 and 5.7GHz, and each band will score separately and contain only one section for all classes of entry. During each activity period, a station may change location once and the definition of a location was given earlier. Contestants may start from a new location for each activity period. Contacts are scored at one point per kilometre and half-points may be claimed by both stations for a cross-band contact if a two-way exchange cannot be accomplished on the same band. Such contacts must be clearly marked in the logs submitted. Two activity periods will count towards the final score for each band. Operation will take place between 0900 and 2000gmt. The closing date for entries is 15 days after the last period. It should be noted that the bands in use are agreed on a year-by-year basis in order to stimulate activity on those bands which are felt to be in need of increased activity levels.

(3) Six 10GHz cumulative activity periods will coincide with the Microwave Cumulatives described above. The same general rules apply, but there are three sections, narrowband, wideband and tv, which are scored separately. Stations may operate in all sections if so desired, provided that separate equipment is available for each mode (excluding preamps, power amplifiers and antennas). Awards are made to the winner, runner-up, leading foreign station and leading fixed station in each section. In this "contest" three activity periods will count towards the final score and stations not able to operate for three periods are encouraged to send in logs as a record of their activity. Such logs will not be eligible for entry but will be recorded in the results tables. The closing date for entry is as (2) above.

(4) Organised by RSGB under the same rules and coincident with the IARU Region 1 Contest, this contest includes all bands from 432MHz up to and including 24GHz, and is likely in the near future to be extended to include bands above 24GHz. It is a 24h contest, running typically from 1400h on day one to 1400h on day two. There are two such contests in the calendar, one in May and the other in October. Scoring is on a radial ring basis for 432 and 1,296MHz and on a one point per kilometre for the other bands, half points scoring for crossband contacts. There are two sections, single-operator and multi-operator.

(5) This RSGB contest is a once-per-year event culminating in the award of the 1,296MHz Trophy.

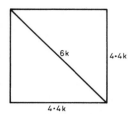

Fig 2.7. The smallest QRA locator square, showing the greatest inaccuracy of ±3km

(6) From 1986 this annual event was extended to cover 70, 144, 432MHz, and 1.3 and 2.3GHz. It is a 24h event and scoring will be on a radial ring basis.

(7) A once-per-year event for both bands.

(8) Known as the RSGB Winter Cumulatives. Five events open to fixed or portable stations, running between October and December, these are short (evenings-only) contests. Entry is the best cumulative score of three from five.

(9) From 1987 in the UK, the first Sundays of the months indicated have been nominated as microwave activity days, to try to encourage portable activity (particularly on 10 and 24GHz) in the winter months.

2.6 MICROWAVE CALCULATIONS

Many of the day-to-day calculations involved in microwave operation centre on the use of trigonometry to determine the distances and beam bearings to distant stations. These calculations can be carried out manually, with the aid of a scientific calculator, a programmable calculator or, more easily, with a pocket-portable or home microcomputer.

The mathematics of such calculations are given first, followed in section 2.7 by several short programs, written in BASIC, which exploit latitude, longitude and "Maidenhead" locator systems as well as the UK-based National Grid Reference (NGR) system to calculate distance and bearing between stations. Two additional programs are given there, one of which allows simple microwave systems analysis while the other gives a graphics plot of the path profile when distance, K-value and obstructions are entered.

2.6.1 Location systems

There are several methods of varying accuracy which can be used, but all depend on some form of map reference system to specify the location of the two stations – in what follows the terms "home" and "distant" refer to operator location and the location of the station to be worked, respectively. Some of the more common methods are:

1. *Latitude and longitude.* This is the most fundamental and universally understood system, consisting of a network of imaginary circles drawn on the earth's surface. It is capable of very great accuracy and is unambiguous. Maps for this system are available worldwide.

Source: Most maps
Accuracy: As great as required

2. *QRA locator.* This is based on latitude and longitude but has several disadvantages for calculation purposes. The references produced are not unique and repeat themselves over large distances. It is not capable of great accuracy and has to be converted back to latitude and longitude for bearing calculations. This conversion is tedious, as the sub-divisions of the squares are non-decimal and a very strange arrangement is used for the last letter of the reference. However, it has been widely used in Europe on the vhf bands.

Source: Same as latitude and longitude but needs a "look-up" table for conversion to QRA

Accuracy: Worst error ±3km; the smallest "square" is about 4.4km square in Europe. See Fig 2.7

3. *National Grid Reference (NGR).* This method uses a rectangular grid of lines on a Mercator projection map of the UK. It is very accurate and can be used directly to calculate bearings. It is very simple to use but is limited to the UK, though its use has been extended to nearby coasts, for example France.

Source: Ordnance Survey (OS) etc
Accuracy: Fractions of a km, as great as required

4. *Universal Transverse Mercator (UTM).* This method is similar to, but not compatible with, NGR. Maps are available worldwide. It has the accuracy and ease of use of the NGR over short ranges but becomes more complicated if the path crosses the boundary between two adjacent zones which occur about every 1,000km.

5. *Bearing and distance from a large town.* This is a very quick but rather inaccurate method since towns are usually quite large and poorly defined in outline.

Source: any map
Accuracy: approximately 5 to 10km

6. *Maidenhead locator.* This is a newer system than the QRA locator, and one which overcomes some of its disadvantages. It is based on lat/long and has worldwide coverage. The standard version is accurate to about 3.5km, but this can be improved by adding further characters to the reference.

Source: maps containing lat/long

What follows is a summary of an article by John Morris, GM4ANB, which appeared in *Radio Communication* October 1984. Entitled "The new locator system", it explains how the then-new system works, and provides much useful and practical information.

"VHF, uhf and microwave operators used the 'new' locator system from 1 January 1985. For the uninitiated, a locator system is a way of giving the location of your station to within a few kilometres as quickly and efficiently as possible.

During the previous decade or so it has become commonplace for stations making dx contacts on the vhf bands and above to exchange their locators, partly to allow the distance to be calculated, but also because collecting locator squares has become a popular sport. In most contests it is part of the rules that locators must be exchanged, again to allow the distance, and hence the score, for the contact to be calculated.

Until recently it was only in Europe that a locator system was in widespread use. The system, commonly called the 'QRA' but in recent years more correctly termed 'QTH locator', was invented somewhere in middle Europe, and gradually spread to the whole continent. Unfortunately it was never really designed for more than local use, and was stretched to serve even Europe. Now other parts of the world, notably North America, are becoming interested in the idea of a locator system, but there is just no way that the QRA can be persuaded to reach across the Atlantic. It is also a rather complicated system, and not too easy to calculate.

The solution was to change to a new system. A single locator system, designed by amateurs to suit the special requirements of amateur radio, has now been adopted by all three regions of the IARU – the international organisation of national radio societies. The adoption means that amateurs all over the world have a single, well-defined way of telling each other their locations with a minimum of fuss and bother.

Some questions often asked:

Q: What difference will this make to operating?

A: Once the changeover is complete there should be little difference on the surface. Instead of sending one string of characters – such as YN27e – you will send a different string – such as IO83QP. After a short while the new system should become just as familiar as the old one, and you will turn your beam south (or whatever) just as automatically on hearing 'IO83QP' as you did on hearing 'YN27e'.

Q: Is my hard-earned collection of squares totally useless, so that I have to start collecting all over again?

A: No. The new system was deliberately designed to have a certain amount of compatibility with the old one, so that square collections, lists, awards and so on can continue as before. The 'big squares' are all in the same places but they have just been given different names. Conversion from old to new squares is quite simple, and will be explained.

Q: How do I find my new locator?

A: There are three ways of doing this. The first is to read and understand the description of the system, and work it out for yourself. The second is to follow the step-by-step procedure given in this article, using nothing more than pencil, paper, a calculator, and a few minutes' time. The third is to use a computer, either your own or perhaps one brought along to the local club. A program to calculate locators from National Grid References will be listed.

Q: What about maps?

A: Maps are available from the RSGB.

How the system works

The world is divided along the lines of latitude and longitude into fields. Each field covers 20° of longitude from west to east and 10° of latitude from south to north, and it takes 324 of them to cover the world. The fields are labelled by two letters, each in the range 'A' to 'R'. The first letter gives the longitude of the field, starting from 180°W, and working eastwards. The second letter gives the latitude of the field, starting from 90°S and working northwards.

For example, take field 'AA'. The first 'A' shows that the field covers 180°W to 160°W. The second 'A' gives the latitude covered by the field as 90°S to 80°S. At the opposite end of the earth is field 'RR', which runs from 160°E to 180°E and 80°N to 90°N.

Most of Britain and Ireland is in field 'IO', which covers 20°W to 0°W and 50°N to 60°N. The Channel Islands, Isles of Scilly, and the Lizard Point in Cornwall are in field 'IN', which covers 20°W to 0°W and 40°N to 50°N. Most of the Shetlands (roughly from Sandwick northwards) are in field 'IP', which covers 20°W to 0°W and 60°N to 70°N. That part of England east of Greenwich, including Norfolk, Suffolk, Essex, Kent and most of Cambridgeshire and parts of other counties is in field 'JO' which covers 0°E to 20°E and 50°N to 60°N.

Each of the fields is divided, again along lines of latitude and longitude, into 100 squares. These are arranged as a 10-by-10 grid, so that each one covers 1° of latitude and 2° of longitude. Two digits, each '0' to '9', are used to label the squares. The first gives the longitude within the field, starting from the west, and the second the latitude, starting from the south.

For example, take square 'IO00'. The field letters, 'IO', show that it is somewhere in the range 20°W to 0°W, and 50°N to 60°N. The first '0' says that the square is at the western end of the field, so that it covers 20°W to 18°W. The second '0' puts the square at the south of the field, giving its latitude coverage as 50°N to 51°N.

It may be noted that the locator squares coincide with the old QRA squares. Thus square 'IO83' is exactly the same as the old 'YN' square; new 'JO01' is the same as old 'AL' square; new 'IN79' is the same as old 'XJ'; new 'IO86' is the same as old 'YQ', and so on.

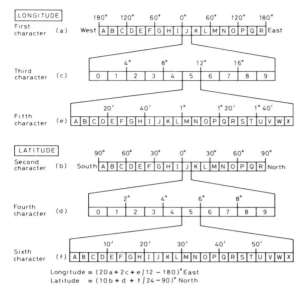

Longitude = (20a + 2c + e / 12 − 180)° East
Latitude = (10b + d + f / 24 − 90)° North

Fig 2.8. New locator system

Each of the locator squares is finally divided into a 24-by-24 grid of sub-squares. Each of these covers 5' of longitude and 2.5' of latitude. They are labelled using two letters, each in the range 'A' to 'X', starting from the southwest corner of the square. The first of the sub-square letters gives the longitude, and the second the latitude.

A full locator reference consists of the two field letters, two square digits, and two sub-square letters. To give a full example, take locator 'IO83QP'. The 'IO' part means that it is in field 'IO', ie 20°W to 0°W, 50°N to 60°N. The '83' part means that it is in square 'IO83', which has its southwest corner at 4°W and 53°N. The 'Q' says that the longitude is between 1°20' and 1°25' east of this. The 'P' gives the latitude as somewhere between 37.5' and 40' north of the southern edge of the square. Thus the area covered by locator 'IO83QP' is from 2°40'W to 2°35'W and 53°37.5'N to 53°40'N. So, if you happen to live in Chorley in Lancashire, your locator is IO83QP.

Fig 2.8 shows how the locator is built up from fields, squares and sub-squares. It may be noted that all of the longitude defining characters – the first, third and fifth – run from west to east, while the latitude defining characters – the second, fourth and sixth – go from south to north. In addition, at all levels the east-west size, in degrees, is always twice the north-south size.

In distance terms, each sub-square is about 4.6km from south to north. The east-west size varies with latitude, but in the middle of Britain (55°N) it is about 5.3km. If you take the accuracy of the system as being

the farthest you can get from the middle of a sub-square without actually leaving it, this gives a maximum error of about 3.5km (at 55° latitude), which is quite adequate for most normal operation. Accuracy can be further improved by subdividing the smallest square in decimal fashion and adding two more digits after the last character of the usual format, although this degree of accuracy (around 300m) is seldom required.

Names

On the air the system should be called simply 'locator', with no 'QTH', 'QRA' or anything else. For example, you might say 'My locator is IO83QP', or ask of another station 'What is your locator?' On cw the recommended abbreviation is 'LOC', so that the cw equivalent of 'What is your locator?' is simply 'LOC?'

The various divisions of the locator, fields, squares and sub-squares have just those names. A vhf dx chaser might claim to have worked '300 squares' or for the real enthusiast '20 fields'.

Just to confuse matters, amateurs in North America seem to have taken to the name 'grid system'. So if you get the question 'What is your grid?' then what is wanted is your locator.

Finding your locator by hand

The following step-by-step procedure can be used to calculate your locator from your latitude and longitude, using nothing more than pencil, paper and a simple calculator.

First of all you must find your latitude and longitude. The latitude should be rounded down to the next half of a minute south, and the longitude to the next whole minute west. If you use an Ordnance Survey map for this you should note that the grid lines do not run exactly north-south and east-west, and should not be used. Instead a long straight edge should be used to read the scales at the edges of the map. The centre page from a large newspaper folded across the corners works quite well. Having established your latitude and longitude the procedure is as follows:

1. First deal with the longitude. Convert the longitude to decimal degrees. This is done by dividing the minutes part by 60 and adding the result to the degrees part.

2. If you are east of Greenwich, add 180.

3. If you are west of Greenwich subtract the value from 180.

Table 2.5. Number-to-letter conversion table for hand calculation of a locator

0	A	5	F	10	K	15	P	20	U
1	B	6	G	11	L	16	Q	21	V
2	C	7	H	12	M	17	R	22	W
3	D	8	I	13	N	18	S	23	X
4	E	9	J	14	O	19	T		

4. Divide the result by two.

5. Now divide the value obtained by 10, and note the figures to the left of the decimal point. These give the first letters of the locator, on the basis of 0 =A, 1 =B, 2=C and so on, as shown in Table 2.5.

6. Multiply by 10, and note the single digit immediately before the decimal point. This is the third character of the locator.

7. Take just the fractional part of the value (the part to the right of the decimal point), and multiply it by 24. The figures to the left of the decimal point give the fifth character of the locator, once again using the table.

8. Now follow a similar process for latitude. Convert the latitude to decimal degrees.

9. If you are north of the equator, add 90.

10. If you are south of the equator subtract the value from 90.

11. Divide by 10, and take the second letter of the locator from the digits to the left of the decimal point, using the table.

12. Multiply by 10, and note the digit to the left of the decimal point. This is the fourth character of the locator.

13. Take the fractional part, and multiply by 24. The figures to the left of the decimal point give the last letter of the locator, again using the table.

As an example, take Edinburgh Castle. From the map, its latitude is somewhere between 55°56.5'N and 55°57'N, and its longitude between 3°11'W and 3°12'W. Rounding to the next half minute south and whole minute west means that latitude 50°56.5'N and longitude 3°12'W are taken. The instructions above are then obeyed. In the following example the steps taken are described on the left, and the result on the calculator shown on the right:

1. Take the minutes of the longitude   12
   Divide by 60   0.2
   Add the degrees of the longitude   3.2

2. The longitude is not east, so do nothing

3. The latitude is west, so subtract from 180   176.8

4. Divide by 2   88.4

5. Divide by 10   8.84
   To the left of the decimal point is '8', so from the table, the first locator character is 'I'

6. Multiply by 10   88.4
   The digit immediately left of the decimal point is '8' so the third character of the locator must also be '8'. The locator so far is thus 'I-8---', where '-' means a character

yet to be determined

7. Take the fractional part   0.4
   Multiply by 24   9.6
   To the left of the decimal point is '9', so the fifth character must be 'J'. The locator becomes 'I-8-J-'

8. Take the minutes part of the latitude   56.5
   Divide by 60   0.941666666
   Add in the degrees part of the latitude   55.94166667

9. The latitude is north, so add 90   145.9416667

10. The latitude is not south, so do nothing

11. Divide by 10   14.5941667
    To the left of the decimal point is '14', so the second character of the locator is 'O'. The locator becomes 'IO8-J-'

12. Multiply by 10   145.9416667
    The digit to the left of the decimal point is '5', so the fourth character of the locator must also be '5', giving 'IO85J-'

13. Take the fractional part   0.94166666
    Multiply by 24   22.59999984
    To the left of the decimal point is '22', so 'W' is the last character of the locator

The full locator for Edinburgh Castle is thus IO85JW.

Square conversions

As has been mentioned, the new locator squares cover exactly the same area as the old locator 'big squares'; only the names have changed. This means that lists and awards can continue uninterrupted. If you have previously worked ZL square under the old system, then you have worked IO91 square under the new system.

Converting squares from old to new systems is fairly straightforward, and if you are a square collector it is worth sitting down and converting your lists of squares worked and confirmed.

There are several ways of doing this. The easiest is to use a computer program. It is almost as easy to use the small card maps of the old and new systems. For each conversion simply look up the square on the old map, find the corresponding square on the new map, and read off the new square name.

Failing all else, the next table can be used. This table works only for the area 40° to 66°N, 12°W to 40°E, but should be adequate for most contacts. To use it, find the first letter of the old locator square in the first column. The first and third characters of the new square can be read off from columns (2) and (3). Then find the second letter of the old locator square in column (4), and read off the second and fourth characters from columns (5) and (6). The procedure is more complicated to describe than to carry out.

Table 2.6. Square conversions

(1)	AB CD	EF GH	IJ KL	MN OP	QR ST	U VW X YZ
(2)	JJJJ	JJJJ	JJKK	KKKK	KKKK	IIII II
(3)	0123	4567	8901	2345	6789	4567 89
(4)	AB CD	EF GH	IJ KL	MN OP	QR ST	U VWX YZ
(5)	NNNN	NNNN	NNOO	OOOO	OOOO	PPPP PP
(6)	0123	4567	8901	2345	6789	0123 45

Key: (1) Old square first letter; (2) new square first character; (3) new square third character; (4) old square second letter; (5) new square second character; (6) new square fourth character. See general text for detailed explanation.

For example, take old square 'BI'. Find 'B' in column (1) and read off 'J' and '1' from columns (2) and (3). Then look up 'I' in column (4) and read off 'N' and '8' from columns (5) and (6). Thus the old square 'BI' corresponds to new square 'JN18'.

Converting locators

In the past, computer programs have been published that claim to convert old locators to new ones and, regrettably, more will probably appear in the future. Why 'regrettably'? Because, briefly, this conversion is just not possible without quite a high probability of error.

The new system was deliberately designed to be compatible with the old at the square level, so that lists and awards could continue without hiatus. This compatibility does not extend to the sub-square level. The smallest squares of the two systems are just not the same. This means that any conversion from old to new locators can quite easily get the wrong answer, and often will.

The technique these programs normally use is to convert from old locator to latitude and longitude, and then from latitude and longitude to new locator. What this overlooks is that an old locator small square does not correspond to just a single point, but to an area of typically 20 or 25km . There is nothing to say that all of this area has to be in the same new locator sub-square. Indeed, often part will be in one sub-square, and part in another.

For example, old locator YK01c covers longitude 3°48'W to 3°52'W. In the new system part of this area is in IO80CW (3°45'W to 3°50'W), and part in IO80BW (3°50'W to 3°55'W). Obviously the old locator just does not give enough information to decide what the new locator is. Fig 2.9 shows the relation between the new locator square and the old locator square.

An equally compelling reason for working out your new locator from scratch, rather than trying to convert from the old one, is that a surprisingly large number of stations have their old locator wrong. The old system is somewhat complicated, making it all too easy to make mistakes in calculating it. Even one ex-VHF Manager of

the RSGB will admit to having sent the wrong locator for several years. Worse still, other stations in the vicinity simply copied and used the same wrong locator!

The message, therefore, is to sit down and work out your new locator from scratch, a matter of 5min at most. That is the only way to be sure that you have it right.

Computer programs

The new locator system is very well suited indeed to computers, rather more so than the old system. There are already several programs around that will do various things with the locator, such as contest scoring, distance and bearing calculation, and so on, and no doubt many more will be appearing in the near future. Several programs are given in section 2.7, which will deal with the kind of calculations most used – locator, latitude/longitude, National Grid Reference, distance and bearing.

If you are a member of a radio club, once you have the program running correctly you might like to take your computer and the local OS map along to a meeting to give others the chance to find their locators."

2.6.2 Bearing calculations

Once the location of each station is known the bearing can be calculated using one or other of the following methods. "Classical" manual methods only are described here. In section 2.7, there are a number of microcomputer programs which carry out similar calculations but much more quickly!

2.6.3 Spherical trigonometry

This can be used with the latitude/longitude (lat/long) system and gives exact values for bearings and distances. The calculations can be carried out with a scientific calculator and the bearings are given relative to true (geographic) north.

First the lat and long of both stations are converted into the form of degrees and decimal fractions of degrees; the distant station's lat and long are referred to as DN and DW (distant north, distant west), and the home station's lat and long are HN and HW (home north and home west). Degrees north and west are positive, south and east negative.

DIFF represents the difference in longitude between the two stations (DW – HW) and A represents the angle in degrees subtended at the centre of the earth by the two stations. The bearings and distance are then calculated as follows:

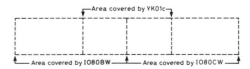

Fig 2.9. Comparison of area covered by old and new locator systems

	Lat	Long	
Distant	DN= ** ***	DW = ** ***	(decimal degrees)
Home	HN= ** ***	HW= ** ***	
		** ***	

DIFF = DW – HW

$$A = \arccos(\ \cos(DIFF)\ \cos(DN)\ \cos(HN)\ + $$
$$\sin(HN)\ \sin(DN)\ )$$

Path length = 111.15 A   km

$$X = \arccos\left(\frac{\sin(DN) - \cos(A)\ \sin(HN)}{\sin(A)\ \cos(HN)} \right)$$

$$Y = \arccos\left(\frac{\sin(HN) - \cos(A)\ \sin(DN)}{\sin(A)\ \cos(DN)} \right)$$

If DW > HW then:

	Bearing TO	= 360 – X
	Bearing FROM	= Y
otherwise:	Bearing TO	= X
	Bearing FROM	= 360 – Y

This method gives the exact great circle bearings relative to true north. It will be found that the bearings TO and FROM are not exactly 180° apart. This is quite correct and other methods which only give one bearing are only approximate.

To illustrate this method the calculation will be done for a path between Snowdon and Peterhead, with Peterhead as the home station.

Snowdon:		53° 04′N		04° 05′W
	DN=	53.067	DW=	+4.083

Peterhead:		57° 24′N		01° 57′W
	HN=	57.4	HW=	+1.95

DW	=	+4.083
HW	=	+1.950
DIFF	=	2.133

$$A = \arccos(\ \cos(2.133)\ \cos(53.067)\ \cos(57.4)$$
$$\sin(57.4)\sin(53.067)\ )$$

= 6.722

$$X = \arccos\left(\frac{\sin(53.067) - \cos(6.722)\ \sin(57.4)}{\sin(6.722)\ \cos(57.4)} \right)$$

= 163.4°

$$Y = \arccos\left(\frac{\sin(57.4) - \cos(6.722)\ \sin(53.067)}{\sin(6.722)\ \cos(53.067)} \right)$$

= 14.8°

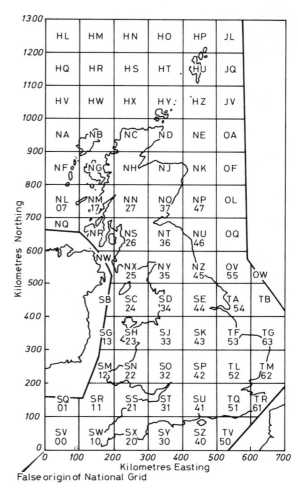

Fig 2.10. The 100km National Grid squares and the letters used to designate them

DW (4.083) is greater than HW (1.95) so:
Bearing TO Snowdon   = 360 – 163.4 = 196.6° true
Bearing FROM Snowdon   = 14.8° true

Note that 14.8 + 180 = 194.8 compared with 196.6.

2.6.4 Simple trigonometry and NGR

This can be used with any rectangular grid system such as NGR or UTM. The National Grid is a rectangular grid drawn on a transverse Mercator projection map of the UK, with the prime meridian at 2°W. This method of calculating the bearings assumes that the paths are straight lines on this map (which is not strictly correct as the map is a flat representation of a near-spherical earth). In practice this method is very accurate over paths up to about 1,000km.

In the NGR system, a point on the earth is usually specified by a two-letter reference for the 100km square and the number of kilometres east and north of the bottom left-hand corner of that square, as in Fig 2.10. Thus SZ710992 represents a point 471.0km east and 99.2km north of the origin of the grid.

An alternative way of describing the point is to specify the 100km square not by its letters, but by its number of kilometres east and north of the grid origin, giving an eight-digit reference. Thus SZ710992 is equivalent to 47100992. The latter method is far more useful for amateur purposes as the eastings and northings can be obtained directly by subtracting the references of the two stations, rather than having to work out where "SZ" square is, relative to the "Home station" square. It is far less prone to errors during calculations which is an important factor if the calculation is being carried out under pressure or in a hurry, such as during portable operation.

The numbers of hundreds of kilometres for each square are shown in Fig 2.10, but they can also be found at each corner of an OS map – in rather small print!

The bearings and distance are calculated using the simple geometry of a right-angled triangle as shown in Fig 2.11. The only numbers required are the difference between the easterly and northerly co-ordinates of the two stations.

If the stations have co-ordinates DE, DN (distant east, distant north) and HE, HN (home east, home north), then the differences are DIFFE = DE – HE and DIFFN = DN – HN, and the angle X is as shown in Fig 2.11. The calculations are as follows:

	km E	km N
Distant NGR	DE	DN
Home NGR	HE	HN
DIFF	DIFFE	DIFFN

Path length (km) = $\sqrt{(\text{DIFFE}^2 + \text{DIFFN}^2)}$

If DIFFE is zero then: (a) If DIFFN is positive, then
$$\begin{aligned}\text{Bearing TO} &= 0\\ \text{Bearing FROM} &= 180\end{aligned}$$

(b) If DIFFN is negative, then
$$\begin{aligned}\text{Bearing TO} &= 180\\ \text{Bearing FROM} &= 0\end{aligned}$$

Otherwise:

$$X = \arctan\left(\frac{|\text{DIFFN}|}{|\text{DIFFE}|}\right)$$

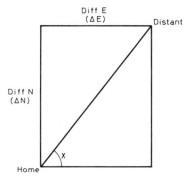

Fig 2.11. The geometry of the right-angled triangle used in simple trigonometrical calculations

(The | | signs mean that the sign of DIFF taken to be positive, even is it is negative.)

If DIFFE is positive then: $\begin{aligned}\text{Bearing TO} &= 90 - X\\ \text{Bearing FROM} &= 270 - X\end{aligned}$

otherwise: $\begin{aligned}\text{Bearing TO} &= 270 + X\\ \text{Bearing FROM} &= 90 + X\end{aligned}$

These bearings are relative to GRID north which differs from true north by a few degrees, the amount depending on the longitude of each station. The exact value is given on each OS map. The difference can be found approximately (in the UK) by taking the difference between the longitude of the station and that of the 2°W line (degrees west are positive, degrees east are negative), but this can be up to about 0.5° in error. Thus:

TRUE bearing TO   = GRID bearing TO
                                     – (Home long – 2)

TRUE bearing FROM   = GRID bearing FROM
                                          – (Distant long – 2)

For example, take a path from Portsmouth to South Wales:

Portsmouth	SZ710992	= 47100992
South Wales	ST260977	= 32601977

DE	= 471.0	DN	= 99.2
HE	= 326.0	HN	= 197.7

DIFFE = 145.0   DIFFN = – 98.5

Path length = $\sqrt{(145^2 + 98.5^2)} = 175\text{km}$

DIFFE is not zero, so

$$X = \arctan\left(\frac{|-98.5|}{|145.0|}\right) = 34.2$$

DIFFE is positive, so

Bearing TO Portsmouth $= 90+34.2=124.2°$ GRID
Bearing FROM Portsmouth $=270+34.2=304.2°$ GRID

Now convert to TRUE bearings:

TRUE – GRID at Portsmouth from map $=0.8°$
TRUE bearing from Portsmouth $= 304.2 + 0.8 =305°$

Longitude of Portsmouth $= +0.994°$
TRUE bearing FROM Portsmouth
$=304.2-(0.994-2) =305.2°$

TRUE-GRID at South Wales from map $= -0.7°$
TRUE bearing to Portsmouth $= 124.2 - 0.7$ $=123.5°$

Longitude of South Wales $= 3.1°$
TRUE bearing TO Portsmouth $=12.42 - (3.1-2) =123.1°$

2.6.5 Drawing a line on a map

This is used mainly when the location is given as a bearing and distance from a town. It requires that both stations are shown on the same sheet of the map which, if it is small enough to be convenient to use, will probably not be accurate enough to give precise details of the location. This method is only suitable for very short paths, or for those stations using quite large beamwidths, since it does not take account of the earth's curvature.

2.6.6 Converting NGR to lat/long

If the NGR is known, the following relationships can be used to calculate the lat and long of the station, so that the more accurate spherical trigonometry method can be used.
    If NG(n) is the number of kilometres north and NG(e) the number of kilometres east from the grid origin, then:

1. $X = \dfrac{NG(n) + 100}{111.166}$

2. $L = 49 + X - 0.000079\,X^2$

3. $B = \dfrac{NG(e) - 400}{111.55}$

4. $LAT = \arcsin(\cos(B)\sin(L))$

5. $Y = \arccos(\tan(LAT)/\tan(L))$

If NG(e) is greater than 400km then longitude $= 2 - Y$
If NG(e) is less than 400km then longitude $= 2 + Y$
    (Degrees west are positive)

In some cases the NGR co-ordinates may become negative if they are extended further south. Provided that the sign is used throughout the calculations, there will be no problems.

To summarise, the method of calculation chosen depends on the accuracy required. For vhf/uhf, QRA or line-drawing are acceptable methods. At the lower microwave frequencies comparatively wide beamwidths are still in use and quite large distances may be involved. Here QRA, Maidenhead, lat/long or line drawing can be used.
    At the higher microwave frequencies beamwidths are very narrow and distances somewhat shorter, often within the boundaries of a country. NGR, Maidenhead and lat/long are sufficiently accurate and quite simple to use, but for international use lat/long has many advantages and is highly accurate, although slightly more involved.

2.7 MICROCOMPUTER PROGRAMS FOR MICROWAVE CALCULATIONS

Most of the programs given here are written in such a way that it would be possible to compile a larger "menu-driven" program in which the user is invited to call a particular routine from the choice offered. Line renumbering would be needed to avoid duplicate line numbers. Although written to run on the BBC Micro, Model B, the user should have little difficulty in translating these programs into their computer's particular dialect of BASIC. It is not claimed that these short programs or routines represent the ultimate in programming elegance, but are given merely as examples of the types of routine which have been found most useful in planning microwave operation.

2.7.1 Program 1: Path profile plot [10]

This program plots a graphical representation of the path profile when given the path length, transmitter and receiver heights, "K"-value and obstructions. It should be of particular use in determining the viability (or otherwise) of paths up to several hundred kilometres, especially on the higher-frequency bands, for instance on 10 and 24GHz, when using wideband modes and low-power, simple equipment rather than high-power, narrowband modes. It presents an alternative to the manual plotting methods using earth-profile paper.

```
 10 MODE4:PRINT:PRINT:PRINT TAB(8)"*** Path Profile Check ***"
 60 PRINT:PRINT TAB(5,10):INPUT "Enter path length in km ";L
 70 XS=INT(1200/L)
 80 PRINT:INPUT "Enter k-value (default = 1.33) ";K
 90 IF K=0 THEN K=1.33
100 DIM H(L)
110 Z=1/(12.74*K)
120 HM=0
130 FOR D= 0 TO L
140 H(D)=D*(L-D)*Z
150 IF H(D)>HM THEN HM=H(D)
160 NEXT
170 PRINT:INPUT"Enter Tx height in m ";TH
180 PRINT:INPUT"Enter Rx height in m ";RH
190 IF TH>HM THEN HM=TH
200 IF RH>HM THEN HM=RH
210 PROCdraw
220 PRINT"Press any key to continue"
230 C=INKEY$(100):IF C$="" THEN 230
240 CLS:INPUT "Enter number of obstacles ";N
250 IF N=0 THEN PROCdraw
260 PRINT:PRINT"Enter each obstacle distance from Tx in km and
      height in m ASL"
270 FOR I=1 TO N
280 PRINT:PRINT"Obstacle   ";I;"   ";:INPUT X,Y:H(X)=H(X)+Y
290 NEXT
300 FOR I=1 TO L
310 IF H(I)>HM THEN HM=H(I)
320 NEXT
330 PROCdraw
340 END
350 DEF PROCdraw
360 CLS
370 YS=950/HM
380 MOVE 0,50
390 FOR D=0 TO L
400 DRAW D*XS,YS*H(D)+50
410 NEXT
420 MOVE 0,YS*TH+50:DRAW XS*L,YS*RH+50
430 ENDPROC
```

2.7.2 Program 2: Lat/long to Maidenhead locator conversion [11]

On entry of latitude in degrees, minutes and seconds (north or south of the equator) and longitude (east or west of the Greenwich meridian), the program will calculate the standard form of the international ("Maidenhead") locator. If the user wishes to build the routine into a menu program, it will be necessary to put the appropriate line number into line 500, otherwise "ELSE GOTO" can be deleted, as can lines 480, 490 and 500.

```
310 CLS
315 PRINT:PRINT"*** Lat/Long to Locator program ***"
320 PRINT:PRINT"Please enter Latitude (D,M,S,N/S)":PRINT
330 INPUT D,M,S,A$
340 IF A$="S" THEN GOSUB 520
350 I=INT(D/10)
360 J=INT(D-I*10)
370 K=INT((M+S/60)*2)/5
380 PRINT:PRINT"Please enter Longitude (D,M,S,E/W)"
390 INPUT D,M,S,A$
400 IF A$="W" THEN GOSUB 520
410 F=INT(D/20)
420 G= INT((D-F*20)/2)
430 H=INT((ABS(D*60-INT(D/2)*120)+M+S/60)/5)
440 PRINT
450 PRINT"Locator:        ";
460 PRINT CHR$(F+74)+CHR$(I+74) +CHR$(G+48)+
    CHR$(J+48)+CHR$(H+65)+CHR$(K+65)
470 PRINT
480 PRINT"Another go  (Y/N)?  "
490 INPUT A$
500 IF A$="Y" THEN CLS:GOTO 320 ELSE GOTO
510 STOP
520 D=-1-D
530 M=59-M
540 S=60-S
550 IF S<60 THEN 580
560 S=0
570 M=M+1
580 IF M<60 THEN 610
590 M=M-60
600 D=D+1
610 RETURN
```

2.7.3 Program 3: Maidenhead locator to lat/long conversion [11]

This program does the reverse of program 2; that is, it will provide the user with latitude and longitude figures

from any locator entered into the program. The same remarks as above apply to lines 980, 990 and 1000.

```
810 PRINT
820 DEF FNA(I)=ASC(MID$(M$,I,1))-65
830 DEF FNB(J)=(J-INT(J))*60
840 CLS:PRINT:PRINT"*** Locator to Lat/Long Calculation ***"
850 PRINT:PRINT:PRINT"Please enter Locator"
860 INPUT M$:IF LEN(M$)<6 OR LEN(M$)>6 THEN PRINT:PRINT"Sorry,that
     is not a valid Locator":GOTO 850
870 D=FNA(2)*10+FNA(4)-73
880 M=FNA(6)*2.5*1.25
890 PRINT:PRINT"Latitude:         ";
900 IF D>=0 THEN PRINTD;SPC(1);INT(M);SPC(1);FNB(M);SPC(1);" N"
910 IF D<0 THEN
    PRINT(-1-D);SPC(1);INT(60-M);SPC(1);60-FNB(M);SPC(1);" S"
920 D=FNA(1)*20+FNA(3)*2+INT(FNA(5)/12)-146
930 M=INT(FNB(FNA(5)/12)*2+5.01)/2
940 PRINT"Longitude:          ";
950 IF D>=0 THEN PRINTD;SPC(1);INT(M);SPC(1);FNB(M);SPC(1);" E"
960 IF D<0 THEN
    PRINT-1-D;SPC(1);INT(60-M);SPC(1);60-FNB(M);SPC(1);" W"
970 PRINT
980 PRINT"Another go  (Y/N) ? "
990 INPUT M$:CLS
1000 IF M$="Y" THEN GOTO 850 ELSE GOTO
1010 STOP
```

2.7.4 Program 4: Bearings from locators [11]

Given "home" and "distant" locators, program 4 will calculate distance and bearing from the home to the distant station. The bearings are "true" bearings. The end-of-routine choice has not been included in this particular routine, although the ability to retain the "home" locator for re-use is built-in.

```
4000 CLS
4010 DIM P(2,2),M$(2)
4020 M=57.2958
4030 DEF FNA(I)=ASC(MID$(M$(J),I,1))-65
4040 GOSUB4480
4050 PRINT:PRINT TAB(11)"Locator to Locator"
4060 PRINT:PRINT TAB(10)"Distance and Bearing"
4070 PRINT:PRINT TAB(12)" (Menu Option 6)"
4080 PRINT:PRINT"Please enter Home station Locator"
4090 J=1
4100 GOSUB4360
4110 PRINT
4120 PRINT"Please enter Distant station Locator"
4130 J=2
4140 GOSUB 4360
4150 A=P(2,1)/M
4160 B=P(2,2)/M
4170 L=(P(1,2)-P(1,1))*2/M
4180 E=SIN(A)*SIN(B)+COS(A)*COS(B)*COS(L)
4190 D=ATN(SQR(1-E*E)/E)
4200 IF D<0 THEN D=180/M+D
4210 IF A>B THEN F=90+(1+ABS(A-B)/(A-B))
4220 IF L<>0 THEN F=90+M*ATN((SIN(A)*E-SIN(B))/(SIN(L)*COS(A)^2))
4230 IF SIN(L)<0 THEN F=F+180
4240 GOSUB 4480
4250 PRINT
4260 PRINT"From ";M$(1);" to ";M$(2)
4270 PRINT
4280 PRINT"Bearing =",INT(F)
4290 PRINT
4300 R=6365.11*D
4310 PRINT"Distance =",INT(R*100)/100;" Km"
4320 PRINT
4340 GOTO 4110
4350 PRINT"Error - try again"
4360 INPUT M$(J)
4370 CLS
4380 PRINT
4390 IF LEN(M$(J))<>6 THEN 4350
4400 FOR I=1 TO 2
4410 A=FNA(I)
4420 B=FNA(I+2)+17
4430 C=FNA(I+4)+.5
4440 IF A<0 OR A>18 OR B<0 OR B>9 OR C<0 OR C>24 THEN 4350
4450 P(I,J)=A*10+B+C/24-90
4460 NEXT I
4470 RETURN
4480 CLS
4490 PRINT
4500 PRINTTAB(11);"Maidenhead Locator"
4510 PRINT
4520 RETURN
```

2.7.5 Program 5: Bearings from NGRs [12]

This program is aimed particularly at the UK operator using the higher bands. For this reason it uses National

Grid Reference and converts the two (home and distant) NGRs to give the eastings and northings in kilometres from the grid origin, the international locator, integer distance between the two stations and the bearing in degrees magnetic. The factor converting grid bearing into magnetic bearing (in this case 7.5) is a compromise magnetic variation based on a location in the centre of the UK. If the user wishes to be more precise, then this factor should be replaced (in lines 5240, 5250, 5260 and 5270) by the *actual* magnetic variation printed on the appropriate ("home") Ordnance Survey map. It will be typically 6° for stations near the east coast and 9° for stations near the west coast of Wales. By omitting the factor completely, bearings in grid north will be obtained, in which case the end of line 5300 should be modified to ...;" Deg (Grid)". Lines 5340 and 5350 are included to allow building into a "menu" program. If not required they can be deleted, together with lines 5320 and 5330.

```
4600 DIMT(24):CA=ASC("A"):CS=ASC(" "):CO=ASC("O")
4610 CLS
4620 PRINT:PRINT"   *** Microwave Path Calculation ***"
4630 PRINT:PRINT TAB(12)"Using NGR"
4640 PRINT TAB(1,10)"Gives :- Eastings/Northings in Km"
4650 PRINT TAB(10)"Lat/Long"
4660 PRINT TAB(10)"Locator  (Maidenhead)"
4670 PRINT TAB(10)"Distance and Bearing"
4680 PRINT"from two NGR entries,Home and Distant"
4690 PRINT TAB(0,20)"To continue,please press SPACE bar"
4700 IF GET$=CHR$(32) THEN CLS:GOTO 4710
4710 PRINT:INPUT"Please enter Home NGR";H$
4720 WH=0:N$=H$:GOSUB4830: IF EF GOTO4790
4730 PRINT:INPUT"Please enter Distant NGR";A$
4740 WH=1:N$=A$:GOSUB4830: IF EF GOTO4790
4750 PRINT:PRINT"Your Home Lat/Long is :-":WH=0:GOSUB5050
4760 PRINT:PRINT"The distant Lat/Long is :-":WH=1:GOSUB5050
4770 GOSUB5200
4780 CLEAR:RETURN
4790 PRINT:PRINT"Sorry, that is not a valid NGR"
4800 FORI=1 TO 2000:NEXTI
4810 ON WH+1 GOTO4710,4730
4820 STOP
4830 REM SCREEN INPUT FOR VALIDITY
4840 L=LEN(N$):EF=0:PT=0
4850 IF L<8 ORL=9 OR L>10 THEN EF=1
4860 FORJ=1 TO L:T=ASC(MID$(N$,J,1))
4870 IF T=CS GOTO4940
4880 PT=PT+1:IFJ>2 GOTO4920
4890 T=T-CA:IF T<0 OR T>26 OR T=8 THEN EF=1
4900 IFT>8 THEN T=T-1
4910 GOTO4930
4920 T=T-CO:IF T<0 OR T>9 THEN EF=1
4930 T(PT+WH*8)=T
4940 NEXTJ:IF EF THEN RETURN
4950 X=WH*8+1:TA=INT(T(X)/5):TC=T(X)-5*TA
4960 TB=INT(T(X+1)/5):TD=T(X+1)-5*TB
4970 E=-1000+500*TC+100*TD+10*T(X+2)+T(X+3)+T(X+4)/10
4980 N=1900-500*TA-100*TB+10*T(X+5)+T(X+6)+T(X+7)/10:GOSUB5190
4990 X=21+WH*2:T(X)=N:T(X+1)=E
5000 T1=(N+5548.79)/6371.28
5010 T2=2*ATN(EXP((E-400)/6389.7))
5020 E=ATN(-COS(T2)/(COS(T1)*SIN(T2)))*180/PI-2
5030 N=SIN(T1)*SIN(T2):N=ATN(N/SQR(1-N*N))*180/PI
5040 X=17+WH*2:T(X)=N:T(X+1)=E:RETURN
5050 REM PRINT OUT LAT & LONG
5060 X=17+WH*2:T2=INT(T(X)):T3=INT(600*(T(X)-T2)+0.5)/10
5070 PRINTTAB(5);T2;" degrees  ";T3;" minutes N"
5080 T1=ABS(T(X+1)):T2=INT(T1):T3=INT(600*(T1-T2)+0.5)/10
5090 IF T(X+1)<0 THEN T$="W"
5100 PRINTTAB(5);T2;" degrees  ";T3;" minutes ";T$
5110 T(X)=T(X)/180+0.5:E=T(X+1)/360+0.5:L$=""
5120 T=CA:F=18:GOSUB5160
5130 T=CO:F=16:GOSUB5160
5140 T=CA:F=24:GOSUB5160
5150 PRINT TAB(6)"       Locator  ";L$:RETURN
5160 REM DETERMINE LOCATOR
5170 N=F*(N-INT(N)):E=F*(E-INT(E)):L$=L$+CHR$(T+E)+CHR$(T+N)
5180 RETURN
5190 PRINT TAB(5)"Eastings = ";E;" Km":PRINT TAB(5)"Northings = ";N
      " Km":RETURN
5200 JE=T(24)-T(22)
5210 JN=T(23)-T(21)
5220 A=ATN(ABS(JE)/ABS(JN))
5230 A=DEG(A)
5240 IF JN>0 AND JE>0 THEN A=A+7.5
5250 IF JN<0 AND JE>0 THEN A=(180-A)+7.5
5260 IF JN<0 AND JE<0 THEN A=(180+A)+7.5
5270 IF JN>0 AND JE<0 THEN A=(360-A)+7.5
5280 D=SQR((JE^2)+(JN^2))
5300 PRINT:PRINT TAB(5)"Bearing = ";INT(A);" Deg (Magnetic)"
5310 PRINT TAB(5)"Distance = ";INT(D);" Km"
5320 PRINT"Another go?      Y/N"
5330 INPUT Z$
5340 IF Z$="Y" THEN CLEAR:GOTO 4600
5350 IF Z$<>"Y" THEN GOTO
5360 END
```

2.7.6 Program 6: System performance analysis [13]

This is a simple system analysis program which will allow a station's potential performance to be assessed and should be of use at all microwave frequencies when considering the "needs" of a particular installation. The user is invited to enter a number of equipment parameters from which the performance will be calculated.

```
5000 REM Microwave System Performance Analysis
5010 DATA 0,2.6,10,16,22:REM Detector thresholds
5020 @%=&20109:REM Optional output formatting
5030 CLS:PRINT:PRINT"** System Performance Analysis **"
5050 PRINT: INPUT "Enter frequency in MHz ";F
5060 L=299.8/F
5070 INPUT "Enter Rx i.f. bandwidth in kHz ";RB
5080 LRB=10*LOG(RB)+30
5090 INPUT "Enter Rx noise figure in dB ";NF
5100 INPUT "Enter Rx antenna gain in dB ";RG
5110 BR=SQR(27000/10^(0.1*RG))
5120 PRINT:PRINT " Nominal 3 dB beamwidth = ";BR;"  Degs."
5130 PRINT:INPUT "Enter Rx feeder loss in dB ";RF
5140 PRINT"Choose type of detector: "
5150 PRINT" 1.            SSB "
5160 PRINT" 2.            AM "
5170 PRINT" 3.            FM "
5180 PRINT" 4.            FM no limiter "
5190 PRINT" 5.            FM slope detection "
5200 PRINT: INPUT " Enter choice ";DT
5210 IF DT<1 OR DT>5 THEN 5200
5220 RESTORE
5230 FOR I=1 TO DT
5240 READ DTH
5250 NEXT
5260 NT=290*(10^(0.1*(NF+RF))-1)
5270 PRINT:PRINT " Effective receiver noise temperature =  ";NT;
      " Deg K"
5280 NT=10*LOG(NT)
5290 ERS=-228.6+LRB+NT+DTH-RG
5300 PRINT:PRINT " Effective receiver sensitivity = ";ERS;"  dBW"
5310 PRINT: INPUT " Enter transmitter power in Watts ";TP
5320 TPL=10*LOG(TP)
5330 INPUT " Enter Tx antenna gain in dB ";TG
5340 BT=SQR(27000/10^(0.1*TG))
5350 PRINT:PRINT " Nominal 3dB beamwidth = ";BT;" degs"
5360 PRINT:INPUT " Enter Tx feeder loss in dB ";TF
5370 EI=TPL+TG-TF
5380 PRINT:PRINT " Transmitter eirp = ";EI;" dBW"
5390 PLC=EI-ERS
5400 PRINT:PRINT " Path loss capability = ";PLC;" dB"
5410 PRINT:INPUT " Is system LOS (L) or troposcatter (T) ";S$
5420 IF S$<>"L"AND S$<>"T" THEN 5410
5430 IF S$="T" THEN 5560
5440 PRINT:PRINT " Options are: "
5450 PRINT" 1.       C/N over a given path"
5460 PRINT" 2.       Maximum range of the equipment"
5470 PRINT:INPUT " Enter choice ";C$
5480 IF C$<>"1" AND C$<>"2" THEN 5440
5490 IF C$="2" THEN 5540
5500 PRINT:INPUT" Enter path length in km ";PL
5510 LO=32.45+20*LOG(F)+20*LOG(PL)
5520 PRINT:PRINT " Nominal path loss = ";LO;" dB"
5530 PRINT:PRINT" Nominal LOS carrier to noise= ";PLC-LO;" dB":END
5540 PL=0.00025*L*(10^(0.05*PLC))/PI
5550 PRINT:PRINT" Max. LOS path length = ";PL;" km" :END
5560 PRINT:INPUT" Enter path length in km ";PL
5570 INPUT " Enter transmitter height in metres asl ";h1
5580 INPUT " Enter transmitter horizon in km ";d1
5590 INPUT " Enter transmitter horizon obstruction height in metres
      asl ";h2
5600 PRINT:INPUT " Enter receiver height in metres asl ";h3
5610 INPUT " Enter receiver horizon in km ";d2
5620 INPUT " Enter receiver horizon obstruction height in metres
      asl ";h4
5630 R=8497:REM mean radio radius of earth
5640 TA=DEG(0.001*(h2-h1)/d1-0.5*d1/R)
5650 TB=DEG(0.001*(h4-h3)/d2-0.5*d2/R)
5660 PRINT:INPUT" Enter mean path refractivity in N units (310
      assumed) ";N$
5670 IF N$="" THEN N=310 ELSE N=VAL(N$)
5680 T1=DEG(PL/R)
5690 TS=TA+TB+T1
5700 LV=10*TA+10*TB-0.2*(N-310)+2*TS/SQR(BT*BR)
5710 TPL=LV+55.45+30*LOG(F)+20*LOG(PL)+10*T1
5720 SN=PLC-TPL
5730 PRINT:PRINT" Path loss capability = ";PLC;" dB"
5740 PRINT:PRINT" Site and coupling loss = ";LV;" dB"
5750 PRINT:PRINT" Normal tropo path loss = ";TPL;" dB"
5760 PRINT:PRINT" Estimated tropo carrier to noise = ";SN;" dB"
5770 END
```

2.7.7 Program 7: Lat/long to NGR conversion

The following additional routine is included as another useful short program using NGR. The REM statements should make it self-explanatory and it converts a latitude and longitude into an NGR, defined in terms of kilometres from the grid origin.

```
1000 REM This program converts a latitude and longitude
1010 REM to an NGR. The accuracy depends upon the distance
1020 REM away from the true origin of the National Grid (at
1030 REM 2 degrees W, 49 degrees N), but is typically within
1040 REM 25m for most of the UK
1050 REM
1060 REM Written by S J Davies, based on the Microwave
1070 REM Newsletter 06/82
1080 PRINT "Latitude (Degrees, Minutes N) ";
1090 INPUT D1,M1
1100 PRINT:PRINT "Longitude (Degrees, Minutes W) ";
1110 INPUT D2,M2
1120 REM Convert to degrees and decimal fractions of degrees.
1130 L1=D1+M1/60
1140 L2=D2+SGN(D2)*ABS(M2)/60
1150 REM Evaluate R, factor to convert degrees to radians
1160 REM This is required because the functions SIN and COS
1170 REM require angles to be given in radians
1180 R=1/57.29577951
1190 REM Evaluate SIN and COS of L1 which are used often
1200 S1=SIN(R*L1)
1210 C1=COS(R*L1)
1220 REM Evaluate variable Y
1230 Y=SQR(1-0.00667054*(S1^2))
1240 REM Calculate Northings in km.
1250 N=-100
1260 N=N+111.0793*(L1-49)
1270 N=N-31.947*SIN(R*(L1-49))*COS(R*(L1+49))
1280 N=N+0.971*((L2-L2)^2)*S1*C1/Y
1290 REM Calculate Eastings in km.
1300 E=400
1310 E=E+111.2651*(2-L2)*C1/Y
1320 E=E-0.0056*((2-L2)^3)*(C1^3)*(((S1/C1)^2)-1)
1330 REM Round off coordinates to 100m
1340 N=INT(N*10+0.5)/10
1350 E=INT(E*10+0.5)/10
1360 REM Print out results
1370 PRINT:PRINT "Conversion to National Grid reference:"
1380 PRINT:PRINT "          Northings = ";N;" km"
1390 PRINT:PRINT "          Eastings  = ";E;" km"
1400 END
```

2.8 CONCLUSIONS

This chapter has attempted to point out the differences in techniques between operation on frequencies above 1GHz and those which are generally practised on the hf, vhf and uhf bands.

The main technical difference is that the path losses are greater, and so the equipment has to have a much higher performance to achieve similar ranges. Much of the improvement is a result of using higher-gain antennas, and this inevitably means that the beamwidths are much narrower.

Thus, much importance is attached to calculating directions, accurately pointing antennas, and optimising equipment performance.

The narrow beamwidths have a major effect on operating techniques; calling "CQ" is much less common, and replies will usually only come from stations that are in the beam. Consequently, on the higher bands most of the contacts are the result of pre-arranged skeds, and a separate talkback link is used. However, enhanced propagation modes are more likely on these bands.

A scientific approach is therefore much more common, and the operator will often estimate the potential of the equipment and path parameters, under normal conditions, in advance of operation. Methods of achieving these ends are described and the effects of power, antenna gain and feeder losses on operating habits (fixed versus portable) discussed.

Several microcomputer programs or routines are given, all of which should aid the operator in the achievement of better microwave operation.

Finally, it is stressed that *method* is considered an important ingredient in the recipe for success.

2.9 REFERENCES

[1] *Test Equipment for the Radio Amateur*, 2nd edn, H L Gibson, G2BUP, RSGB.

[2] "Tropospheric scatter propagation", J N Gannaway, G3YGF, *Radio Communication*, Vol 57, p710.

[3] "Wideband horn feed for 1.2 to 2.4GHz", Peter Riml, OE9PMJ, *Dubus* 2/86, pp110–111.

[4] "Log periodic antenna feed for 1.0 to 3.5GHz", Hans Schinnerling, DC8DE, *Dubus* 2/83, pp99–101.

[5] "Multiband feed for 1 to 12GHz", Klaus Neie, DL7QY, *Dubus* 2/80, pp66–76.

[6] *Practical Astronomy with Your Calculator*, Peter Duffett-Smith, Cambridge University Press. ISBN 0 521 29636 6.

[7] *Amateur Radio Software*, John Morris, GM4ANB, RSGB. ISBN 0 900612 71 1.

[8] P E H Day, G3PHO, *RSGB Microwave Newsletter* 05/85 (June 1985).

[9] *Safety on Mountains*, John Jackson and others, British Mountaineering Council, Crawford House, Precinct Centre, Manchester University, Booth Street East, Manchester M13 9RZ or camping/mountaineering shops. ISBN 0 903908 20 4.

[10] B Chambers, G8AGN, *RSGB Microwave Newsletter* 05/85 (June 1985).

[11] Modified from ideas by J M Howell, G4BXZ, and W B Kendal, G3DGU, *Radio and Electronics World* December 1984. Radio and Electronics World Magazines, Sovereign House, Brentwood, Essex CM14 4SE. ISSN 0262–2572.

[12] "The new locator system", J Morris, GM4ANB, *Radio Communication*, Vol 61, 1985, modified by M W Dixon, G3PFR and R A Cole.

[13] B Chambers, G8AGN, *RSGB Microwave Newsletter* 03/85 (April 1985).

CHAPTER 3

System analysis and propagation

3.1 INTRODUCTION

A basic communication system is shown in Fig 3.1. It consists of a transmitter and a receiver, each with its associated antenna, the two being separated by the path to be covered. In order to generate an intelligible output, the receiver requires a certain minimum signal to be collected by its antenna and presented to its input socket. Whether or not signals can be passed between any particular transmitter and receiver will thus depend primarily on the power of the transmitter, the sensitivity of the receiver and the loss associated with the path between them – the path loss.

In practice, the size of transmitters and antennas and the sensitivity of receivers can be varied over a wide range. For example, the difference at a particular frequency between a "small" transmitter and a "large" one can be a factor of 1,000:1 or 10,000:1. The overall antenna gain may vary over a similar range, and there is potentially a fair range of choice of basic receiver sensitivity which is controlled by the amount of information that needs to be transmitted. This means that it is possible to design equipment having the capacity to cope with paths for which the path loss may differ by a factor of billions.

Usually the transmitter will generate a much stronger signal than the minimum required by the receiver, hence a large loss of signal between the two antennas can be tolerated. Despite this, for many paths of interest, the actual losses will be much greater and communication therefore impossible.

An added complication is that, even over a given path, the variation in path loss over a period of time can be large, and this may lead to problems. For example, if communication is to be maintained for a high proportion of the time, and 99.5 per cent is a common requirement for a professional link, then relatively powerful equipment will be required in order to cope with poor propagation conditions. Under favourable conditions, however, severe overloading may occur, and the equipment must be designed to cope with this also. On the other hand, if it is acceptable to be able to communicate only during periods of very favourable propagation conditions, then relatively simple equipment can be

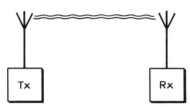

Fig 3.1. A basic communication system

surprisingly effective, as the results obtained by amateurs over the years can testify.

It is probably true to say that communicating at microwave frequencies rather than at hf or vhf demands a more critical attitude to factors which affect propagation. The reasons are a mixture of practical and theoretical:

(a) At hf and vhf some degree of success can be virtually guaranteed from most sites when using relatively low power, inexpensive equipment with simple antennas – success meaning communication over paths tens, hundreds or thousands of kilometres long according to the norm currently accepted. In this sense, operating at these frequencies can be regarded as being uncritical.

(b) By contrast, communication via microwaves over paths even a few kilometres in length may often prove impossible even though relatively powerful equipment is being used. This can be due to the effect of obstructions which, in terms of wavelength, appear larger as the frequency of transmission increases. Consequently, marginal changes in the path, produced by moving the transmitter or receiver a short distance, may have a large effect on the propagation loss and consequently determine whether or not signals can be passed.

(c) In more general terms, while the propagation of microwaves obeys the same laws as other forms of electromagnetic radiation, there is a tendency for one particular propagation mode to dominate to a greater extent than at vhf, for example, where signals beyond the horizon are usually received by a number of modes such as diffraction, refraction and reflection. Microwave

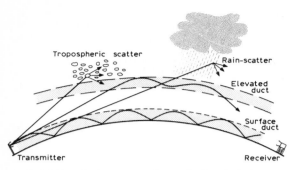

Fig 3.2. Trans-horizon propagation mechanisms in the lower atmosphere

propagation therefore tends to be more of a "go/no-go" phenomenon.

(d) Except in certain specialised areas, it is rare for amateurs operating at hf or vhf to attempt to correlate equipment parameters with performance. This is often done at microwave frequencies, however, and has proved invaluable as a creative tool in directing attention away from impractical objectives and towards more useful possibilities, sometimes with most surprising results.

For these reasons, the relationship between propagation characteristics and equipment parameters can be regarded as being of particular significance at microwave frequencies.

3.1.1 Communication system analysis

As we have already seen, whether or not communication is possible between two sites will depend on the characteristics of the transmitter, the receiver and the path between them. The objective of system analysis is to quantify these factors so that the performance of a communication link can be predicted. It can be used to determine the initial design of equipment for a link, to determine the suitability of existing equipment to communicate over a given path and, if the way in which the path loss varies with time is also known, it enables one to predict the percentage of the total time that communication is practical or whether it is possible at all. In the latter case, the analysis will also indicate by how much the potency of the equipment needs to be increased to produce an acceptable level of communication.

The accuracy of the predicted performance will obviously depend on the reliability of the basic data. In general terms, equipment parameters such as transmitter power and antenna gain can be measured under the best conditions to within fractions of a decibel. Consequently, errors from this source are likely to be small compared with the uncertainty in the path loss. For this reason, even "guesstimates" of equipment parameters

can provide a useful guide to the performance of the equipment and can prevent gross mistakes being made in either underestimating or overestimating its potential.

It can thus be seen that system analysis is of great practical value. Amateurs traditionally exploit the trial-and-error approach to their activities, including radio communication, and, while this philosophy has produced notable successes, it is suggested that system analysis deserves more attention for the following reasons:

(a) It may help to prevent the waste of effort on impossible tasks.

(b) It can direct attention towards areas of investigation which do not have obvious attractions.

(c) By providing a quantitative framework, it helps to isolate the factors which are controlling the performance of an equipment from those which are connected with propagation phenomena or operating techniques.

(d) As will be seen later, it can be used to provide a rough check on the overall performance of an equipment. This is of course especially valuable for those without elaborate test equipment.

3.1.2 Microwave propagation

Many of the propagation modes encountered at vhf and uhf are also applicable at microwave frequencies, with the exception of those which rely on ionised media such as aurora and sporadic-E. Along unobstructed paths, propagation will be via line-of-sight, whereas trans-horizon propagation will usually rely on mechanisms such as diffraction, ducting or tropospheric, rain, or aircraft scatter, as shown in Fig 3.2 [1]. EME is also a possibility, especially on the lower microwave bands.

3.2 ANALYSIS OF COMMUNICATION SYSTEM PERFORMANCE

Consider the communication link shown schematically in Fig 3.3. As was noted in the introduction to this chapter, a receiver requires a certain minimum signal power at its input in order to generate a useful intelligible audio output. The transmitter power potentially available vastly exceeds this minimum signal, and consequentially communication can take place between the

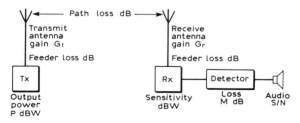

Fig 3.3. Schematic of a communication system

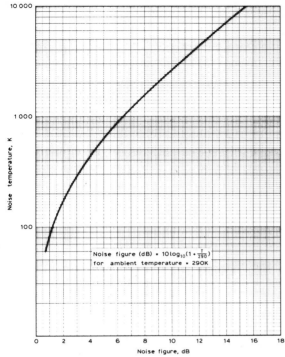

Fig 3.4. Relationship between noise temperature and noise figure

(Within figure:)

Noise figure (dB) = $10 \log_{10}(1 + \frac{T}{290})$
for ambient temperature = 290K

Noise temperature, K

Noise figure, dB

would be required to be radiated from an isotropic antenna to produce the same signal at the receiver as does the actual transmitter-antenna combination. Thus:

$$\text{eirp} = P \times G_t \text{ watts}$$

where P is the transmitter output power in watts and G_t is the gain of the transmitting antenna in absolute terms.

In practice, it is convenient to convert all units into decibels with the reference power as 1W, ie 1W = 0dBW. An alternative reference level of 1mW is also sometimes used and this is indicated by the use of the term "dBm". Values given in dBW and dBm thus differ by a factor of 1,000, ie 30dB. It is important to recognise that the value of the antenna gain is with reference to an isotropic radiator (as opposed, for example, to a dipole), and is the gain in the direction of the receiver. Feeder losses also need to be taken into account and can be included at this stage. Hence in terms of decibels:

eirp (dBW) = power generated (dBW)
              + antenna gain (dB)
              − feeder losses (dB)

As an example, consider a transmitter operating at 1.3GHz.

Transmitter power of 20W	=	+13dBW
34-element antenna, gain	=	+19dB
Loss of 10m of RG9 cable	=	− 2dB
Thus eirp	=	+30dBW

Receiver

The figure of merit of a receiver can be defined in terms of the minimum power its antenna must collect in order that the receiver may generate an intelligible output. This power is conveniently referred to as the "effective receiver sensitivity" (ers) and is defined as:

ers (dBW) = minimum detectable signal at
             receiver input (as a positive number)
             + antenna gain (dB)
             − feeder losses (dB)

This relationship is seen to have a form similar to that corresponding to the eirp of a transmitter as described previously.

The effective receiver sensitivity can be quantified as follows:

(a) The noise power generated internally by a receiver is given by the value of kTB, where:

k = Boltzmann's constant, 1.38×10^{-23} W/K/Hz
B = receiver noise bandwidth (Hz). This can be taken to be equal to the receiver i.f bandwidth.
T = noise temperature of the receiver (K). This is related to the noise figure of the receiver by the equation:

transmitter and the receiver despite a huge loss of signal – the path loss – between them. In simple terms, the ratio of the power generated by the transmitter to that required by the receiver is a measure of the maximum path loss that a particular equipment can tolerate. This maximum path loss may be referred to as the "path-loss capability" (plc) of the particular system.

$$\text{Thus} \quad \text{plc} = \frac{\text{effective power of transmitter}}{\text{minimum power to operate receiver}}$$

If the actual path loss exceeds the plc of the equipment, signals cannot be heard. If it is less, however, then signals will be heard, the signal-to-noise ratio of which will improve as the difference between the two increases. Thus the plc simply reflects the potency of a given transmitter-receiver combination.

3.2.1 Path-loss capability calculations

These require the specification of the transmitter, receiver and antenna characteristics as discussed below.

Transmitter

The figure of merit of a transmitter and its associated antenna is given by its "effective isotropic radiated power" (eirp), which is defined as that power which

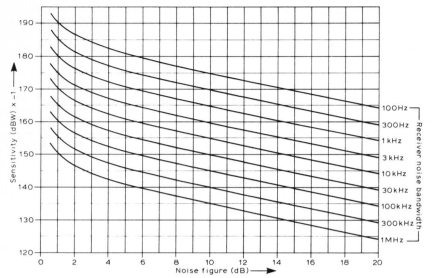

Fig 3.5. Effect on receiver sensitivity of variations in the noise figure and bandwidth

noise figure (dB) = 10 log(1 + T/290)

This relationship is shown in graphical form in Fig 3.4. In terms of decibels the noise power generated is given by:

$$\text{noise power} = -228.6 + 10\log(B) + 10\log(T)$$
$$\text{(dBW)} \qquad\qquad \text{(Hz)} \qquad \text{(K)}$$

As an example, the noise power generated by a receiver having an i.f bandwidth of 3kHz and a noise figure of 5dB, ie a noise temperature of 627K, is given by:

noise power (dBW) = $-228.6 + 10\log(3,000) + 10\log(627)$

$= -228.6 + 34.8 + 28.0$

$= -165.8$ dBW

Values for kTB as a function of receiver bandwidth and noise figure obtained in this way are summarised in Fig 3.5.

(b) The audio quality of a signal is directly related to the ratio of the audio power of the signal to that of the noise power generated by the receiver, and this obviously needs to be specified. As a guide, skilled operators can in some cases understand signals which are several decibels below the audio noise. For many practical purposes, therefore, the minimum acceptable signal-to-noise ratio can be taken as 0dB.

(c) During the detection process, the signal-to-noise ratio of the pre-detector (ie the i.f) signal may suffer significant degradation on conversion into an audio signal. Therefore, in order to maintain audio quality, it is necessary to increase the pre-detector signal by an amount M decibels equivalent to this loss. Approximate values of M for various detectors are given in Table 3.1.

(d) Antenna gain: G_r decibels.

(e) Losses such as feeder losses: L decibels.

Putting these factors together:

$$\text{ers(dBW)} = -228.6 + 10\log(B) + 10\log(T)$$
$$+ \text{snr} + M - G_r + L$$

where snr is the audio signal-to-noise ratio. As an example, consider the following receiver system:

Boltzmann's constant k	= −228.6dBW
Bandwidth B = 3kHz; 10log(3,000) =	34.8dB
NF = 5dB; T = 627K; 10log(T) =	28.0dB
Audio snr	= 10.0dB
Product detector M	= 0dB
Antenna gain G_r	= 19.0dB
Cable losses L	= 3.0dB

Hence, the effective receiver sensitivity (ers) =−171.8dBW. Note that, for many practical cases, the

Table 3.1

Type of detector	Relative loss (dB)
Linear (product, diode quadrature detector, diode with high bfo injection)	0
Envelope (diode detector)	2.6
FM discriminator	
(with limiter)	10
(without limiter)	16
Slope detector	22

value corresponding to the first three factors can be taken directly from Fig 3.5.

Although in most cases the value for the ers as calculated by the above method will be accurate enough, this may not be so when considering the influence of feeder loss on the effective noise performance of a receiver having a very low intrinsic noise figure. In such a case a more accurate estimate of the receiver ers is obtained by adding the feeder loss directly to the receiver noise figure before the conversion to effective noise temperature. Hence for the previous example:

noise figure + cable loss = 5 + 3   = 8.0dB

T=1,540K (previously 627K); 10log(1,540) = 31.9dB

Hence ers (previously −171.8dBW)   = −170.9dBW

Although the difference in the values of the ers predicted using the two methods is small (0.9dB), this may be very important in the context of, say, the implementation of an eme system.

In all cases, the effective receiver sensitivity will correspond to a very small power which will be represented by a large negative number in terms of decibels. As the overall sensitivity of the receiver system increases, the ers becomes more negative in value. Any additional losses in the receiver are added to this number to make it less negative.

Path-loss capability

The path-loss capability (plc) of a system is obtained by dividing the effective radiated power by the effective receiver sensitivity. When these values are expressed in decibels:

$$plc\,(dB) = eirp\,(dBW) - ers\,(dBW)$$

Using the previously worked examples:

$$plc\,(dB) = 13 + 19 - 2 - (-170.9)$$
$$= 200.9dB$$

3.2.2 Calculation of path loss

The final step in the overall system analysis is that of determining the actual transmission loss of the path separating the transmitter and the receiver. If this loss is less than the plc of the system then communication is possible. The actual loss of a given path will depend critically upon whether it is unobstructed (corresponding to line-of-sight propagation) or obstructed, and whether or not anomalous propagation conditions are present. These cases will be considered in turn.

Line-of-sight propagation

This is represented by a transmitter and a receiver operated in free space. As there are no effects due to obstacles (including the atmosphere), this is a simple

form of propagation for which the path loss can be calculated precisely from basic physical principles. Due to this fundamental nature, it is a reference mode against which path losses associated with other propagation modes are usually judged.

As will be familiar to many readers, the radiation emitted from an isotropic antenna spreads out equally in all directions and this means that the radiation intensity decreases as the square of the distance from the antenna. The path loss corresponding to this behaviour obeys the same law. Hence, a convenient form of the equation relating path loss, frequency and distance is:

$$path\,loss\,(dB) = 32.45 + 20log(f) + 20log(d)$$

where f is the frequency in megahertz and d is the path length in kilometres. As an example, the loss associated with a 100km path at 1,300MHz is given by:

$$path\,loss\,(dB) = 32.45 + 20log(1,300) + 20log(100)$$
$$= 32.45 + 62.28 + 40.0$$
$$= 134.73dB$$

For many purposes this can be rounded to the nearest decibel, ie 135dB.

At higher frequencies, it is often more convenient to describe frequencies in terms of gigahertz rather than megahertz. The equivalent equation is then:

$$path\,loss(dB) = 92.45 + 20log(f) + 20log(d)$$

Values for the free-space path losses over terrestrial distances at some specific frequencies of amateur interest are given in Fig 3.6.

As noted earlier, the path loss associated with this propagation mode is relatively low compared with most other modes. This can be illustrated by calculating the transmitter power required to send signals corresponding to a single ssb speech channel over a 100km path. Using the following parameters:

Frequency	= 1.3GHz
Combined antenna gains	= 38dB
Receiver i.f bandwidth	= 3kHz
Receiver noise figure	= 5dB
Audio snr required	= 10dB
Product detector, M	= 0dB
Total cable losses	= 6dB

then the path loss, as calculated previously, is 134.73dB. The plc of the equipment specified, as calculated by the method given earlier, is:

$$plc\,(dB) = P + 186.9$$

where P (dBW) is the transmitter power.

Since the plc of the equipment must at least equal the path loss, then

$$P + 186.9 = 134.73$$

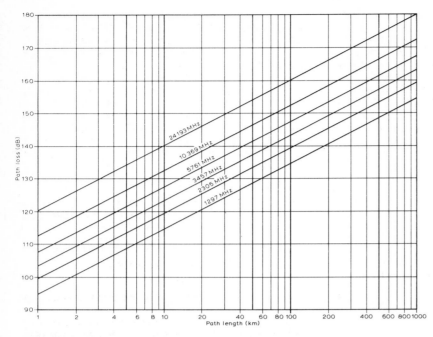

Fig 3.6. Free-space path loss as a function of path length and frequency

from which P = −52.2dBW. This value corresponds to a power level of roughly 6μW. Similar equipment for 10GHz would require a transmitter power of roughly 0.4mW, or the combined gain of the antennas to be increased by about 18dB. In practice, transmitter powers of this level are easily achieved with the minimum of facilities. This implies that normally there will be a large reserve of power available to cope with additional losses such as those incurred when perhaps the path is obstructed and communication can only be achieved via diffraction or indirectly by reflection. Such cases will be considered later.

3.2.3 Free-space path loss during anomalous propagation conditions

Under normal propagation conditions, then, the free-space path loss increases as the square of the distance between the transmitter and the receiver due to the spreading out of the transmitted energy in both the horizontal and vertical directions. Under certain conditions of anomalous propagation, however, the transmitted energy may be partially confined in the vertical direction and energy spreading then occurs mainly in the horizontal direction. This confining process leads to a reduction in the path loss such that in the ideal case of perfect confinement in the vertical direction it increases with distance rather than with the square of the distance, hence:

$$\text{path loss (dB)} = 92.45 + 20\log(f) + 10\log(d)$$

where f is in gigahertz and d is in kilometres.

For the 100km path at a frequency of 1.3GHz discussed earlier, the path loss under ideal anomalous propagation conditions is given by:

$$\begin{aligned}\text{path loss (dB)} &= 92.45 + 20\log(1.3) + 10\log(100)\\ &= 92.45 + 2.28 + 20.0\\ &= 114.73\text{dB}\end{aligned}$$

This should be compared with the value of 134.73dB obtained under normal free-space or line-of-sight propagation conditions. The difference, 20dB, indicates why anomalous propagation conditions are so desirable, from an amateur point of view, since they enable contacts over much longer distances or over slightly obstructed paths to be made with no improvement in equipment specification.

The conditions under which anomalous propagation can occur are discussed in detail later in this chapter.

3.2.4 Path loss for propagation via troposcatter

This propagation mode requires that both antennas be pointed along the great-circle path between the two stations at as low an angle of elevation as possible. The two beams will then intersect in a common volume of the atmosphere near the centre of the path, as shown in Fig 3.7. Propagation will be line-of-sight to the common volume from the transmitter. A very small fraction of the power passing through this volume will then be scattered in all directions by the irregularities in the atmosphere, and some of it will be in the direction of the receiver. This power then propagates by line-of-sight to the receiver. The height of the bottom of this scattering volume will depend on the path length, and to some extent on the horizons of the sites used at each end, but will be typically 600m on a 100km path and 10km on a 500km path. The loss in the scattering process is usually so large that the equipment is unlikely to have enough spare capacity to overcome the extra losses introduced by any additional obstructions in the path. The path loss increases by about 10dB for every degree of horizon angle at each station, and on paths of over 100km by about 9dB for every extra 100km of path length, so the choice of a site with a good horizon is vitally important since it can make a difference of several hundred kilometres to the range obtained.

The angle through which the signal is scattered is an important characteristic of a troposcatter path, as the loss involved increases with angle; the angle involved being usually only a few degrees. The relevant details of a troposcatter path are shown in Fig 3.7. The heights of each station are h_1 and h_3, and h_2 and h_4 are the heights of the obstructions forming the horizon at each station, at distances of d_1 and d_2 respectively. All heights are with respect to sea level. R is the mean effective radio radius of the earth, 8,497km. θ_s is the scattering angle which is determined by the path geometry, and consists of three terms: one depending on the overall path length, and two being characteristic of the sites at each end.

$$\theta_s = \frac{180D}{\pi R} + \frac{180}{\pi}\left(\frac{(h_2-h_1)}{d_1} - \frac{d_1}{2R}\right)$$
$$+ \frac{180}{\pi}\left(\frac{(h_4-h_3)}{d_2} - \frac{d_2}{2R}\right)$$

The path loss can now be expressed as the sum of several components:

(a) The free-space loss, as already defined in section 3.2.2.

(b) The loss in the scattering process:

$$L_s = 21 + 10\theta_s + 10\log(f) \qquad \text{(dB, deg, MHz)}$$

This is an empirical expression derived from observed signal levels, and shows the variation of scattering efficiency with frequency and scattering angle. The loss increases by 10dB per degree of scattering angle.

These expressions are plotted in Fig 3.8, which shows the free-space loss and the sum of the free-space and scatter losses for comparison, indicating that much greater losses are involved in troposcatter, and that they increase very rapidly with distance.

(c) The aperture-to-medium coupling loss:

$$L_{am} = 2 + 2\theta_s/\alpha \qquad \text{(dB, deg)}$$

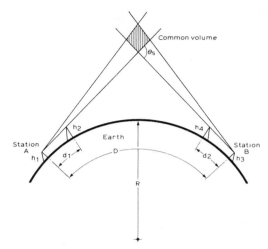

Fig 3.7. The geometry of a troposcatter path

where α is $\sqrt{(\theta_1 \times \theta_2)}$, the geometric mean of the two antenna beamwidths. This takes into account the size of the two beams and the way in which they intersect in the atmosphere, which affects the efficiency of coupling between them. It implies that there is no point in increasing the size of the antennas above a certain gain on a given path, as the expected increases in gain will not be realised when very-high-gain antennas are used. This condition occurs when the antenna beamwidths approach the scattering angle, ie a few degrees.

(d) Loss due to the variation of the mean radio refractive index of the atmosphere:

$$L_n = 0.2(N - 310) \qquad \text{(dB)}$$

where N is the refractive index expressed in millionths above unity. If N varied by 30 units, this would affect the path loss by 6dB, so it has a significant effect and

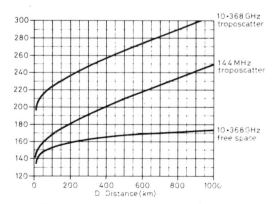

Fig 3.8. Comparison of troposcatter and free-space path loss

Table 3.2. Correction to path loss given in Fig 3.9 for different frequencies

Band (GHz)	Correction (dB)
1.3	-27
2.3	-20
3.4	-15
5.6	-8
10	0
24*	11

* An additional allowance must be made for water-vapour absorption on this band.

probably accounts for the seasonal variations mentioned later.

The total troposcatter loss is the sum of all these terms. It is convenient to split it into two parts; one being the basic path loss and the other being the variable losses due to the nature of the sites used and the climatic conditions.

The first part, the troposcatter loss between two stations on a smooth earth, is obtained by taking the terms which are either constant or depend on path length or frequency.

$$L = 55.5 + 20\log(D) + 30\log(f) + \frac{1{,}800\ D}{\pi\ R} \quad \text{(dB, km, MHz)}$$

This loss is plotted against distance in Fig 3.9 for a frequency of 10,368MHz. The graph can be used at other frequencies by adding $30\log(F/10{,}368)$ to the value read from the curve. Values of this term for various amateur bands are given in Table 3.2.

The remaining terms are the variable ones which depend on the sites or propagation conditions and weather, so these should then be added to the loss obtained from the graph.

$$L_v = \underset{\text{(site A)}}{10\theta_a} + \underset{\text{(site B)}}{10\theta_b} + \frac{2\theta_s}{\alpha} - 0.2\,(N{-}310) \quad \text{(deg, dB)}$$

For most purposes the total loss can be taken as the loss from the graph plus the contribution from each site. The other two terms will have little effect, and the value of N is not likely to be known accurately.

Once the details of the sites are known, the values of θ_a and θ_b can either be calculated using the expression for θ_s given earlier, or the loss $(10\theta_a)$ can be found directly using Fig 3.10. In this, d is the distance to the first obstruction, and dh is the height of the obstruction above the site, see Fig 3.7.

$$dh = h_{obstruction} - h_{site}$$

The actual height of the site does not appear explicitly in the expressions, only in as much as it determines where the first obstruction is and its height relative to a site. It can be seen from the original expression for θ_s that both

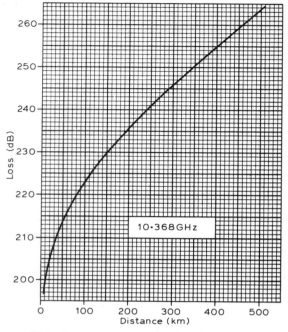

Fig 3.9. Troposcatter path loss variation with distance

the elevation angle that the obstacle presents and its distance from the site are the important parameters in determining the path loss. A distant horizon is the key feature of a good site which, in simple terms, might be described as a place having a "good view".

It is also very useful to calculate the loss from the site-dependent terms separately, as it provides a means of comparing the merits of various sites and is independent of frequency. Path profile plots should be performed for each direction of interest at each site to find the object causing the horizon and thus the values of d and h. A very good site can give negative values of this loss and so reduce the overall path loss. This loss is typically in the range −5 to +10dB.

As an example of a troposcatter path loss calculation, consider the Oxford–Hayling Island path, a distance of 110km. Taking the distances from the path profile shown in Fig 3.11, the site losses are:

$$\theta_a,\ \text{Oxford} = 57.3 \left(\frac{184-77}{26{,}000} - \frac{26}{17{,}000} \right)$$

$$\theta_a = 0.23 - 0.09 = 0.14° \qquad \text{Loss} = 10\theta_a = 1.4\text{dB}$$

$$\theta_b,\ \text{Hayling Island} = 57.3 \left(\frac{199-18}{18{,}000} - \frac{18}{17{,}000} \right)$$

$$\theta_b = 57 - 0.06 = 0.51° \qquad \text{Loss} = 10\theta_b = 5.1\text{dB}$$

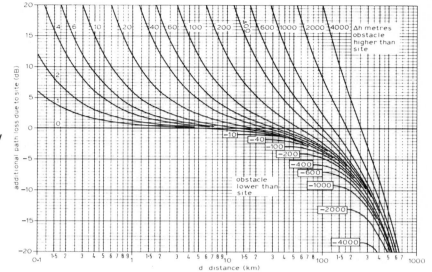

Fig 3.10. The effect of site geography on path loss

The total loss due to the site is 6.5dB. The same result can be obtained by using the following values of dh and d in Fig 3.10.

Site A: d = 26km, dh = 107m
Site B: d = 18km, dh = 181m

Next, θ_s is needed to calculate the coupling loss. θ_s is the sum of the horizon angles at each site, plus the term in the total path length, 57.3d/R.

$$\theta_s = \quad \theta_a \quad + \quad \theta_b \quad + \quad 57.3d/R$$
$$\quad\quad 0.14 \quad\quad 0.51 \quad\quad 57.3 \times 110/8,497$$

Oxford (a)   Hayling Is. (b)   Path length term

Now the coupling loss can be found. The antennas, 0.6m and 1.3m dishes, have beamwidths of 4° and 2° at 10GHz, so the mean is 2.5°. The coupling loss is thus 2.8/2.5, approximately 1dB. The path loss from Fig 3.9 is 224dB; hence the total loss at 10,368MHz is:

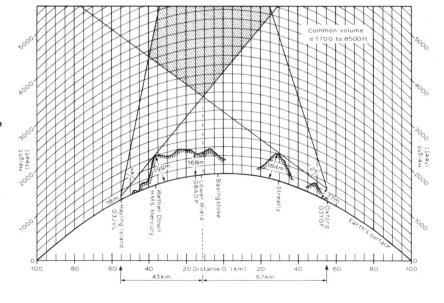

Fig 3.11. Path profile plot for the Oxford to Hayling Island path

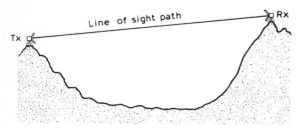

Fig 3.12. A line-of-sight path

$$224 + 6.5 + 1 = 232dB$$

This value is the mean value of the loss averaged over a year. There are many factors that will affect this value slightly, and these are discussed later.

Knowing the path loss, the next step is to calculate the plc of the equipment at each end of the path. Hence:

G3JVL (transmit)		
Transmitter output	=	7dBW
Feeder loss	=	− 2dB
Antenna gain, 0.6m dish	=	34dBi
EIRP	=	39dBW

G3YGF (receive)		
Receiver, nf 8dB, bandwidth 500Hz	=	169dBW
Antenna gain, 1.3m dish	=	39dBi
Feeder loss	=	− 2dB
Threshold (cw)	=	0dB
ERS	=	206dBW
Hence plc	=	245dB

Since the path loss has been calculated as 232dB, the predicted signal-to-noise ratio is 13dB. This should be compared with the mean observed value of 10dB. The discrepancy is probably due to the seasonal and climatic variations, for which no allowance has been made, although there will always be a few decibels of uncertainty in the equipment parameters.

3.2.5 The potential of troposcatter communication

Details of various systems and the range that can be expected between two stations using them are given in Table 3.3 to illustrate the performance that should be expected under flat conditions from good sites. The site-loss contributions are assumed to be zero, and the figures are given for a signal-to-noise ratio of 0dB in a 100Hz bandwidth, representing a weak cw signal. The range expected when using ssb in a 2kHz bandwidth is about 130km less on each band.

Table 3.4 gives the estimated troposcatter range between two systems which are capable of eme communication to illustrate the relative magnitudes of the problems involved. For distances approaching 1,000km,

Table 3.3. Range obtainable by troposcatter propagation on various amateur bands

Band (GHz)	Path loss (dB)	Range (km)	Equipment	Antenna gain (dBi)
1.3	258	760	100W, 3dB nf, 4x25ele Yagi	24
2.3	262	720	50W, 3dB nf, 1.8m dish	31
10.3	234	240	100mW, 10dB nf, 1.3m dish	39
10.3	254	440	1W, 3dB nf, 1.3m dish	39

Receiver bandwidth of 100Hz in all cases.

the challenge represented by the two modes of communication can be seen to be comparable. These tables also show that in theory the range attainable by troposcatter need not vary much with frequency. In practice, however, physically smaller antennas tend to be used on the higher frequencies, and it is also harder to generate comparable powers on the higher bands.

3.3 MICROWAVE PROPAGATION

In the following sections, the various modes of propagation applicable at microwave frequencies will be considered. An appreciation of these will enable the amateur to estimate, as part of the system analysis procedure already discussed, how the transmission loss over a given path is likely to be affected, not only by the frequency of operation and the nature of the terrain along the path, but also by weather-related phenomena.

3.3.1 Free-space propagation

This is represented by a transmitter and a receiver operated in space. Since there are no effects due to obstructions to be considered, the path loss can be calculated precisely from basic physical principles, as discussed earlier in this chapter. It can be seen from Fig 3.6 that the transmission losses corresponding to path lengths of practical interest are very large. Nevertheless, this propagation mode is one of the least lossy.

Practical examples of this mode arise in space-to-space and earth-to-space communication at frequencies at which atmospheric absorption losses can be ignored.

3.3.2 Line-of-sight paths

As shown in Fig 3.12, a so-called "line-of-sight" path between two sites exists when the transmitting and the

Table 3.4. Troposcatter range of equipment capable of eme operation

Band (GHz)	EME path loss (dB)	Tropo range (km)	Equipment	Antenna gain (dBi)
1.3	271	890	500W, 3dB nf, 500Hz, 5.2m dish	34
2.3	276	860	100W, 3dB nf, 500Hz, 5.2m dish	40
10.3	289	790	50W, 3dB nf, 1kHz, 3.9m dish	50

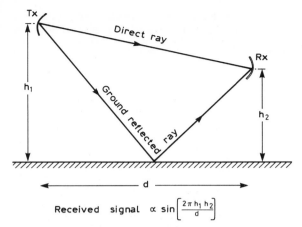

Received signal $\propto \sin\left[\dfrac{2\pi h_1 h_2}{d}\right]$

Fig 3.13. Propagation close to the ground

receiving antennas are so elevated that there is no obvious obstacle between them. That is, the transmitter can "see" the receiver and vice versa. This does not necessarily imply, however, that a person standing next to the receiving antenna literally can see the transmitter, assuming that his eyesight is good enough and the atmosphere is clear and still, since a path which is obstructed at optical frequencies may be line-of-sight at microwave frequencies.

Provided that atmospheric effects are small, and that all potential obstacles are well removed from the propagation path, the propagation conditions approximate closely to the free-space mode discussed above. Consequently, even if the transmitting and receiving antennas have only modest gain, the transmitter output power required to pass a signal over a line-of-sight path which may be several hundreds of kilometres long is generally only a few milliwatts. Also, it is a fairly simple matter to calculate the system power budget for a given line-of-sight path and hence to estimate the probable signal-to-noise ratio at the receiver. A measurement of the actual received signal-to-noise ratio will then provide a check on the overall performance of the system. This approach is most useful since it does not rely on the amateur having access to sophisticated test equipment, only a calibrated attenuator.

In practice, effects due to path obstructions and the atmosphere can be of major significance; these will be discussed in the following sections.

3.3.3 Propagation over flat terrain

A simplified view of a communication link operating over a short terrestrial path is shown in Fig 3.13. The surface of the terrain is assumed to be smooth and the curvature of the earth has been neglected. Due to the proximity of the ground to the line-of-sight path, the received signal now has a contribution from the ground-reflected wave in addition to that from the direct wave. Hence for a fixed transmitting antenna height h_1 the strength of the received signal will be found to vary periodically through a series of interference maxima and minima as the height h_2 of the receiving antenna is varied. Such maxima are characteristically broad and the minima are sharp. The vertical separation s between adjacent receiving antenna positions for maximum and minimum signal strength is approximately given by:

$$s(m) \;=\; \frac{7.5 \times 10^4\, d}{h_1\, f} \qquad \begin{array}{l}(km) \\ (m, MHz)\end{array}$$

Hence, for a 10GHz transmitter at a height of 200m above ground level and operating over a 50km path, s = 3.75m.

In practice this simplified behaviour will be modified due to the effects of ground roughness at the reflection point, wave polarisation and earth curvature. Nevertheless, it does show that, especially when operating over marginal paths, the height of the receiving antenna and/or the transmitting antenna should be adjusted for best results whenever possible.

3.3.4 Propagation via reflection

Even if the direct path between the transmitter and the receiver is obstructed, it is sometimes still possible to achieve contact by reflecting signals from an object which is in view from both ends of the path. As can be seen from Fig 3.14, the transmission loss between the transmitter and the receiver will be proportional to:

$$\frac{1}{(d_1\, d_2)^2}$$

Hence for minimum transmission loss the reflecting object should be situated close to one end of the path. This

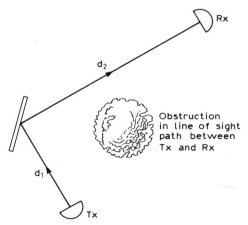

Fig 3.14. Propagation via reflection

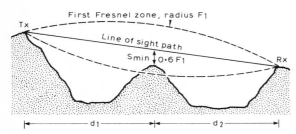

Fig 3.15. Fresnel zone surrounding line-of-sight ray on a microwave path

principle forms the basis of the periscope antenna configuration discussed in Chapter 4.

3.3.5 Knife-edge diffraction

If the transmitting and receiving antennas are not sufficiently elevated for the line-of-sight ray to propagate well away from any intervening obstruction, then additional transmission loss over the path will be incurred due to diffraction around the obstruction. In practice the microwave signal will not propagate from the transmitter to the receiver as a single ray but as a collection of rays or a wavefront. The received signal is thus made up of contributions from a number of these rays, the final combination of which will be determined by the amplitudes and phases of individual components. Hence an obstacle, such as a hill, situated near to the line-of-sight ray may block some of the contributing rays or change their phases relative to others, thus normally leading to a decrease but possibly even an increase in the received signal level compared to its value in the absence of the obstacle. It is usually assumed that the obstacle will have a negligible effect on the received

signal if it is situated more than a certain minimum distance away from the line-of-sight ray, as shown in Fig 3.15. Normally, this minimum distance is taken to be 0.6 of the first Fresnel zone (often denoted as F_1) or:

$$S_{min}(m) > 0.6F_1$$

$$S_{min} > 10.4 \sqrt{\left(\frac{d_1 d_2}{(d_1 + d_2) f}\right)}$$

where d_1 and d_2 are in kilometres and are the distances from each end of the path to the potential obstruction, and f is in gigahertz.

If an obstacle is closer to the line-of-sight ray than the distance S_{min}, or the line-of-sight ray is actually obstructed, then normally the strength of the received signal will be diminished. To obtain an estimate of the additional path loss due to the obstacle it is often assumed that the latter can be replaced by a simple knife edge, the diffraction loss properties of which are well known. Fig 3.16 shows the ideal diffraction loss for a knife-edge obstacle as a function of the clearance S of the line-of-sight ray, expressed in wavelengths. From this it can be seen why the value of S_{min} is often chosen to be $0.6F_1$ since this corresponds to the case of no diffraction loss. Note also that when the line-of-sight ray just touches the obstacle (S = 0), the diffraction loss is 6dB. A more useful representation of Fig 3.16 is shown in Fig 3.17. This enables the minimum diffraction loss of a single knife-edge obstacle to be determined easily. Although drawn for 10GHz, values read from Fig 3.17 can be adjusted for other amateur bands by adding the correction factors given in Table 3.5.

It should be noted that the values for the diffraction loss obtained from Fig 3.17 have been found, in practice, to be optimistic by 6 to 15dB at 10GHz. This discrepancy is due almost certainly to the fact that real obstacles are usually rounded rather than sharp-edged, and have a rough surface due to the presence of vegetation, trees or buildings. It is difficult to quote definitive values for the additional losses due to such roughness effects since they will depend on frequency and, more importantly, on the water content of the object in question. As a rough guide, however, measurements made at a frequency of 3.3GHz [3] suggest that the following should normally be regarded as opaque to microwaves:

(a) rows of trees in leaf, if more than two in depth;

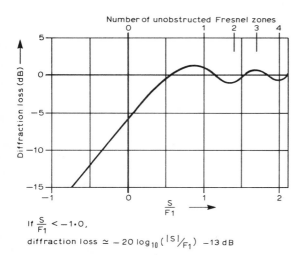

If $\frac{S}{F_1} < -1.0$,

diffraction loss $\simeq -20 \log_{10}\left(\frac{|S|}{F_1}\right) - 13\,dB$

Fig 3.16. Diffraction loss due to an ideal knife-edge obstacle

Table 3.5

Band (GHz)	Diffraction loss correction factor for Fig 3.17
1.3	–9
2.3	–6
3.4	–5
5.7	–3
10	0
24	4

(b) trunks of trees, whether leafless or in leaf;

(c) walls of masonry, if more than 20cm in thickness;

(d) any but the lightest of wooden buildings, particularly if containing partitions.

In spite of these rather gloomy conclusions and their implications for propagation at microwave frequencies through an urban environment, tests at 3.4GHz have shown that signals can be received through hedges and individual trees in leaf, and in one case over a 1km path through a housing estate, the transmitting and receiving antennas being inside houses on opposite sides of a hill some 30m high. The lesson to be learned from this latter test is clear; even if on paper a particular path is not line-of-sight, it is still possible on occasion to transmit signals over it, as other propagation mechanisms may come to the rescue.

Techniques exist for dealing with the calculation of diffraction losses due to several obstacles lying along a single path, but these are outside the scope of this review. Further details may be found elsewhere [4].

3.3.6 Atmospheric refraction

Terrestrial paths inevitably involve the propagation of signals through the lower part of the atmosphere, the troposphere. This is a medium whose properties vary from place to place with factors such as pressure, temperature and humidity. The effect of these variations is to alter the refractive index of the medium which in turn affects how signals are bent or refracted in passing from the transmitter to the receiver.

Normally the earth's atmosphere has a refractive index n, the value of which is only slightly greater than unity, typically 1.0003. It is more convenient, therefore, to work in terms of the refractivity N, which is defined as:

$$N = (N-1) \times 10^6$$

Thus the refractivity corresponding to a refractive index of 1.000320 is 320.

In temperate climates at frequencies up to about 30GHz, the dependence of N on air pressure, temperature and humidity is given by:

$$N = \frac{77.6 \times p}{T} + \frac{3.733 \times 10^5 e}{T^2}$$

where p = the atmospheric pressure (mb)
   e = the water vapour pressure (mb)
   T = the air temperature (K)

The first term on the right-hand side of this equation corresponds approximately to the optical value of the refractivity; the second term, which must be included at microwave frequencies, accounts for the presence of water vapour in the atmosphere. Hence when propagating

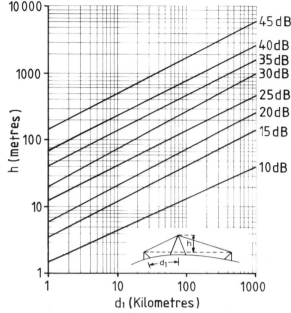

Fig 3.17. Minimum obstacle loss at 10GHz

through the latter, light waves and microwaves are affected differently.

The normal variation of air pressure, temperature and humidity with height above the ground results in the refractivity decreasing in an approximately linear fashion with increasing height up to about 1km. The effect of this is to bend signals down towards the earth rather than allowing them to propagate in a straight line, as assumed earlier. If the refractivity remains substantially constant along the length of a path, the usual assumption except along mixed land-water paths, then the signals will follow a smooth curve whose radius of curvature normally is somewhat greater than that of the earth.

Over a greater range of heights, the mean value of the refractive index may often be well approximated by:

$$n(h) = 1 + N_s \times e^{(-b.h)} \times 10^{-6}$$

where N_s = refractivity at the surface
    h = height (km)
and b is a constant determined from

$$e^{-b} = 1 + dN/N_s$$

where dN is the difference in N values at a height of 1km above the surface and at the surface.

It has been shown from long-term studies of meteorological data that dN is in general correlated

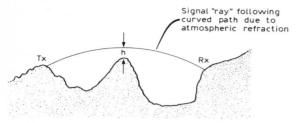

Fig 3.18. Path profile showing curvature of signal ray due to atmospheric refraction

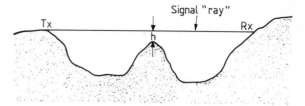

Fig 3.19. Path profile drawn using the modified earth's radius factor K to give a straight signal ray

with the surface value N_s but in a way that differs with the climate or region of the world, for example:

$$dN = -3.95 \times e^{(0.0072Ns)} \qquad \text{in the UK}$$

$$dN = -9.30 \times e^{(0.004565Ns)} \qquad \text{in the FRG}$$

$$dN = -7.32 \times e^{(0.005577Ns)} \qquad \text{in the USA}$$

Although these expressions can be used to estimate dN when only surface meteorological data are available, this approach must be used with some caution, since the presence of anomalous propagation conditions, especially at the lower microwave frequencies, cannot usually be inferred only from a knowledge of conditions at the surface [5].

3.3.7 K factor

Under normal propagation conditions, signals follow a curved path, its radius of curvature being related to the refractivity of the intermediate atmosphere. To determine the proximity of potential obstacles to the line-of-sight ray, a path profile is plotted, on which the surface of the terrain immediately below the signal path is compared with the curved path of the signal ray itself. This is illustrated in Fig 3.18.

A more convenient technique avoids the need to plot the curved path of the signal ray. In this, the apparent radius of curvature of the earth is increased by such an amount that the relative positions of the terrain and the signal ray are maintained when the latter is taken to follow a straight path. This is shown in Fig 3.19. The ratio of the apparent radius of curvature of the earth to the actual value is known as the K factor, ie:

$$K = \frac{\text{apparent radius of earth}}{\text{real radius of earth}}$$

Since the curvature of a signal ray is related directly to both K and the refractivity N, then obviously K and N are related also. This relationship is given by:

$$K = \frac{1}{1 + (\frac{a}{n_s} \times \frac{dn}{dh})}$$

where a = real radius of the earth

n_s = surface value of n

and $\dfrac{dn}{dh}$ = gradient of n at heights below 1km

Under average conditions near to the earth's surface, the refractivity N decreases with height at the rate of about 40 N units per kilometre. Then taking n as typically 1.0003 results in a value for K of 1.33 (ie 4/3) which is the most commonly adopted starting value used in checking paths for line-of-sight conditions.

In practice the mean value of K can vary over wide limits. In a temperate maritime climate such as that of the UK, K can vary between about 1.32 in NE Scotland in February to about 1.45 in Cornwall in July or August [6]. Over the continental USA the variation in the mean value of K is even greater, ranging from about 1.25 in winter up to about 2 in summer [7]. Charts showing the worldwide distribution of N_s and N, from which mean values of K can be determined, are also available [8].

Since the troposphere is not homogeneous, the value of K will not only vary with time at a given location but also along a given path at a fixed time. Table 3.6 gives an estimate [9] of the percentage of the total time that the mean value of K at a particular location on land in a temperate climate will exceed a certain value. It is clear from this that enhanced propagation conditions are likely to prevail for a surprisingly large fraction of the total time.

When checking to see whether a given path is likely to be line-of-sight it is prudent to use a value of K averaged along the path rather than the value at any particular point since the variability of this path-averaged value

Table 3.6

K value	Proportion of total time for which this value will be exceeded (per cent)
1	99
1.33	65
1.55	50
3.85	10
5	8
infinity	1.8

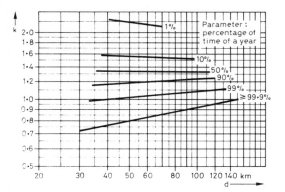

Fig 3.20. Frequency distribution of the modified earth's radius factor K as a function of the path length (from *Planning and Engineering of Radio Relay Links*, Brodhage and Hormuth, Siemens AG, Berlin and Munich, 1977)

will be less than the variability at a point. The path-averaged value of K which is exceeded for 99.9 per cent of the time is shown in Fig 3.20 as a function of path length for continental temperate climates [10]. Clearly, the longer the radio path, the greater is the minimum path-averaged value of K. In hot and wet climates the value of K will be higher, whereas in a dry climate it will be lower. For example, over a 50km path the average value of K commonly taken as the lower limit for path-checking calculations is K = 1 for wet climates, K = 0.8 for temperate climates and K = 0.6 for desert climates.

3.3.8 Line-of-sight path calculations

Whether or not a line-of-sight path exists between two sites can obviously be checked by plotting the path profile between them and determining if the signal ray would meet any obstruction. This tends to be a time-consuming operation, especially if a range of values for K needs to be considered. Fortunately, simple calculations can indicate quickly the likelihood of a line-of-site path being present and therefore if a more detailed examination of the path profile is justified.

Consider the path shown in Fig 3.21. From simple geometrical considerations it can be shown that the distance from an elevated site to the horizon is given by:

$$d_1 = \sqrt{(2Ka(h_1 - h_3))}$$

where a = the real radius of the earth
h_1 = height of the site, asl
h_3 = height of terrain at the horizon, asl
K = the ratio of the earth's effective to its real radius

Note that d, h and a are in the same units.

In the case where the horizon is at sea level, then h_3 is zero. In other cases it is necessary to estimate the value

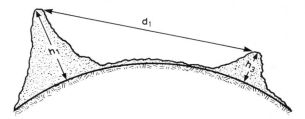

Fig 3.21. Distance to the horizon for a line-of-sight path

of h_3. This can usually be done by inspection of a map to find an approximate value for h_3, using this value to calculate the position of the horizon more precisely, from which a better value for h_3 can be determined and so on.

Assuming a mean value for the earth's radius of 6,371km, and specifying h in metres, then the equation for the distance to the horizon becomes:

$$d \text{ (km)} = 3.57 \sqrt{(K(h_1 - h_3))}$$

The equivalent equation in imperial units is:

$$d \text{ (miles)} = 1.22 \sqrt{(K(h_1 - h_3))}$$

Actual values of the distance d for various values of K and h are given in Table 3.7.

In checking whether or not a line-of-sight path exists between two sites, three main cases can be distinguished, as shown in Fig 3.22. These are:

(a) Signals from both sites share the same horizon. That is, signals can pass from one site to the other by just grazing the intermediate terrain. In this case, the overall path length is equal to the sum of the two distances to the horizon, and this represents the maximum value for d that can be achieved. Thus:

$$dmax = d_1 + d_2$$
$$= \sqrt{(2Ka \times (h_1 - h_3))} + \sqrt{(2Ka \times (h_2 - h_3))}$$

(b) Signals from the two sites overlap. In this case, d is less than the sum of d_1 and d_2 and signals can pass

Table 3.7

h (m)	Distance to horizon d (km)		
	K = 1	K = 1.17	K = 1.33
100	36	39	41
200	51	55	58
300	62	67	71
400	71	77	82
500	80	87	92
1,000	113	122	130
3,000	196	212	226

Note: K = 1 corresponds to no atmosphere; K = 1.17 corresponds to the average optical value; K = 1.33 corresponds to the average microwave value.

directly from one site to the other above the intermediate terrain.

(c) Signals from each site do not reach the other's horizon. In this case, d is greater than the sum of h_1 and h_2 and the terrain forms a significant obstruction in the path.

The equations given above can be used to estimate the absolute maximum line-of-sight path potentially available in a given country. The greatest distance to the horizon is from the highest mountain to sea level, and the maximum path length cannot exceed twice this value. Practical line-of-sight paths may be considerably shorter; the longest available in the UK is in the region of 260km.

If the simple checks outlined above indicate that a given path may be marginal then it is sometimes necessary to draw a detailed terrain profile to check where potential obstructions may occur and to enable an estimate of additional path losses to be made. Techniques for constructing such profiles are given in Chapter 2 [11].

Anomalous propagation

As discussed previously, the effective earth radius K is determined from:

$$K = \frac{1}{1 + (\frac{a}{n} \times \frac{dn}{dh})}$$

where a   = real radius of the earth
          dn/dh = gradient of n below 1km

Taking n and a to have values of 1.0003 and 6,371km, respectively, and substituting:

$$n = 1 + (10^{-6}) \times N,$$

then K is given by $$K = \frac{157}{157 + \frac{dN}{dh}}$$

where (dN/dh) is the gradient of the refractivity expressed in N units per kilometre. On average (dN/dh) has been found to have a value of −40 N units per kilometre. This results in K = 1.33 (4/3) and hence normal refraction of the signal ray in passing from the transmitter to the receiver. Under normal propagation conditions, therefore, the presence of the troposphere results in the radio horizon being about 15 per cent further away than if the earth were *in vacuo*. For light waves, however, the corresponding value is only about seven per cent, since at optical frequencies N is independent of the presence of water vapour in the troposphere. Hence a transmitter which is invisible to the eye may be "visible" over the horizon to a receiver.

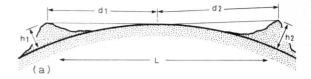

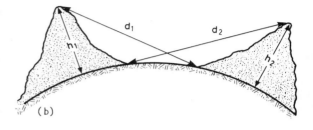

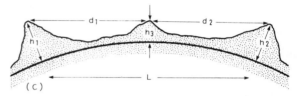

Fig 3.22. Preliminary path checks for line-of-sight conditions where (a) signals from both sites share the same horizon; (b) signals from the two sites overlap; (c) signals from each site do not reach the other's horizon

In practice the gradient of N can vary over a wide range of values. It is of interest, therefore, to examine the variation of K with (dN/dh) since this will establish the tropospheric conditions necessary for long-distance microwave propagation to occur.

If (dN/dh) has a value of less than −40 N units per kilometre, the value of K is increased and above-average refraction will occur. Hence the radius of curvature of the microwave ray passing from the transmitter to the receiver will become more nearly equal to the radius of curvature of the earth and the distance to the radio horizon will be increased. When (dN/dh) has the critical value of −157 N units per kilometre then, from the equation given earlier, K becomes infinite, ie the radii of curvature of the microwave ray and the earth are equal. Under these conditions, if the earth were smooth, the radio horizon would be unlimited!

If the value of (dN/dh) becomes less than −157 N units per kilometre, K becomes negative. When this happens, "ducting" is said to occur and a microwave signal propagates as though confined vertically inside a type of waveguide. This confinement in the vertical plane results in a reduced transmission loss, which in the case of a perfect duct (ie complete vertical confinement), would be proportional to d, the path length, rather than d^2 as in the case of normal free-space propagation. It is this property of ducting which is so attractive to the microwave dx enthusiast.

Finally, if the value of (dN/dh) is greater than −40 N units per kilometre then below-average propagation conditions will occur. For example, if K has a value less than unity (ie (dN/dh) becomes positive) then the radius of curvature of the microwave ray will become smaller than that of the earth and the situation may arise that a distant transmitter can be seen with the eye but no signal can be received from it since the radio horizon is now less than the optical one.

3.3.9 Meteorological conditions associated with anomalous propagation

Having discussed the manner in which the gradient of the refractive index of the atmosphere close to the earth's surface can influence microwave propagation conditions, it now remains to examine how such gradients can arise in practice, since an appreciation of the meteorological conditions which, for example, give rise to super-refraction and ducting can enable the amateur to make the best use of such phenomena.

The meteorological conditions which appear to be associated with the formation of super-refractive layers in the lower atmosphere are those of subsidence, advection, radiation, evaporation and the passage of weather fronts.

3.3.10 Subsidence

The air which descends slowly within an anti-cyclonic weather system (ie a region of high air pressure) becomes progressively heated by compression and, due to its high-altitude origin, it contains virtually no moisture. As shown in Fig 3.23, the subsidence is normally halted at some height when opposed by forces in the air underneath, and the warm air then spreads out in an elevated layer without significant mixing with the cooler air below. This results in a temperature inversion across the boundary region, and a corresponding sharp drop in the dew point.

If the subsidence inversion exists within about 2,000m of the surface, it imparts stability to the air below by suppressing convection air currents. This stability greatly increases the probability of ducts being formed through the advective and radiative effects described below.

Occasionally over the British Isles, and more frequently over the continental mainland, the subsidence inversion descends to within a few hundred metres of the surface and has a more direct influence on propagation. The very pronounced inversion layers which result at low levels are frequently super-refractive and form laterally extensive, elevated ducts. Land and sea areas are equally affected in this way and, due to the elevated position of the duct, it is reasonably insensitive to the roughness of the transmission path underneath.

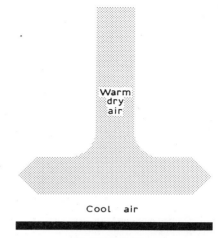

Fig 3.23. Subsidence

Subsidence often continues for several days at a time and, when present at low levels, can enable long-distance contacts at microwave frequencies to be achieved.

3.3.11 Advection

Advective conditions are characterised typically by warm, dry air passing over a colder, wetter surface. For example, the air flow around anti-cyclonic weather systems over central Europe produces a drift of warm, dry air from the mainland out over the cooler, very moist air of the sea, as shown in Fig 3.24. There is little convection turbulence over the sea and, when the winds are light, the overlay of warm air continues without mixing. The result is the formation of surface ducts which can extend for hundreds of kilometres. Over the southern North Sea protracted periods of advection are known to produce enhanced propagation at 11GHz for more than 10 per cent of the time, often persisting through both night and day. While advection is considered to be the most important over-sea propagation mechanism, it also affects low-lying coastal areas where the sea breeze draws cool moist air inland to meet air which is warmer and drier. The upper surface of the sea breeze where it meets the land air is thus a region where suitable humidity and temperature gradients may form, giving rise to a super-refracting layer.

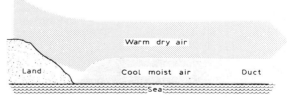

Fig 3.24. Advection

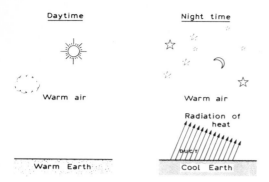

Fig 3.25. Radiation

A different advective situation exists when cold, dry air blows over a warmer, wet surface. Evaporation into the dry air produces a steep humidity lapse so that, despite the temperature lapse which is also set up, a duct is still formed. Examples include dry Arctic air blowing over the warmer sea, or cold, dry air behind a cold front which crosses land that has been wetted by heavy rain.

3.3.12 Radiation

Ducts are often formed due to nocturnal cooling of the earth's surface by radiation. As shown in Fig 3.25, conditions for duct formation are most favourable when the land has been heated by the sun to a high temperature during the day and there is little or no cloud cover during the subsequent night, together with little wind. A temperature inversion starts to form after sunset as the earth radiates heat rapidly into space, and it intensifies throughout the night to become most pronounced at about dawn. The cooling of the air near to the surface of the ground results in mist, fog or ground frost, all of which are indications of moist air within the inversion layer. As the sun rises, the ground surface temperature increases, there being little or no cloud, and gradually the inversion is destroyed and the moisture becomes dispersed throughout the atmosphere as the mist, fog, dew or ground frost disappear.

Ducts due to radiation are most prevalent over barren, dry land such as desert. However, even though other types of land surface may exhibit less extreme diurnal temperature variations, these may still be large enough to produce a temperature inversion in the lowest layer of the air due to contact with a cooler earth's surface. Nocturnal radiation is the most frequent cause of enhanced propagation conditions over land areas in the UK but, as the events tend to be of fairly short duration, it is likely that they will be less available to the average amateur than the periods of subsidence.

The influence of radiation cooling in coastal areas has been found to extend over sea paths between the Netherlands and the UK. However, over areas of deep water, for example oceans, ducts are not produced in this manner since the diurnal changes of surface temperature are too small.

3.3.13 Evaporation

A shallow duct exists frequently over most oceanic areas of the world in the form of the so-called "evaporation duct". This arises from the fact that the air layer which is in immediate contact with the sea surface is saturated with water vapour due to evaporation, whereas the air some distance above the sea surface generally is not. This decrease of water vapour concentration with increasing height gives rise to a duct, the mean thickness of which ranges from about 6m in the North Sea up to about 15m in tropical regions. Such a duct will have a profound effect on nautical microwave propagation at frequencies up to about 40GHz. At higher frequencies, however, it is expected that the normally lower path losses due to duct propagation will be offset by scattering and absorption effects.

3.3.14 Weather fronts

Recent evidence from both amateur [12] and professional [13] experiments at microwave frequencies tends to suggest that propagation enhancement can also result from the movement of weather fronts into the area of a weakening anti-cyclonic weather system. The period of enhancement tends to be short and seems to result from super-refraction occurring somewhere within the frontal structure. However, the exact nature of the enhancement mechanism is still under investigation.

3.3.15 Propagation in ducts

A good insight into the way that microwaves are influenced by the presence of a duct can be gained by tracing out the paths taken by a microwave ray when launched at various angles with respect to the horizontal in the vicinity of the duct. In the discussion which follows the duct is assumed to extend uniformly in the horizontal plane, the only variation in refractivity being with height. It is convenient at this stage to introduce another variable in order to describe the refractive properties of the atmosphere. This is the modified refractive index M, defined as:

$$M = N + 10^6 \, h/a$$

where h is the height above the ground in kilometres, and N and a have already been defined. When dealing with propagation in ducts it is more convenient to work in terms of M rather than N since the former is so defined that its vertical gradient (dM/dh) vanishes at any height h (h ≈ a) for which the path of a ray launched horizontally is a circular arc concentric with the surface of the earth, ie (dM/dh) = 0 when K = infinity. This method of defining M means that (dM/dh) = 0 at all heights in a homogeneous atmosphere over a flat earth. M itself would thus be constant, having at all heights the

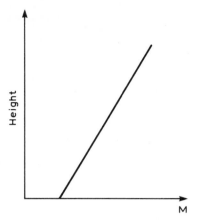

Fig 3.26. M profile for a standard atmosphere

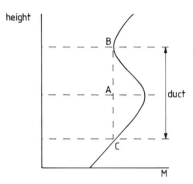

Fig 3.28. M profile for an elevated duct

same value that it has at ground level. Hence a procedure based on the use of M rather than N is termed an "earth-flattening" procedure.

It was noted previously that under average propagation conditions (dN/dh), the refractivity gradient close to the earth's surface, has a value of about –40 N units per kilometre. Substituting this into the above equation and letting a = 6,371km gives for (dM/dh), the gradient of M, the value of 117 N units per kilometre. The M profile for the so-called "standard atmosphere" is thus a straight line with a positive slope, as shown in Fig 3.26. In contrast, the idealised M profile for a typical ground-based duct is shown in Fig 3.27. Here the gradient of M vanishes at the point B and the approximate width of the duct is given by the length AB, since below point A the gradient of M is negative.

As in the case of a ground-based duct, the occurrence of an elevated duct is possible only when the gradient of M is negative over a range of heights. A typical idealised

M profile for this case is shown in Fig 3.28, where the edges of the duct are marked approximately by the points B and C.

Returning now to the case of a ground-based duct, Fig 3.29 shows the paths of a number of microwave rays launched at various elevation angles into the duct from a transmitter T on the ground. It can be seen that there is a critical angle at which the ray must be launched in order for it to reach the (dM/dh) = 0 level without passing through it and thus escaping from the duct. When the launching angle exceeds this critical angle, the ray escapes; when the angle is less than the critical angle, however, the ray reaches a maximum elevation which is closer to the (dM/dh) = 0 level the nearer the launching angle is to the critical angle. The ray then returns to the ground from its point of maximum elevation via a path which is a mirror image of that taken on its upward journey. If the ground is horizontal and specularly reflecting, a reflected ray will then traverse a path which is symmetrical with respect to the incident ray, reaching the same elevation as the incident ray and returning to the ground for a possible second reflection. Such a ray is said to be trapped inside the duct which can then be

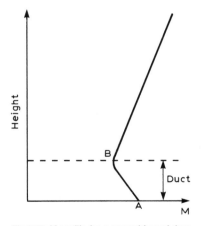

Fig 3.27. M profile for a ground-based duct

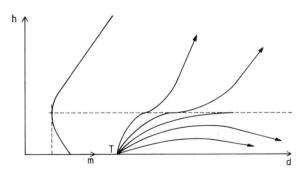

Fig 3.29. Paths of rays launched from the ground at various angles into a ground-based duct (from *The Physics of Microwave Propagation*, Donald C Livingston. ©1970. Reprinted with permission of Prentice-Hall Inc, Englewood Cliffs, NJ, USA)

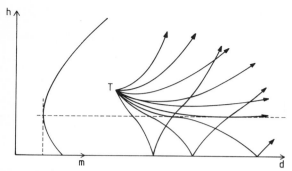

Fig 3.30. Paths of rays launched at various angles from a point above a ground-based duct (from *The Physics of Microwave Propagation*, Donald C Livingston. ©1970. Reprinted with permission of Prentice-Hall Inc, Englewood Cliffs, NJ, USA)

considered to extend from the surface up to the elevation at which $(dM/dh) = 0$.

Fig 3.30 shows the situation in which a transmitter is situated above a ground-based duct and a receiver is inside the duct. Again it is possible for signals to be trapped inside the duct, provided that the launching angle is below some critical value.

Ray path diagrams for a transmitter located inside and outside an elevated duct are shown in Figs 3.31 and 3.32, respectively. When the transmitter is located inside the duct, rays which are launched over a wide range of elevation angles above and below the horizontal may be trapped. When the transmitter is outside the duct, however, only the ray which is launched at a critical angle below the horizontal from a point above the top of the duct can become trapped. It is for this reason that elevated ducts may appear to be of less interest to the amateur since signals launched from below the duct cannot be trapped, but there is also the possibility that signals might be reflected from the underside of the duct to give enhanced range or to clear obstacles, as shown in Fig 3.33.

Having established the existence of a critical angle for the trapping of a microwave signal inside a duct to occur, some estimate of the size of this angle will be of interest. In fact it depends on the total change in refractivity across the width of the duct, ie:

$$\text{critical angle} = \pm 0.0002\sqrt{(dN)} \quad \text{radians}$$

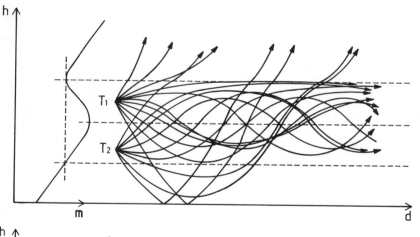

Fig 3.31. Paths of rays launched at various angles from points within an elevated duct (from *The Physics of Microwave Propagation*, Donald C Livingston. ©1970. Reprinted with permission of Prentice-Hall Inc, Englewood Cliffs, NJ, USA)

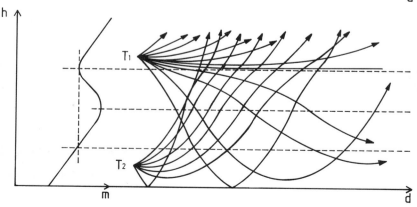

Fig 3.32. Paths of rays launched at various angles from points above and below an elevated duct (from *The Physics of Microwave Propagation*, Donald C Livingston. ©1970. Reprinted with permission of Prentice-Hall Inc, Englewood Cliffs, NJ, USA)

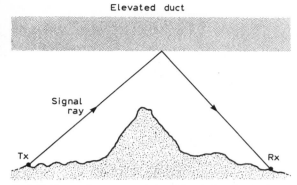

Fig 3.33. Propagation over an obstructed path via reflection from an elevated duct

For a typical maximum value of dN of 40, the critical angle is about ±0.5°; thus only those signals which are launched almost horizontally will be trapped by the duct.

Although the ray tracing procedure outlined above explains in qualitative terms how a duct can cause guiding of an electromagnetic wave, it also tends to suggest that any duct will guide waves of any frequency. In fact this is not so and a more exact analysis of wave propagation inside ducts shows that a wave of a given frequency can only be guided by a duct if the latter has a large enough lapse of N across it. For horizontally polarised waves, the minimum duct thickness is related to the wavelength of the signal and the gradient of N by:

$$d^{(3/2)} = \frac{\lambda}{2.5\sqrt{\left(\dfrac{dN}{dh}\right)}} \quad \text{metres}$$

This expression has been evaluated for various values of dN/dh and frequency; the resulting curves are shown in Fig 3.34. Since shallow ducts are more prevalent than deep ones, it is to be expected from Fig 3.34 that duct propagation should be much more frequent at microwave frequencies than at, say, vhf. Thus microwave propagation conditions may be very good even at times when the vhf and uhf bands appear to be normal.

3.3.16 Propagation via troposcatter

Paths that involve only line-of-sight propagation are not very common, and usually the signals will have been scattered off or diffracted around several obstacles on the way. As the length of the path increases, so does the number of obstructions or the angles through which the signals have to be diffracted. Under these conditions signal levels will decrease very rapidly with distance, and signals arriving by other propagation mechanisms may be stronger. Propagation beyond the horizon can occur by a variety of methods, such as ducting, as already

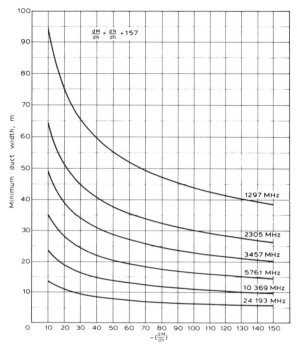

Fig 3.34. Dependence of minimum duct width on the lapse rate dM/dh

discussed, or by the signals being scattered off an object which is high enough to be visible to both stations, such as an aircraft. However, these phenomena are only short-lived and a more permanent mechanism would be desirable. Satellites or eme are more predictable but, apart from the case of geostationary satellites, can only be used for some of the time.

Troposcatter uses the weak but reliable reflections that can be obtained from the dust particles, clouds, and refractive index variations that occur in the atmosphere in the region 300 to 15,000m asl, and this mechanism can be used for reliable dx working over distances of many hundreds of kilometres. As has already been discussed, the refractive index of the atmosphere depends on such properties as its temperature, pressure and humidity so variations in any of these can scatter the signals. The scattering process is more efficient at lower altitudes where the atmosphere is denser, and where turbulence associated with the weather can have marked effects on the signal levels and characteristics.

3.3.17 Characteristics of troposcatter signals

Several different types of fading are experienced on troposcatter signals [14]. The effects are more severe at high frequencies, and so are easier to observe and describe. At 10GHz the note of the carrier can appear quite rough, being modulated by the scattering process

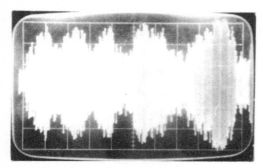

Fig 3.35. Oscilloscope trace showing rapid fading on troposcatter signals received from G3JVL on 10,368MHz over a 110km path in March 1979 (continuous carrier, 50ms/cm, showing fading at around 10Hz)

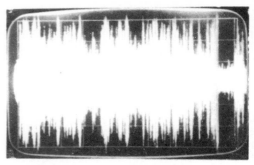

Fig 3.37. Continuous carrier showing fadcing on a longer time scale, 0.6s/cm

at frequencies up to about 50Hz. An example of this rapid fading is shown in Figs 3.35 and 3.36 which are oscilloscope photographs of a continuous carrier received over a 110km path from G3JVL to G3YGF, showing both the depth of the fading and the range of frequencies over which it occurs. At times it produces a waveform that resembles 100 per cent modulation. Fig 3.37 shows the fading on a longer time scale, and the occasional very deep fades can corrupt cw; this is shown in Fig 3.38 where the dash in the "V" of G3JVL has been broken up into two dots.

There is also fading over a period of minutes and, in the longer term, signals tend to show a diurnal variation of about ±5dB, often peaking in the afternoon when atmospheric turbulence caused by convection currents from the warm ground is at a maximum. Plots of signal level showing this effect are given in Fig 3.39. There is also an annual variation of similar amplitude, with signals peaking in the summer and being at a minimum in the winter. The daily and annual variations are probably the result of corresponding variations in the average value of N over the path.

The rapid fading is caused by the signal being scattered from various regions of air, each of which may be

in turbulent motion, and moving relative to each other. This motion can cause both frequency and amplitude modulation of the signals. Frequency modulation results from the signals being scattered from air masses that are moving at different velocities, so there will be random doppler shifts on the signals. At 10GHz a velocity of 50kmph will produce a shift of about 500Hz, and this effect can spread the energy of the carrier out over 1kHz or more, heavy rainstorms producing a sound rather similar to an auroral signal. These storms can

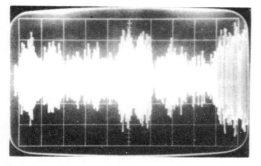

Fig 3.36. Continuous carrier, 50ms/cm, showing more random fading

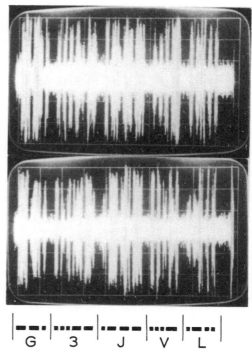

Fig 3.38. Morse code from G3JVL showing occasional deep fading, 0.6s/cm

also increase the signal levels by around 10 to 20dB, as the raindrops scatter the signal more effectively. Amplitude modulation results from variations in the scattering efficiency or interference effects between signals arriving by different paths.

3.3.18 Tropospheric propagation above 10GHz

So far it has been assumed that the troposphere is perfectly transparent to microwaves. In practice, however, some absorption or scattering of a signal will occur due to the presence of the constituent gases and hydrometers, ie rain, snow or hail. Those gases which have the greatest effect at microwave frequencies are water vapour and oxygen. Water has a permanent electric dipole moment and oxygen a permanent magnetic moment; hence both exhibit resonance absorption effects. Fig 3.40 shows the attenuation due to absorption as a function of frequency. It can be seen that absorption losses are negligible at frequencies below about 10GHz but become significant at higher frequencies due to oxygen resonances around 60GHz and 119GHz, and water resonances at about 22GHz and 183GHz.

The amateur band most affected by oxygen absorption is thus likely to be that at 120GHz where the range of signals even in dry air is unlikely to exceed a few kilometres. Significant additional attenuation can also be caused by water vapour. It should be noted, however, that it is the absolute mass of water held in the atmosphere which matters; thus there may be more water in the atmosphere on a fine summer day than on a wet winter one. If the air temperature is below zero then the water content will be very low; long-distance communication will be much easier, therefore, in arctic conditions or between mountains above the snow line.

At frequencies up to about 20GHz the attenuation of microwaves by hydrometers is proportional to the liquid water content. Thus rain and wet snow will cause the greatest attenuation, whereas hail and dry snow are of less significance. Below 10GHz the dominant loss mechanism when hydrometers are present is absorption since the wavelength is large compared with the drop size. Above 10GHz the dominant loss becomes that due to scattering. Figs 3.41 and 3.42 show the attenuation due to fog, clouds and rain as a function of frequency. It can be seen that only the attenuation due to rain is of significance except at the higher frequencies. Even this is not so high as might appear at first, since in general a given path will not be subjected simultaneously to the same rainfall intensity over the whole of its length due to the cellular pattern of rainfall.

Bearing in mind the above, the estimated potential for long-distance communication in the millimetric amateur bands is summarised in Table 3.8. From this the following conclusions may be drawn:

(a) It is expected that amateurs should be able to work paths at least tens of kilometres long on most of the

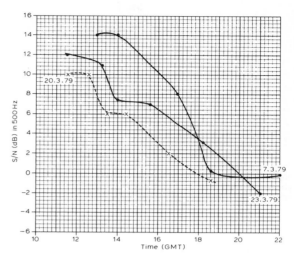

Fig 3.39. Variation of troposcatter signal strength with time, showing diurnal varaiations

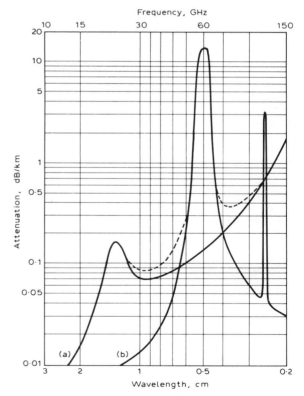

Fig 3.40. Microwave attenuation due to water vapour and oxygen (from *The Services Text Book of Radio – Volume 5*. Reproduced with the permission of The Controller of Her Majesty's Stationery Office)

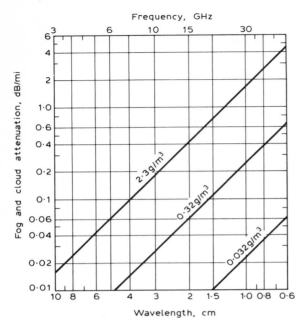

Fig 3.41. Microwave attenuation due to fog and clouds (from The Physics of Microwave Propagation, Donald C Livingston. ©1970. Reprinted by permission of Prentice-Hall Inc, Englewood Cliffs, NJ, USA)

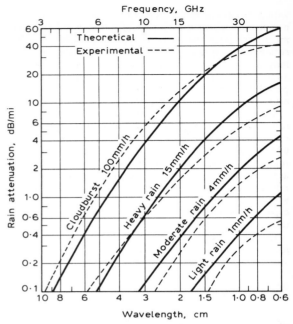

Fig 3.42. Microwave attenuation due to rain (from The Physics of Microwave Propagation, Donald C Livingston. ©1970. Reprinted by permission of Prentice-Hall Inc, Englewood Cliffs, NJ, USA)

millimetric bands even under conditions of high humidity.

(b) Ranges of hundreds of kilometres can be expected on most bands under conditions of low humidity, for instance over deserts or where the air temperature is below 0°C.

(c) Due to the high attenuation of signals by oxygen in the atmosphere at frequencies around 120GHz, propagation ranges on this band are likely to be restricted to a few kilometres.

(d) Although rain will cause high path losses on all the millimetric bands, these can often be avoided in amateur operation by judicious timing.

3.3.19 Propagation over earth– space paths

Many of the factors which affect microwave propagation over terrestrial line-of-sight paths will also be present over earth–space paths, especially if the elevation angle from the ground station to the satellite is small. At such angles, which will occur when a ground station, situated at a high latitude, is communicating

Table 3.8. Performance of simple equipment on the millimetric bands

Band (GHz)	PLC	Margin (dB)						Max range (km) for 10dB margin		
		1km		10km		100km		space	dry	humid
		dry	humid	dry	humid	dry	humid			
24	177	57	56	37	34	15	−15	220	120	50
47	187	63	62	43	37	3	−32	350	70	48
76	197	67	65	47	34	−3		700	65	30
120	205	71	41					1,100	2	2
142	208	72	69	51	21	22		1,300	70	13
241	216	76	71	56	3	33		2,000	500	9

These figures were obtained for equipment having the following parameters. Transmitter: output power = 1mW. Antennas: 20cm diameter dishes with low-efficiency (25 per cent) feeds. Receiver: noise figure = 20dB; i.f bandwidth = 10MHz. In all cases the signal-to-noise ratios shown are pre-detection.

with a geosynchronous satellite or is maintaining communication with a non-geosynchronous satellite for the maximum time that it is above the horizon, ground reflections, variations in refractive index and ducting may all be of significance. At much larger elevation angles, however, their effects will become small compared with other mechanisms such as absorption and attenuation due to hydrometers.

The extent to which a steady decrease in refractive index with increasing height causes refraction of a microwave ray has been discussed already. For a path which extends throughout the atmosphere, however, refraction causes the apparent elevation angle of a ray, as seen from the ground, to be greater than if the atmosphere were not present. The effects due to ray bending will be important only at very small elevation angles and especially when narrow-beamwidth antennas are being used.

As on a terrestrial path, the free-space transmission loss on an earth–space path will be increased by absorption due to oxygen and water vapour, and by scattering due to hydrometers. This additional loss will depend on the elevation angle since this defines the effective thickness of the atmosphere. To a first approximation, then, the effective distance for oxygen absorption can be taken as the distance the wave would have to travel if the atmosphere were replaced by one having constant density reaching upwards from the ground to a height of 4km, with a vacuum above. The corresponding height for water vapour is 2km. This gives a theoretical total one-way attenuation due to the combined effects of oxygen and water vapour of approximately 1.5dB at 1GHz, 2dB at 5GHz and 6dB at 15GHz, for a horizontal path (ie one tangential to the earth's surface). These values reduce as the elevation angle increases to become, in the limit, when the signal take-off direction is vertical, about 0.1dB at 15GHz, with only 1dB at the 22GHz water absorption peak.

3.4 REFERENCES

[1] "The identification of trans-horizon interference propagation conditions from meteorological data", M T Hewitt and A R Adams, *Proc URSI Commission F*, Symposium on effects of the lower atmosphere on radio propagation at frequencies below 1GHz, Lennoxville, Quebec, Canada, May 1980, pp7.2.1–7.2.6.

[2] "Tropospheric scatter propagation", J Gannaway, *Radio Communication*, Vol 57, 1981, pp710–714 and 717.

[3] "Some experiments on the propagation over land of radiation of 9.2cm wavelength, especially on the effect of obstacles", J M McPetrie and L H Ford, *J IEE*, Vol 93, IIIA, 1946, pp531–538.

[4] "Multiple knife-edge diffraction of microwaves", J Deygout, *IEEE Trans on Ant and Prop*, AP14, 1966, pp480–489.

[5] *VHF/UHF Manual*, ed G R Jessop, Chapter 2 (by R Flavell), RSGB.

[6] "The radio refractive index over the British Isles", J A Lane, *J Atmos Terr Phys*, Vol 21, 1961, pp157–166.

[7] "Forecasting television service fields", A H Lagrone, *Proc IRE*, Vol 48, 1960, pp1009–1015.

[8] *Radio Meteorology*, B R Bean and E J Dutton, NBS Monograph 92, 1966.

[9] *CCIR Green Book*.

[10] *Planning and Engineering of Radio Relay Links*, H Brodhage and W Hormuth, Siemens-Heyden, 1977.

[11] "Microwave path checking", B Chambers, *Radio Communication*, Vol 54, 1978, pp122–126.

[12] *RSGB Microwave Newsletter*.

[13] "Frontal disturbances in anti-cyclonic subsidence – a cause of microwave interference propagation beyond the horizon", M T Hewitt, A R Adams and R G Flavell, *URSI XXth General Assembly*, Washington DC, USA, Aug 1981.

[14] "Results of propagation tests at 505 and 4,090MHz on beyond the horizon paths", K Bullington, W J Inkster and A L Durkee, *Proc IRE*, Vol 43, 1955, pp1306–1316.

CHAPTER 4

Microwave antennas

4.1 INTRODUCTION

If you are interested in working dx, you are interested in high-performance antennas. This means antennas which give high gain with good radiation patterns, and what this means in practice should become apparent in this chapter.

A special characteristic of microwave antennas is the relative ease with which high gains can be achieved from manageable-sized hardware, compared with lower frequencies. Values between 20 and 45dB with respect to an isotropic source are quite common. Gain is normally quoted in dBi, referred to an isotropic source. Since the isotropic antenna is a theoretical concept and does not exist, another reference, used mainly by amateurs, is dBd, in which case the gain is referred to a dipole. A dipole in free space has a gain of 2.15dB relative to the point source of the imaginary isotropic radiator.

The temptation to take advantage of antenna gain is great, since it is the most socially aware method of increasing one's station effectiveness on both transmit and receive. By concentrating the radiated energy into a beam, several advantages result. The operator seeking to work at the extremes of propagation is always dealing with signals near the noise threshold. Here, even one or two extra decibels becomes significant, making the difference between a contact or no contact. Using a well-designed beam allows concentration of energy, not only in the desired direction, but also at a low angle onto the

horizon where it is more effective over terrestrial paths. For eme the target is, in angular terms, very small and radiated power not hitting the target is power wasted. The use of beams can lead to less interference to and from other stations using adjacent frequencies and can also minimise rf interference to other services, including domestic electrical equipment. However, the beamwidths become quite small and therefore extra skill is required in handling these antennas effectively. This skill is rapidly acquired and it is very soon realised that many of the remote locations are not quite where you thought they were.

Antenna gain is achieved by concentrating the radiated energy within angular confines to form a beam. In general, the smaller the angle, the higher the gain. The angular size of this beam reduces as the size of the array is increased, be it either the diameter of a dish or the boom length of a Yagi-type antenna. Gain may also be increased by combining a number of individual antennas. By increasing the gain of the antenna, the effective power of a transmitter or the sensitivity of a receiver is increased, but the price to be paid is the need to align the antenna more precisely in the desired direction.

The ideal form of the polar diagram of a typical high-gain antenna is shown in Fig 4.1(a). This ideal state is never achieved and a poorly designed antenna might have a polar pattern like that of Fig 4.1(b). The general form of the polar diagram of a practical, well-designed antenna is shown in Fig 4.2, where the 1dB, 3dB and 10dB beamwidths represent the angles through which the antenna may be rotated before the power transmitted or received falls respectively by 26 per cent (–1dB), 50 per cent (–3dB) or by 90 per cent (–10dB) of the maximum value. The 10dB level also represents the beamwidth within which most of the power is concentrated. The –1dB beamwidth should be considered the limit for normal pointing accuracy. The approximate relationship between gain and beamwidth is shown in Fig 4.3, normalised to permit performance on any frequency to be assessed.

The assumption has been made that the beamwidth in both planes is the same, as this is normal for long arrays or large-diameter dishes. This figure gives a guide to the accuracy with which the antenna needs to be pointed.

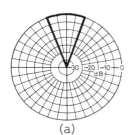
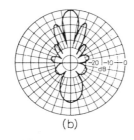

(a)   (b)

Fig 4.1 (a) Idealised radiation pattern of high-gain antenna, with flat-nosed main lobe and no sidelobes at all. (b) Unacceptable radiation pattern, with pointed main lobe and excessive side and back lobes

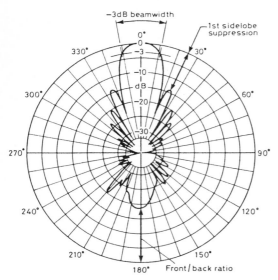

Fig 4.2. E-plane pattern of a good long Yagi. Note the general symmetry and the deep nulls at ±90°

For example, the 3dB beamwidth of an antenna having a gain of 35dB is about 3°. To receive weak signals close to the threshold requires that the antenna be pointed within half this angle, ie within the 1dB beamwidth or about 1.5°. For strong signals, the 10dB beamwidth may apply, but even this is still only about 5°. That this is

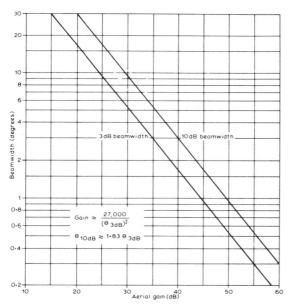

Fig 4.3. Approximate relationship between antenna gain and beamwidth

regularly achieved by amateurs, even under contest conditions, is a measure of the progress that has been made in acquiring the necessary skills. It should be stressed that if the heading for a station has been determined by the use of a lower frequency, this can lead to errors which may mean no contact.

The main problems are the comparative beamwidths and the likelihood of the deep nulls on either side of the main lobe being directed at the remote station. These nulls are located at approximately the main beam's 3dB angular width (3dB beamwidth) either side of the true heading. The recommended method uses good maps and a calculator or computer programmed to give the results and accuracy required. The availability of such devices now means that complex calculations may be made with little or no effort, even when out on portable sites.

However, these factors do not remain constant and consideration of which antenna to use as the frequency increases is recommended. It becomes evident that when the highest bands are considered the obvious choice is a dish. Then the question is "which f/D (focal length to diameter) should I use?" The feed becomes the next choice to be made; several are discussed and are described for specific bands but the theory applies to any other band.

4.2 TYPES OF ANTENNA

4.2.1 The five main types

The five main types of antenna used on the microwave bands are:

1. Yagi types, where only one element or a small group of elements is fed with power, the rest being elements.

2. Phased arrays, including log periodics and waveguide omnis, where all elements are fed.

3. Horns, which are developed from waveguide and may be flared in one or both planes.

4. Parabolic reflectors, which are the best-explained type, due to their similarity to optical reflectors.

5. Omni slots, now used on microwave frequencies as beacon and repeater radiators.

4.2.2 Antennas suited to particular applications

Antennas of the Yagi type have been very popular on 1.3GHz for some time and are also now finding their place on 2.3GHz, where their low windage and weight compare well with dishes having the same gain. Both are, of course, difficult to design and to adjust for optimum performance but both will repay the effort with good results, the choice being left to the users' needs. However, on the higher bands dishes present an easier choice when the optimum result is required. It is not suggested that the design and adjustment of the Yagi types is impossible, as has often been demonstrated, but better results can be achieved with less work using a dish. Antennas such as helicals, corner reflectors and cylindrical paraboloids are now little used, mainly due to their low gain relative to their volume. They do, however, have specific applications to which they are well suited.

As already mentioned, various forms of Yagi antennas are now in use at 1.3 and 2.3GHz, where formerly dishes were used. Dishes less than about 10λ in diameter are rather inefficient and other simpler or less wind catching types are recommended for 1.3GHz as even these smaller dishes may be inconvenient in many installations. Dishes are almost mandatory for applications such as eme. This is because high gain is essential and several bands can be catered for by just exchanging the feed. Large arrays of Yagis can be used, but their use will be limited to a single band.

Helicals are used in applications such as satellite communication where circular polarity is often required. However, even this case may be better served by cross-polarised Yagi types which permit polarity to be selected. One exception is the eme worker who wishes to optimise a circularly polarised feed horn. To do this requires a pair of "opposite"-sense eight-turn helicals. By using these as measuring antennas, it is possible to obtain very good circularity while adjusting the dish feed. The "same"-sense helix will give maximum output, and the "opposite"-sense helix will give minimum output when used in this way (see the 1.3GHz chapter in Volume 3).

Reference should be made to section 4.11 for general antenna alignment and adjustment recommendations.

4.3 YAGI-TYPE ANTENNAS

4.3.1 High-performance standard Yagis

This section presents a description of the general design principles of standard long Yagis, based on an article by G3SEK [1].

Fig 4.4 shows claimed and measured gain figures for 144MHz, 432MHz and 1.3GHz long Yagis, plotted against boom length in wavelengths. All gains are expressed in dBd, ie decibels above a half-wave dipole. With one or two exceptions, the gains claimed by antenna manufacturers lie far above the independent measurements of the same Yagi, and have not been included. Doubling the boom length of a long Yagi, and hence nearly doubling the gain, would reduce both the E-plane and H-plane beamwidths to about 70 per cent of their previous values. This follows from the so-called Kraus formula relating gain to E-plane and H-plane beamwidths:

$$B_e \times B_h = 25{,}000/(\text{antilog}(G/10))$$

where the beamwidths are in degrees and G is in dBd. Since the two beamwidths are almost equal for a long Yagi, you can estimate them both with reasonable accuracy.

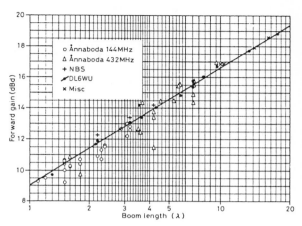

Fig 4.4. Forward gain is proportional to boom length

The Kraus formula is *not* accurate enough to estimate the gain from the beamwidths. The presence of sidelobes, together with quite minor inaccuracies in beamwidth measurement, can totally blur the difference between a good Yagi and a poor one.

Several conclusions emerge from detailed analysis of the data summarised in Fig 4.4:

(a) Gain *is* proportional to boom length. The solid points and the straight line are from one consistent series of measurements, and verify the proportionality to almost 20λ. Variations between measurements from different sources obscure the trend but do not negate it.

(b) Quads, loop Yagis, "quagis", "parrot-perches" and "motleybeams" are all represented, but they do not stand out from the ordinary Yagis.

(c) For a given boom length, the difference in gain between a good Yagi and a mediocre one is only a decibel or two.

(d) The same gain can be achieved with various numbers of elements on the same overall boom length. The number of elements does affect many other characteristics of the antenna, and more will be said about this later.

(e) The Yagis represented by the solid points will be worth a closer look.

When assessing a Yagi design, you can get far more information from a critical study of the directional radiation pattern than you can from simple tables of claimed gain and front/back ratio. Fig 4.2 shows a typical pattern, calibrated 360° around the compass, and inwards in decibels. Maximum power is radiated at the peak of the main lobe; this point is always plotted at the top of the diagram (0°, 0dB). Radiated powers in other directions can be plotted down to typically 40dB below the peak of the main lobe. Although usually called a radiation pattern, Fig 4.2 could equally well be called a reception pattern, for antennas behave the same in receive and transmit modes alike, ie they are reciprocal.

For dx working, the antenna should be horizontally polarised – not from mere convention, but because horizontal works better for dx. Thus the most important radiation pattern, the one you observe when you turn the rotator, is the one in the same plane as the Yagi, which is called the "E-plane". The pattern in the H-plane (the vertical plane for a horizontally polarised Yagi) is very similar to the E-plane pattern. The longer the Yagi, the more alike the E-plane and H-plane patterns become, the main differences being that the E-plane pattern always has nulls at 90°, and the H-plane pattern always has a slightly broader main lobe and higher sidelobe levels.

Fig 4.2 also summarises the points to look for in a good radiation pattern. The main lobe is distinct, and the pattern is generally clean with good suppression of minor lobes. The pattern should be symmetrical and there should be deep nulls at 90° in the E-plane – if not, there is something wrong with either the Yagi or the measurements.

Low levels of minor lobes in the polar pattern are almost as important as gain. The two features are in fact closely related, since any beam works by concentrating rf energy into the wanted direction at the expense of radiation in unwanted directions. The better the suppression of the minor lobes, the more energy can go into the main lobe. On receive, good suppression of the minor lobes means a stronger signal from the wanted direction, and less interference with stations in other directions. You cannot judge the minor-lobe suppression by simple "magic numbers" like front/back ratio. The problem with front/back ratio is that it is too easy to optimise that one aspect of performance while letting the other sidelobe levels run wild. A better general indicator of minor-lobe suppression is the level of the first sidelobes on either side of the main lobe. These "rabbit ears" are present in all long Yagis, though in a good design they would be suppressed to about –15dB.

The higher the gain of a beam, the harder it becomes to aim it in the right direction. The reason is very simple; you can't get away from this, but you can considerably ease your aiming problems by choosing a Yagi design which gives a well-shaped main lobe.

The ideal would be the fan-shaped main lobe shown in Fig 4.1(a), with maximum gain across the whole beamwidth for ease of aiming, and no sidelobes at all. Such perfection is not even attainable in theory; we have to accept that the edges of the main beam will always be rounded, and sidelobes will always be present.

Even so, there is no reason to accept a main lobe like the one in Fig 4.1(b), which is sharply pointed and has less than 10dB of sidelobe suppression. If a Yagi has a pattern like that, there is something fundamentally wrong with it, no matter how high the maximum gain may be.

This is not just a matter of aesthetics: a beam with a pointed main lobe is really awkward to use. It is too difficult to peak a station right on the point of the main lobe, and too easy to peak on a sidelobe by mistake. The best achievable shape for the main lobe is shown in Fig 4.2; there is no doubt about finding the main lobe, yet its fairly flat nose makes peaking the signal quite uncritical.

To sum up all the desirable aspects of antenna performance, an optimised Yagi will have:

(a) high forward gain, for its boom length;

(b) a generally clean polar pattern (in particular, first sidelobes at about –15dB);

(c) a well-shaped main lobe which causes no undue problems in aiming.

There are no fundamental conflicts between good performance in all of these areas, provided we do not go blindly chasing the maximum possible gain. In a modern optimised long Yagi, all the above objectives can be achieved together.

Modern long Yagi designs have evolved through a long process of trial and error – mostly error. Designs for shorter Yagis have been adopted and extended, in the hope of producing workable longer Yagis with higher gain. The early work on long Yagis was done in the 'fifties and 'sixties, by investigators who seemed largely unaware of each other's activities. Subsequently, the most successful designers are those who straightened out the historical tangles and built upon the work of their predecessors, rather than starting yet again from scratch. Thus there has evolved a definite "mainstream" of long Yagi design.

The mechanical dimensions required for optimum performance are usually found by experiment. Countless thousands of man-hours and tons of aluminium have gone into the optimisation of high-performance long Yagis. Computer analysis is increasingly used to assess potential improvements, and can save a great deal of experimental effort, but successful computer optimisation is a lot harder than it might seem. Yagi design still begins with ideas in someone's head, and ends with measurements on real antennas.

Throughout the whole history of amateur-band antennas, there have been frequent claims of "miracle" beams which break the gain/size barrier. Electrically small (eg two-element) beams can beat the odds to a small extent, but the reasons for this are clearly understood, and they do not apply to long Yagis. Unfortunately, since accurate gain measurements are so difficult, it is all too easy for people to obtain results which they proclaim with fervour and total sincerity, but which are in fact wrong.

Far more is known about Yagis using simple rod-type dipole elements than about other types of Yagis using loops or more elaborate element shapes. The latter may offer slightly higher theoretical gain, but even in theory this advantage dwindles away as the Yagi gets longer.

The existing body of knowledge about conventional elements can provide only hints about the behaviour of other element shapes, so the designer who chooses to use unconventional elements is starting again from scratch. In accurate comparisons, few of the more elaborate Yagis have come even close to competing with well-designed conventional Yagis. The G3JVL loop-quad Yagis are a rare example of a well-developed alternative approach, and the performance of the later versions is running neck-and-neck with the best of the plain Yagi designs.

Mainstream long-Yagi design is based on some definite ideas about how a successful long Yagi should work. It is sometimes useful to think of a long Yagi launching a travelling wave along its structure and away into space. Thus you can divide the Yagi into two parts: a "launcher" consisting of the driven element, reflector and first few directors; and a travelling-wave structure consisting of all the rest of the directors. Although that is not necessarily the best all-purpose description of how a Yagi works [2], it eliminates a lot of random cut-and-try by focusing on those combinations of element lengths and positions that show the most promise of launching and propagating a travelling wave.

The history of long-Yagi design starts with the work of Ehrenspeck and Poehler [3], who made a major investigation of uniform long Yagis whose directors were all the same length and equally spaced along the boom. Although short uniform Yagis can work very well, Ehrenspeck and Poehler found that they fail to achieve the expected increase in gain with boom length. In other words, uniform long Yagis are an evolutionary dead end. The next step forward came from investigations of the effects of tapering. In the language of long-Yagi design, "tapering" has two alternative meanings. Tapering the element spacings means that successive directors are spaced further and further apart, going forwards along the boom (Fig 4.5(a)). Tapering the element lengths means that each director is shorter than the one before (Fig 4.5(b)). The two kinds of tapering should have very similar effects on a travelling wave. So, to keep the experimental work within manageable bounds, it seemed sensible to optimise either director spacing or director length, leaving the other one constant at some initially chosen value. This generation of long Yagis has since been called "singly optimised".

Most experimenters have agreed that tapering should be quite pronounced in the launcher section, close to the driven element. Directors further along the boom need not be so strongly tapered. Tapering of spacings was investigated by W2NLY and W6QKI [4], who developed some quite successful Yagis in which all directors were the same length, and the director spacing initially increased and then became constant. The optimum value for this constant spacing seemed uncritical between 0.3λ and 0.4λ, though the wider spacings obviously involve fewer elements and less wind load.

Tapering of director lengths, with the spacings held constant, is the basis of the well-known "NBS" Yagis, derived from the work of Peter Viezbicke of the US National Bureau of Standards in the 'fifties [5]. This mammoth effort included full investigations of length-tapering schemes and of the effects of different element diameters and mounting methods. It culminated in a set of designs including long Yagis with boom lengths of 3.2λ and 4.2λ. Joe Reisert, W1JR, and others have explained how to design "NBS" beams from Viezbicke's charts [6, 7]. NBS long Yagis are good, but they cannot be extended; and much has happened in the three decades since they were developed.

The two single-optimisation techniques produced the best long Yagis available at the time, and these designs have been enshrined in the amateur literature ever since. But single-optimisation fails to produce Yagis which can be extended satisfactorily to meet today's requirements for longer Yagis with higher gain. So the next step was to combine the experience from tapering either the lengths or the spacings, and to taper them both. W2NLY and W6QKI found some improvement in bandwidth from length-tapering their spacing-optimised designs. Carl Greenblum [7] independently investigated double-tapering at about the same time as the single-optimization work was going on. Together, all these experiments formed the basis of some classic Yagi designs of the 'sixties and 'seventies.

The most promising of the modern-day long Yagi designs come from Gunter Hoch, DL6WU. He has thought carefully about ways of improving earlier designs, and his extensive experimental results have been obtained using professional test facilities. DL6WU considered first the director-spacing aspect of tapering. W2NLY and W6QKI showed that this is important in the launcher section, but can be stopped once the spacing has been gradually increased to about 0.4λ. Further increases in spacing in the travelling-wave part of the Yagi are counter-productive.

This spacing scheme seemed close enough to optimum, so DL6WU turned his attention towards optimizing the element-length tapering as well. The result was to be a highly successful family of doubly optimised, long Yagis [8]. The simplest form of director-length tapering would be to make each director shorter than its

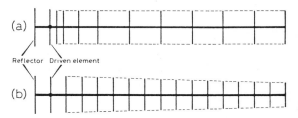

Fig 4.5. Single-optimization schemes. (a) Optimised tapering of director spacing. (b) Optimised tapering of director lengths

Design frequency = 1296.0 MHz   Number of elements = 26

Boom diameter = 12.700 mm   Element diameters: driven = 2.500mm
                                               parasitic = 2.500mm

Electrical boom length = 1975 mm

Suggested stacking distances :
  horizontal = 754.7mm = 29.7 inches = 3.26 wavelengths
  vertical = 747.6 mm = 29.4 inches = 3.23 wavelengths

Elements are SECURELY CONNECTED to the metal boom.

CUMULATIVE SPACING			ELEMENT LENGTH	
mm	inches		mm	inches
Zero	Zero	REFL	120.32	4.737
50.50	1.988	D.E.	108.66	4.278
69.53	2.737	D 1	108.12	4.257
108.28	4.263	D 2	106.72	4.201
158.56	6.243	D 3	105.27	4.145
217.03	8.545	D 4	103.94	4.092
281.85	11.097	D 5	102.78	4.046
351.86	13.853	D 6	101.78	4.007
426.25	16.782	D 7	100.92	3.973
504.45	19.860	D 8	100.17	3.944
585.99	23.071	D 9	99.51	3.918
670.53	26.399	D 10	98.91	3.894
757.79	29.834	D 11	98.37	3.873
847.51	33.367	D 12	97.88	3.854
939.52	36.989	D 13	97.43	3.836
1033.64	40.694	D 14	97.01	3.819
1127.75	44.400	D 15	96.62	3.804
1221.86	48.105	D 16	96.25	3.789
1315.98	51.810	D 17	95.91	3.776
1410.09	55.516	D 18	95.58	3.763
1504.21	59.221	D 19	95.28	3.751
1598.32	62.926	D 20	94.99	3.740
1692.44	66.632	D 21	94.71	3.729
1786.55	70.337	D 22	94.45	3.718
1880.67	74.042	D 23	94.20	3.709
1974.78	77.748	D 24	93.96	3.699

Fig 4.6. Construction details of a 26-element DL6WU long Yagi

predecessor by a constant amount. This works if the Yagi is not extended too far, but eventually the forward gain bleeds away into increased levels of minor lobes. If you extend the Yagi far enough, subtracting a constant amount from each successive director, you eventually arrive at a director length of zero – a dead end, if ever there was one!

DL6WU's answer to that problem is one of those brilliant ideas which seem so obvious in hindsight: taper each successive director length by a constant *fraction*. This logarithmic tapering makes the director lengths decrease quite sharply in the launcher section, but less markedly further along the array. No matter how far the Yagi is extended, the director lengths can never reach zero, and the logarithmic tapering seems to confer some degree of frequency independence. Various people have come close to this approach in the past, but only DL6WU has spelt it out as a design rule, and then followed it through to develop a whole family of successful long Yagis.

The shortest in the DL6WU family of long Yagis consists of only the launcher section with its gradually increasing director spacings. Longer Yagis can then be designed simply by adding more directors at a constant spacing of 0.4λ, with the appropriate logarithmic tapering of element lengths. The performance of the DL6WU Yagis is a tribute to Gunter Hoch's clear thinking about the problem. Without any further optimisation, all the Yagis built from DL6WU's design charts have clean patterns and well-shaped main lobes, and therefore their forward gains are as high as their chosen boom lengths will allow. These are the long Yagis represented by the solid points in Fig 4.4, and the straight line shows every promise of extending beyond 20dBd – that is, if you care to build a Yagi 24 wavelengths long! Perhaps the most remarkable feature of the whole family of DL6WU Yagis is the way that the patterns remain so consistent as the Yagis are extended. Naturally the main lobes become narrower as the Yagis become longer, but the patterns remain clean and the suppression of the first sidelobes remains consistently good at about 15–20dB. In short, DL6WU long Yagis show every sign of working *properly*.

The success of the DL6WU family of long Yagis has demolished several cherished myths and moans.

"Long Yagis can't be extended". They can, if you do it right.

"Ordinary Yagis don't work on microwaves". Oh yes, they do! The longest Yagis on Fig 4.4 were all developed on 1.3GHz. It is not suggested that Yagis are the best antennas for the higher microwave bands, but there is absolutely no reason why they should not work *if scaled properly* to the wavelength.

"Element dimensions for long Yagis are extremely critical". If some people were to be believed, the element lengths of the 1.3GHz Yagis would each need to be accurate to 0.1mm. In fact the logarithmic director taper appears to be very forgiving of constructional errors [8].

"Bandwidths of long Yagis are extremely narrow". With logarithmic tapering, the Yagi itself is quite wideband [1]; the frequency-conscious part is usually the method of matching the feedline to the driven element.

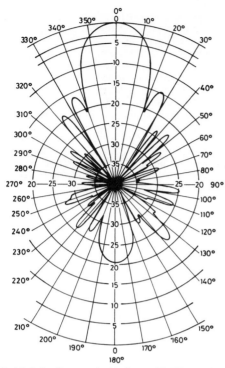

Fig 4.7. Polar diagram of a 26-element DL6WU long Yagi

Table 4.1. Typical dimensions of loopquad antenna

1,296MHz				2,320MHz		
		Boom dia **0.5in**	**0.75in**			**Boom dia** **0.5in**
Rp	**Rw**	**R1**	**R1**	**Rpw**	**Rph**	**R1**
140	115	252	254	80	65	143
Elements 2.5mm dia		**De** 230	**De** 232	**Elements** 1.6mm dia		**De** 130
Directors				**Directors**		
D01-D12		213	215	D01-D12		121
D13-D20		206	208	D13-D20		117
D21-D30		198	200	D21-D30		113
D31-D40		193	195	D31-D40		110
D41-D55		190	192	D41-D55		108
D56-D63		189	191	D56-D63		107

Cumulative spacings

	1,296MHz				2,320MHz		
RP	0	RL	79	RP	0	RL	44
DE	103	D1	131	DE	58	D1	73
D2	152	D3	198	D2	85	D3	110
D4	243	D5	275	D4	136	D5	153
D6	333	D7	424	D6	186	D7	237
D8	514	D9	605	D8	287	D9	338
D10	695	D11	785	D10	388	D11	439
D12	876	D13	966	D12	489	D13	540
D14	1,057	D15	1,147	D14	590	D15	641
D16	1,238	D17	1,328	D16	691	D17	742
D18	1,418	D19	1,509	D18	792	D19	843
D20	1,599	D21	1,690	D20	893	D21	944
D22	1,780	D23	1,871	D22	994	D23	1,045
D24	1,961	D25	2,051	D24	1,095	D25	1,146
D26	2,142	D27	2,232	D26	1,196	D27	1,247
D28	2,323	D29	2,413	D28	1,297	D29	1,348
D30	2,503	D31	2,594	D30	1,399	D31	1,449
D32	2,684	D33	2,775	D32	1,500	D33	1,550
D34	2,865	D35	2,956	D34	1,601	D35	1,651
D36	3,046	D37	3,136	D36	1,702	D37	1,752
D38	3,227	D39	3,317	D38	1,803	D39	1,853
D40	3,408	D41	3,498	D40	1,904	D41	1,954
D42	3,589	D43	3,679	D42	2,005	D43	2,055
D44	3,769	D45	3,860	D44	2,106	D45	2,156
D46	3,950	D47	4,041	D46	2,207	D47	2,257
D48	4,131	D49	4,222	D48	2,308	D49	2,358
D50	4,312	D51	4,402	D50	2,409	D51	2,459
D52	4,493	D53	4,583	D52	2,510	D53	2,560
D54	4,674	D55	4,764	D54	2,611	D55	2,661
D56	4,855	D57	4,945	D56	2,712	D57	2,762
D58	5,035	D59	5,126	D58	2,813	D59	2,863
D60	5,216	D61	5,307	D60	2,914	D61	2,964
D62	5,397	D63	5,487	D62	3,015	D63	3,064

All dimensions are in millimetres except where stated.

"You can't feed a long Yagi with a simple dipole". Yes you can, and it does not need help from quad-loops, log-periodics or ZL-specials either.

Yagis based on the work of DL6WU are now appearing worldwide, both from individual amateurs and from professional manufacturers. They are highly recommended for use at 1.3GHz.

The design of 27- and 32-director singly optimised Yagis was discussed in the fourth edition of the RSGB *VHF/UHF Manual* and these still represent simple, tried and tested designs for the beginner. However, the standard Yagi included here is a 26-element DL6WU design. The parameters were calculated using a computer program written by KY4Z, W6NBI and G4SEK based on articles and design data by Gunter Hoch, DL6WU. The boom length is 8.45 λ or 1,955mm plus overhang. The estimated performance figures are:

Gain	=	18.5dBi
Horizontal beamwidth	=	22.4°
Vertical beamwidth	=	22.8°

Suggested stacking distances are 528mm horizontally and 518mm vertically. Fig 4.6 gives the detail required to construct this antenna. Fig 4.7 shows its polar diagram. The equivalent-length "27-element loopquad" has 20dBi gain.

4.3.2 The G3JVL "loopquad" antenna

The design of this antenna is shown in Figs 4.8 and 4.9, and example dimensions for 1,296MHz and 2,320MHz in Table 4.1, which should be used in conjunction with Fig 4.9. The example values shown in the table will

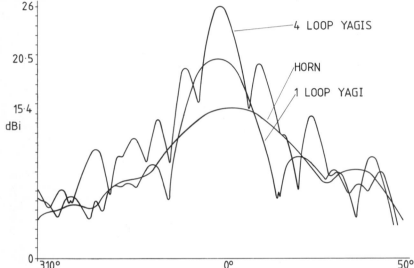

Fig 4.8. (a) A G3JVL "loopquad" antenna. (b) Polar diagram of the loop-quad antenna

provide detail for any boom length, eg a 27-element version will include all elements up to D24. The construction of the loopquad is quite straightforward, but the dimensions given must be closely adhered to: after all, at 1.3GHz 2.5mm (0.1in) error represents about one per cent of a wavelength, or a change in frequency of 13MHz.

When drilling the boom, for example, measurements of the position of the elements should be made from a single point by adding the appropriate lengths; if the individual spacings are marked from the preceding position, then errors may accumulate to an unacceptable degree. Elements other than the driven element may be made from flat aluminium strip. The two holes are drilled or punched before bending, with a spacing equal to the circumference specified in Fig 4.9.

The radiator may be brass or copper strip. This form is by far the easiest to home-construct but the mechanical strength is rather poor. A much superior form uses

mild or stainless steel wire (welding rods) for all the elements. The parasitic element lengths should be cropped, folded and brazed or silver soldered onto M4 countersunk screws. The whole assembled antenna may be zinc plated to protect and possibly improve conductivity at low cost.

The driven element differs in that it uses a countersunk M6 by 25mm long screw which has been drilled through at 3.6mm diameter. The element is brazed or silver soldered with its open end around the hole. The hole may need clearing or redrilling carefully after brazing. To allow the connection of the semi-rigid coaxial cable, saw through the element at its top mid-point. The cut ends should be shaped to accept the coaxial cable as shown in Fig 4.9. To enable soldering it will be necessary to use an acid flux. Examples are Bakers Fluid or Multicore's ARAX fluxed solder. Both of these require that any residue is washed off to prevent long-term corrosion effects. Once the steel has been properly

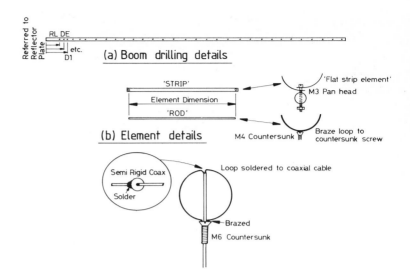

(a) Boom drilling details

(b) Element details

(c) Driven Element details

Fig 4.9. Construction of loopquad antenna (see Table 4.1 for typical dimensions)

"tinned", use normal non-corrosive flux to complete the joint to the cable. The coaxial cable outer should be pre-trimmed to allow the connector to be fitted.

The whole assembly, including the coaxial cable, may be plated after completion. However, it is advisable to leave the ptfe covering the inner. This is because the zinc plating is very difficult to solder. Even after plating the radiator and all screws and soldered joints should be protected with polyurethane varnish, followed by a coat of paint on all surfaces. If inadequate attention is paid to this protection, then the gain of the antenna may decrease with time as a result of corrosion. However, there is only a very small chance of this occurring with the brazed wire elements, as no surface-to-surface contact is involved. The zinc plating is intended to retain a good appearance but its long-term properties can be a little unpredictable. The additional protection of varnish or paint will help to maintain the finish and is strongly recommended.

Where the specified materials are not available, changes may be made to the diameter of the boom and the thickness and width of the elements. Compensation may be achieved by altering the length of all elements by applying the correction factors CF as detailed in Table 4.2. It may be found an advantage to use thicker, wider elements to increase the strength of the antenna, for example a 19mm (0.75in) diameter boom, and 6.35mm by 1.6mm (0.25in by 0.063in) loops. The element dimensions will therefore need correcting by (0.9 − 0.3 + 0.6) = 1.2 per cent. Thus all elements (the reflector, the driven element and the directors) should be made 1.2 per cent longer, but the element spacing is not altered. Provided that the antenna is constructed carefully, its feed impedance will be close to 50Ω.

If a vswr or impedance bridge is available, very small final adjustments may be made by altering the spacing of the reflector loop a little by bending with respect to the driven element. However, it is recommended that the method of adjustment is by altering the driven element length very carefully. As an alternative the G3JVL-designed "looperiodic" wideband feed, as shown in Fig 4.10, may be used. This should result in a reasonable vswr which is less critically dependent on frequency and which permits much wider coverage of the 1.3GHz allocation, for example.

Several versions of this antenna have been constructed for 432MHz, 1.3, 2.3, 3.4 and 10GHz. The dimensions of these have been derived by scaling linearly all the antenna dimensions and applying correction factors (derived from experimental work by G3JVL in 1974–5) as necessary. The parameters concerned are the thickness, width and circumference of the elements and the boom diameter.

The design program listed below permits any amateur to construct this antenna using any size of materials available. This program was derived by G3JVL from the

Table 4.2

Thickness (mm) (in)		CFx100 (%)	Width (mm) (in)		CFx100 (%)	Boom dia (mm) (in)		CFx100 (%)
0.71	0.028	0.0	2.54	0.10	0.4	0.00	0.00	−0.7
1.63	0.0625	0.6	4.76	0.1875	0.0	12.7	0.50	0.0
Other values are			6.35	0.25	−0.3	19.0	0.75	+0.9
determined by			9.53	0.375	−0.95	25.4	1.00	+2.1
plotting a straight								
line through the			Construct a graph to extend these values or					
values given.			use the program listed to obtain all parameters.					

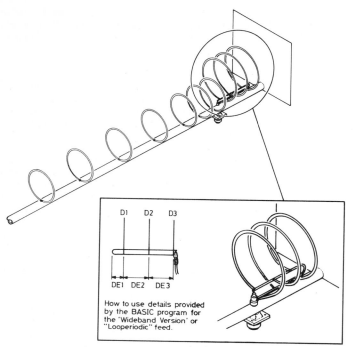

Fig 4.10. The G3JVL "looperiodic" wideband feed

How to use details provided by the BASIC program for the 'Wideband Version' or "Looperiodic" feed.

work previously mentioned and is the original, from which others have been derived. Copyright exists for commercial use.

The completed array can be mounted using a standard clamp from tv antenna suppliers. However, it is essential that the antenna be mounted on a vertical mast. Horizontal supports in close proximity to the antenna can cause severe mistuning. It has been determined that the spacing from any such objects should be at least equivalent to the largest element diameter – much less than was previously suggested. Note that when the antenna is mounted with the loops to one side the polarisation is vertical and the spacing data just detailed also applies but, in this case, from the mast. It is recommended that the antenna be mounted to produce horizontal polarisation in order to benefit from the improvement in performance when working beyond-the-horizon paths. This shows up in the form of a less-rapid rate of fading (QSB) and thus easier communication, especially over troposcatter paths.

If the choice of strip or rod elements is desired the BASIC program that follows is for you, and will accept any size and combination of all the parameters required.

4.3.3 BBC BASIC loopquad design program

```
100 REM ************************
110 REM *       LOOPQUAD        *
120 REM *    By M.H.Walters     *
130 REM * Updated to 31 MAR 87  *
140 REM *    and rewritten      *
150 REM *    By D.F.Walters      *
155 REM ************************
160 REM BBC version translated from PC Microsoft version.
170 DIM LE(6,9),SP(9)
```

```
180 MODE3:PROCtitle
190 PRINT"Do you want printed results (Y/N) : ";
200 PRN$=GET$:IF PRN$<>"N" AND PRN$<>"Y" THEN 200 ELSE PRINT;PRN$
210 INPUT"Enter required centre frequency (GHz) : " FC:SF=1.296/FC
220 INPUT"The number of elements required is " NE
230 PRINT"Do you want the old or new style (O/N) ";
240 STYLE$=GET$:IF STYLE$<>"O" AND STYLE$<>"N" THEN 240 ELSE
    PRINT;STYLE$
250 PROCreaddata
260 PRINT"Will you use rod or strip elements (R/S) ";
270 M$=GET$:IF M$<>"R" AND M$<>"S" THEN 270 ELSE PRINT;M$
280 PRINT"Narrow- or Wideband (N/W) ";
290 BAND$=GET$:IF BAND$<>"N" AND BAND$<>"W" THEN 290 ELSE
    PRINT;BAND$
300 IF M$="S" THEN 330
310 INPUT"Enter the rod diameter (mm) : " ED
320 WE=ED*0.82:TE=WE:GOTO350
330 INPUT"Enter the element thickness (mm) : " TE
340 INPUT" and  the element width     (mm) : " WE
350 INPUT"Enter the boom diameter (inches) : " BD
360 IF BD<>0 BD=BD*25.4:GOTO380
370 INPUT"Enter the boom diameter (mm) : " BD
380 BE=BD/SF:C2=(BE*BE*4.6500093E-5)-(BE*3.93700787E-5)-0.007
390 T1=TE/SF:W1=WE/SF
400 C3=T1*0.006671-0.0047444:REM Thickness CF if mm used
410 C4=T1*0.1694404-0.0047444:REM Thickness CF if inches used
420 Z1=W1/25.4:Z2=2.458*Z1*Z1*Z1-5.8888*Z1*Z1-2.67*Z1+0.7
430 C5=INT(Z2*100+.5)/100:CT=C2*100+C3*100+C5
440 TF=SF*(1+CT/100)
450 IF PRN$="Y" VDU2,1,27,108,1,20:VDU1,&E ELSE CLS:VDU14
460 PRINT"DETAILS for THE SCALING TO : ";INT(FC*1000+.5)/1000;" GHz";
470 IF STYLE$="O" PRINT"OLD STYLE" ELSE PRINT"NEW STYLE"
480 IF PRN$="Y" VDU1,&F
490 PRINT'"BOOM CF       = ";INT(C2*10000+.5)/10000;
500 PRINT" or ";INT(C2*1000000+.5)/10000;"%"
510 PRINT"THICKNESS CF = ";INT(C3*10000+.5)/10000;
520 PRINT" or ";INT(C3*1000000+.5)/10000;"%"
530 PRINT"WIDTH CF      = ";INT(C5*100+.5)/10000;
540 PRINT" or ";INT(C5*10000+.5)/10000;"%"
550 PRINT'"The total CF therefore is ";INT(CT*10000+.5)/10000;"%"
560 PRINT"Therefore the frequency scaling factors are :"'
570 PRINT;INT(SF*10000+.5)/10000;"%  ,  ";INT(TF*10000+.5)/10000;
580 PRINT"% (corrected)"
590 PRINT"Equivalent sizes at 1.296 GHz are shown thus ( )"
600 IF M$="S" THEN 630
610 PRINT"Element Material is ";INT(ED*100+.5)/100;" mm Dia  (";
620 PRINT;INT(ED/SF*100+.5)/100;")":GOTO670
630 PRINT"Element Width     = ";INT(WE*100+.5)/100;
640 PRINT" mm       (";INT(WE/SF*100+.5)/100;")"
650 PRINT"Element Thickness = ";INT(TE*100+.5)/100;
660 PRINT" mm       (";INT(TE/SF*100+.5)/100;")"
670 PRINT"The Boom diameter = ";INT(BD*100+.5)/100;
680 PRINT" mm       (";INT(BE*100+.5)/100;")"
690 PRINT"Element Lengths are :"
700 PRINT"RP Width  = ";INT(LE(0,0)*SF*100+.5)/100;
710 PRINT" inches ";INT(LE(0,0)*SF*2540+.5)/100;" mm"
720 PRINT"RP Height = ";INT(LE(0,1)*SF*100+.5)/100;
```

```
730 PRINT" inches ";INT(LE(0,1)*SF*2540+.5)/100;" mm"
740 IF BAND$="W" THEN 800
750 PRINT"RL Length = ";INT(LE(0,2)*TF*100+.5)/100;
760 PRINT" inches ";INT(LE(0,2)*TF*2540+.5)/100;" mm"
770 D=LE(0,3)*0.9895637*TF
780 PRINT"DE Length = ";INT(D*100+.5)/100;
790 PRINT" inches ";INT(D*2540+.5)/100;" mm":GOTO870
800 PRINT"Wide-band Driven element"
810 PRINT"DE1 Length  = ";INT(24700*TF+.5)/100;" mm"
820 PRINT"DE2 Length  = ";INT(23500*TF+.5)/100;" mm"
830 PRINT"DE3 Length  = ";INT(22300*TF+.5)/100;" mm"
840 PRINT"DE1 spacing = ";INT(2900*SF+.5)/100;" mm"
850 PRINT"DE2 spacing = ";INT(2100*SF+.5)/100;" mm"
860 PRINT"DE3 spacing = ";INT(2700*SF+.5)/100;" mm"
870 PRINT"D01-12  = ";INT(LE(1,1)*TF*100+.5)/100;
880 PRINT" inches = ";INT(LE(1,1)*TF*2540+.5)/100;" mm"
890 IF NE<13 THEN 1070
900 PRINT"D13-20  = ";INT(LE(1,6)*TF*100+.5)/100;
910 PRINT" inches = ";INT(LE(1,6)*TF*2540+.5)/100;" mm"
920 IF NE<21 THEN 1070
930 PRINT"D21-30  = ";INT(LE(2,4)*TF*100+.5)/100;
940 PRINT" inches = ";INT(LE(2,4)*TF*2540+.5)/100;" mm"
950 IF NE<31 THEN 1070
960 PRINT"D31-40  = ";INT(LE(3,4)*TF*100+.5)/100;
970 PRINT" inches = ";INT(LE(3,4)*TF*2540+.5)/100;" mm"
980 IF NE<41 THEN 1070
990 PRINT"D41-50  = ";INT(LE(4,4)*TF*100+.5)/100;
1000 PRINT" inches = ";INT(LE(4,4)*TF*2540+.5)/100;" mm"
1010 IF NE<51 THEN 1070
1020 PRINT"D51-60  = ";INT(LE(5,4)*TF*100+.5)/100;
1030 PRINT" inches = ";INT(LE(5,4)*TF*2540+.5)/100;" mm"
1040 IF NE<61 THEN 1070
1050 PRINT"D61-66  = ";INT(LE(6,4)*TF*100+.5)/100;
1060 PRINT" inches = ";INT(LE(6,4)*TF*2540+.5)/100;" mm"
1070 IF PRN$="Y" THEN 1090
1080 PRINT"Press a key to continue";:ANS$=GET$:CLS:VDU14
1090 PRINT"CUMULATIVE SPACINGS (mm)"'
1100 PRINT"RP   0.0000";
1110 CL=SF(0)*SF*25.4
1120 PRINTTAB(30)"RL ";INT(CL*10000+.5)/10000
1130 CL=CL+(SF(1)*25.4*SF)
1140 PRINT"DE  ";INT(CL*10000+.5)/10000;
1150 CL=CL+(SF(2)*25.4*SF)
1160 PRINTTAB(30)"D1 ";INT(CL*10000+.5)/10000
1170 FOR I%=3 TO NE STEP 2
1180 IF I%>9 THEN 1240
1190 GA=SP(I%)*SF*25.4:CL=CL+GA
1200 PRINT"D";I%-1"   ";INT(CL*10000+.5)/10000;
1210 IF I%<>9 GA=SP(I%+1)*SF*25.4
1220 CL=CL+GA
1230 PRINTTAB(30)"D";I%;" ";INT(CL*10000+.5)/10000:GOTO1280
1240 CL=CL+GA
1250 PRINT"D";I%-1;"  ";INT(CL*10000+.5)/10000;
1260 CL=CL+GA
1270 PRINTTAB(30)"D";I%;" ";INT(CL*10000+.5)/10000
1280 NEXT:VDU3:VDU15:END
1290 :
1500 DEFPROCtitle
1510 PRINTTAB(20)"G3JVL LOOPQUAD DIMENSION SCALING PROG"
1520 PRINTTAB(20)"====================================="
1530 PRINTTAB(20)"           (VERSION 2D)"'
1540 PRINT"Transferred to PC 6th FEB 86 by M.H.Walters"
1550 PRINT"Updated to 6th JUL 86 by D.P.Walters"
1560 PRINT"Translated onto BBC MAR 87 by D.P.Walters"'
1570 REM ALL DATA IS CONVERTED TO 1.296 GHz SIZES
1580 ENDPROC
1590 :
1600 DEFPROCreaddata
1610 IF STYLE$="N" RESTORE 1700 ELSE RESTORE 1800
1620 FOR I%=0 TO 9
1630 READ SP(I%)
1640 NEXT
1650 FOR I%=0 TO 6
1660 FOR J%=0 TO 9
1670 READ LE(I%,J%)
1680 NEXT:NEXT:ENDPROC
1690 :
1700 DATA 0.00,2.05,0.82,1.86,2.32,2.88,3.10,3.56,3.56,3.56
1710 REM SPACING FOR NEW STYLE
1720 DATA 4.54,3.70,0.00,9.21,8.26,8.26,8.26,8.26,8.26,8.26
1730 DATA 8.26,8.26,8.26,8.26,8.26,8.26,8.00,8.00,8.00,8.00
1740 DATA 8.00,8.00,8.00,8.00,7.70,7.70,7.70,7.70,7.70,7.70
1750 DATA 7.70,7.70,7.70,7.70,7.50,7.50,7.50,7.50,7.50,7.50
1760 DATA 7.50,7.50,7.50,7.50,7.40,7.40,7.40,7.40,7.40,7.40
1770 DATA 7.40,7.40,7.40,7.40,7.35,7.35,7.35,7.35,7.35,7.35
1780 DATA 7.35,7.35,7.35,7.35,7.31,7.31,7.31,7.31,7.31,7.31
1790 REM LENGTHS FOR NEW STYLE
1800 DATA 3.10,0.95,1.12,0.83,1.78,1.78,1.25,2.31,3.56,3.56
1810 REM SPACING FOR OLD STYLE
1820 DATA 5.50,4.50,9.77,9.23,8.26,8.26,8.26,8.26,8.26,8.26
1830 DATA 8.26,8.26,8.26,8.26,8.26,8.26,8.00,8.00,8.00,8.00
1840 DATA 8.00,8.00,8.00,8.00,7.70,7.70,7.70,7.70,7.70,7.70
1850 DATA 7.70,7.70,7.70,7.70,7.50,7.50,7.50,7.50,7.50,7.50
1860 DATA 7.50,7.50,7.50,7.50,7.40,7.40,7.40,7.40,7.40,7.40
1870 DATA 7.40,7.40,7.40,7.40,7.35,7.35,7.35,7.35,7.35,7.35
1880 DATA 7.35,7.35,7.35,7.35,7.31,7.31,7.31,7.31,7.31,7.31
1890 REM LENGTHS FOR OLD STYLE
```

Note that the shift key cannot be used to resume scrolling of the screen for designs above about 35 directors when the message "press any key" is displayed.

A Turbo Pascal version of this program is available on request, to run on machines using CP/M or PC MS-DOS operating systems. This runs very much faster than the BASIC version.

4.3.4 Stacking Yagi antennas

More than one antenna may be stacked to achieve extra gain. However, several points should be borne in mind when this is done, or the results obtained may be rather poor. Perhaps the most critical factor is the impedance matching of the antennas. This is illustrated by Table 4.3 which shows how the stacking gain is reduced when two antennas of differing impedances are combined, assuming the worst-case condition for the antenna impedances.

Note that no power is actually lost in either of the antennas. All that happens as the mismatch between the antennas becomes worse is that the gain and radiation pattern of the array just tends to that of one antenna.

It can be seen from this table that even quite small vswrs can seriously degrade the stacking gain, and that for near-optimum results the antennas should possess a vswr of better than 1.1:1. The actual reference for the vswr measurement is less critical – it could be anywhere around 30–70Ω since the vswr of the array as a whole can be largely compensated for in the preamplifier and the transmitter tuning. The important criterion is the relative vswrs of the two antennas. Great care should therefore be taken in their construction and their impedance should preferably be measured and optimised.

It is also most important to ensure that the antennas are correctly phased. This means that, for example, the outer of the feeders should go to the same side of all the driven elements when the antennas are mounted in the array. It is worth checking that this is the case with the antennas installed, as it is easy to make mistakes. Needless to say, equal lengths of cable (multiples of half wavelengths) should be used to join each antenna to the power combiner or divider.

The stacking distance is the one parameter which may require some experiment. If the antennas are out of phase the resulting pattern will display a null in the desired direction of radiation. The result of unequal cable lengths will be an offset to the main beam. If the cables are as much as half a wavelength different, the combined pair will be out of phase and will produce a null on the "boresight". Either side there will be two

Table 4.3

VSWR of each antenna	Max Z/min Z	Worst case stacking gain (dB)
1.0	50	3.0
1.1	55/45	2.6
1.2	60/42	2.2
1.5	75/33	1.6
2.0	100/25	1.0
3.0	150/17	0.5

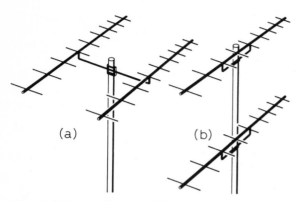

Fig 4.11. (a) Bayed (side-by-side) Yagi antennas. (b) Stacked Yagi array

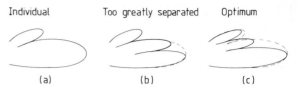

Fig 4.13. The effect of stacking distance on the polar pattern of loopquad antennas

equal but narrower than expected lobes, both having gain. This effect can also be caused by combining the antennas out of phase due to a reversed driven element. It is easily detected when mounting side by side or baying (Fig 4.11(a)). However, when the antennas are vertically combined or stacked (Fig 4.11(b)) the resulting lobes will be above and below the horizon, giving rise to a very poor performance indeed, which is difficult to understand. Too large a stacking distance will result in an increased sidelobe level and an excessive narrowing of the main beam. Conversely, too small a stacking distance may result in lower than optimum gain for the array.

4.3.5 G3JVL's findings on stacking distance

When two antennas are stacked vertically or bayed horizontally, the distance between them is usually set by recommendation or by guesswork. This is due to a lack of definitive theoretical references dealing with this aspect. A number of references covering the combination of arrays of dipoles have been available for a long time. The optimising programs that have been developed require a starting design and may improve it where possible. There are now design programs as previously mentioned that will give good theoretical results. A more theoretical approach to stacking by G8DIC (see

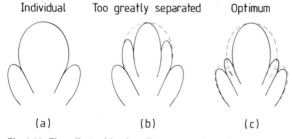

Fig 4.12. The effect of baying distance on the polar pattern of loopquad antennas

below) gives a better idea of what to expect, but still only provides a guide which may be less than optimum.

In practice it has been found that in order to get the best compromise the closer spacings should be chosen. This is to ensure that the pattern obtained is not excessively narrowed and the first pair of sidelobes enhanced. Associated with this, the mainlobe width is less than it ought to be and the gain may also be reduced. The lost gain may be due to too much energy being radiated in unwanted directions in the sidelobes. These sidelobes are unavoidable but the amplitude of them should be as low as possible. In a good design the optimum compromise is the aim. The factors relating gain and sidelobe levels are in opposition. Care should be taken to ensure that the phase relationship between the individual antennas is correct. Deliberate reversal of the phasing will result in the cancellation of the mainlobe and transference of the power almost completely to the first pair of sidelobes, which both then have some gain and also a reduced beamwidth.

The desirable spacing gives both the increased gain and the expected beam narrowing, ie when one is vertically over the other the width in the azimuth plane (around the horizontal) will remain unaltered. But in the elevation plane (vertically) it should be reduced to 50 per cent of its previous value for two antennas. It is also likely that gain may be lost if too close a spacing is used. This value is very dependent upon the presence of nearby objects (other similar antennas in this case). If practical, it is preferable to lengthen the antenna to realise more gain. Practical limitations are very individual to the user's needs, but boom lengths of 4 to 6m are quite practical. The extra components required when stacking antennas will detract from the advantage expected. Very careful design and construction of a combiner or divider and cable preparation is essential. A suggested stacking or baying distance for the 27-element loopquad is 2.6 wavelengths and the 44/47-element version should be tried at 3.3 wavelengths. Fig 4.12 shows the effect of increasing separation and Fig 4.13 the stacking distances for arrays of antennas.

G8DIC offered the following observations concerning stacking antennas in order to improve overall system gain. Generally speaking, an array of two antennas will give a gain increase of 3dB. A further 3dB gain is obtained each time the number of antennas stacked is doubled. However, if antennas are stacked too far apart then large sidelobes may be generated. If the spacing is too small there may be excessive mutual coupling or detuning between the individual antennas which can cause the potential 3dB increase to be reduced or even lost completely. The following analysis attempts to explain how to determine the optimum spacing. The spacing is, generally speaking, not very critical and it is usually best to use the second null of the array pattern to split the first side lobe of the individual antenna pattern.

Although the following is difficult to grasp at first, it is well worth reading and re-reading with reference to the diagrams. The array polar diagram is not the final result, but is the "stacking effect polar diagram" which is used to determine the final result when added to the "actual" polar diagram of one of the individual antennas which make up the stack.

Refer to Fig 4.14 in which A and B are two antennas spaced d apart and angle T is the bearing of the source relative to the main beam direction. The array's polar diagram can be deduced by adding the two received signals at A and B then observing how this sum varies with angle T. Since the source is at a great distance from the array, the two paths can be considered parallel and thus the two signals received are equal in amplitude. Departure from this is a reason why scattered signals frequently do not appear to be stronger when received on such an array.

With reference to the vector diagram, Fig 4.15, the signal from each antenna is half voltage and the phase difference between the two signals is twice angle P degrees. It is readily shown that the resultant varies as the cosine of angle P. We now need to know how angle P varies with angle T. In the diagram it is shown that the signal must travel the product of d and the sine of angle T further to get to antenna A than to antenna B, therefore the signal will be:

$$\frac{360\times(d\times sin(angle\ T))}{\lambda}$$

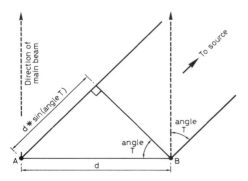

Fig 4.14. Diagram of two spaced antennas for pattern analysis

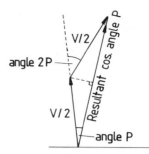

Fig 4.15. Vector diagram of spaced antennas for pattern analysis

in electrical degrees later at A than at B, and λ is the wavelength. Hence:

$$angle\ P = \frac{d\times sin(angle\ T)\times 180}{\lambda}$$

The array polar diagram is given by:

$$\frac{cos(180\times d\times sin(angle\ T))}{\lambda}$$

Fig 4.16 shows the magnitude of cos(angle P) plotted against angle P and also:

$$\frac{(180\times d\times sin(angle\ T))}{\lambda}$$

plotted against angle T for various values of d. To find the magnitude of:

$$\frac{cos(180\times d\times sin(angle\ T))}{\lambda}$$

for a given value of d and angle T, look up angle T on the vertical axis of the lower graph, then move horizontally until the curve for the value of d to be used is encountered, then vertically until the curve for cosine angle P is also encountered. The value of cosine angle P is then read from the vertical axis of the upper graph. This process shows that for large values of d a number of peaks and nulls occur in the array polar diagram. The overall stacking polar diagram, Fig 4.17, of an array of antennas is given by the product of the array polar diagram and the individual antenna polar diagram. If you are working in decibels you simply add the two.

From this it is obvious that when either polar diagram drops into a null then the composite polar diagram will have a null, and also when the array polar diagram is at a maximum (at angle P = 0, 180, 360° etc) the composite polar diagram will have the same value as the individual antenna polar diagram. For a normal antenna with the first sidelobes at around 10dB down it is usually best to position the second null of the array polar diagram (angle P = 270°) at the bearing of the first sidelobe of the antenna. However, some antenna types

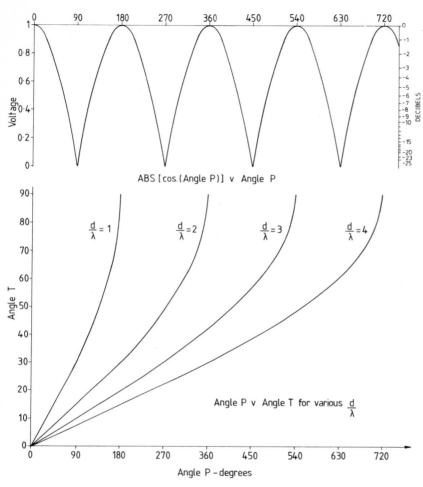

Fig 4.16. Graph of cos(angle P) etc

with inherent good first sidelobe figures (dishes and horns) may benefit from consideration of the first sidelobe level of the composite antenna (approximately for angle P = 180°). In either case:

$$d = \frac{angle\ P \times \lambda}{180 \times \sin(angle\ T)}$$

gives the stacking distance required to get a particular feature of the array polar diagram at angle P to correspond to a bearing of angle T. For example an antenna with the first sidelobe at 30° bearing will require stacking at:

$$d = \frac{270 \times \lambda}{180 \times \sin 30} = 3\lambda$$

for the second array null to coincide with the first sidelobe. In this case the first sidelobe of the array polar diagram will be approximately the first sidelobe of the composite antenna and correspond to angle P = 180°, or a bearing of:

$$
\begin{aligned}
angle\ T &= asn\left(\frac{angle\ P \times \lambda}{180 \times d}\right) \\
&= asn\left(\frac{180}{180 \times 3}\right) \\
&= 19.5°
\end{aligned}
$$

The first array null will correspond to angle P = 90°, or a bearing of approximately 9.6°.

$$angle\ T = asn\left(\frac{90}{180 \times 3}\right) = 9.6°$$

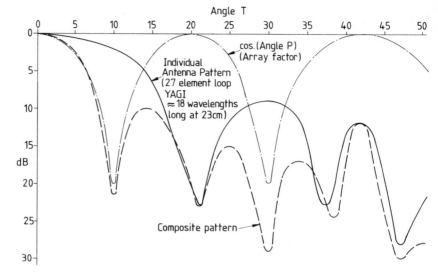

Fig 4.17. Overall polar diagram for a multiple array

4.3.6 Stacking more than two antennas

It can be shown that for n antennas spaced d apart the stacking polar diagram of the array is given by:

$$\frac{\sin(n \times \text{angle P})}{n \times \sin(\text{angle P})}$$

This function has a value of 1 at angle P = 0, 180, 360, 540° etc. It has nulls at n×angle P = 180, 360, 540, 720 and 900° etc, except where the mainlobes occur. (Note that n = 6 in this example.)

Fig 4.18 is a diagram showing the plot for n = 6 as an example (all antennas to be in one plane). It has sidelobes at n×angle P = 270, 450, 630 and 810° etc with level:

$$\frac{1}{n \times \sin(\dfrac{90 \times 3}{n})} , \qquad \frac{1}{n \times \sin(\dfrac{90 \times 5}{n})} ,$$

$$\frac{1}{n \times \sin(\dfrac{90 \times 7}{n})} \quad \text{and} \quad \frac{1}{n \times \sin(\dfrac{90 \times 9}{n})}$$

4.3.7 Power splitters or combiners

The power splitters shown in Fig 4.19 enable either two, four, six or eight antennas of a given impedance to be fed from a single coaxial cable. The unit consists of a length of fabricated coaxial line which performs the appropriate impedance transformations. The inner is made exactly one half wavelength (electrically) long (or any odd multiples of half-wavelength) between the centres of the outer connectors. The outer is made

approximately 38mm (1.5in) longer. The outer may be made from square-section aluminium tubing. The open ends and the access hole, allowing the centre connector to be soldered, may be sealed by covering with aluminium plates secured with an adhesive. Alternatively copper or brass tubing may be used, and the plates soldered.

Any size of inner or outer may be used provided that the ratio of the inside dimension of the outer to the diameter of the inner conductor is unchanged. The

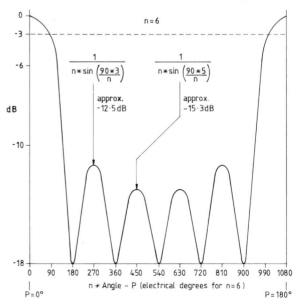

Fig 4.18. Array polar diagram for n = 6 (all six stacked in one plane)

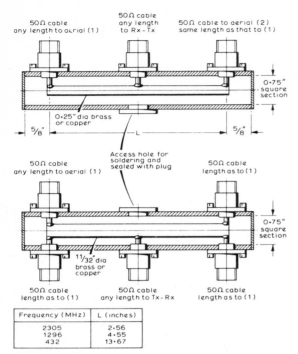

Frequency (MHz)	L (inches)
2305	2·56
1296	4·55
432	13·67

Fig 4.19. 50Ω splitters for connecting two or four antennas to a common feeder

maximum size that may be used is governed by the requirement that *no waveguide modes are to be permitted in the structure*. Practically, this means that the outer must not approach λ/2 (ie below cut-off).

	50Ω system	
	2 - way $Z_o = 72\,\Omega$	4-way $Z_o = 50\,\Omega$
d / D (square, round inner)	2·82	1·96
d / D (round, round inner)	3·32	2·31
d / D (square, flat inner)	1·54	—
d / D (round, flat inner)	1·66	—

Fig 4.21. Ratios of d/D for other useful coaxial configurations

Other forms of coaxial line should work just as well. The most adaptable inner is one cut from sheet metal. The width of the required strip may be calculated with reference to Fig 4.20. Fig 4.21 gives the design details for a number of configurations.

Two-way (half-wave)

The impedance of the centre conductor to match two 50Ω antennas back to 50Ω may be determined from $Z_t = Z_o \times Z_l$, where Z_t is the transforming section impedance, Z_o is the coaxial cable impedance and Z_l is the load to be matched. In this case the transforming-section impedance should be 71Ω. When using a square section outer which measures 25.4mm and has walls of 18swg or 1.2mm, the internal dimension is 23mm. From Fig 4.20, the ratio required is seen to be 0.33. The centre conductor is therefore calculated from 23×0.33 = 7.59mm diameter.

Four-way (half-wave)

This version requires a transforming impedance of 50Ω which makes the centre conductor to outer ratio 0.47. The centre conductor is therefore determined from 23×0.47 = 10.81mm. The diameter of the centre conductor is quite critical, and it has been shown that a 10 per cent error will result in a poor match even when the loads (antennas) present a perfect 50Ω impedance. For this reason it is not good enough to use the nearest standard-size rod.

Lengths of inner and outer

The dimensions shown in the examples shown include an extension of the outer of 14mm beyond the centre conductor's theoretical length. This allows N-type connectors to be mounted on the side wall.

Flat-strip conductor in a square outer

The flat strip version is indicated in Fig 4.20 and is discussed further here. It is an alternative design that is much less demanding in terms of machining as it uses a

Table 4.4. Examples of a flat-strip condctor in a square outer

	Frequency (MHz)	Flat inner (mm)	Round inner (mm)	Outer length (half-wave) (mm)
Two-way	432	344	340	349
Four-way	432	344	340	366
Two-way	934	164	160	169
Four-way	934	164	160	186
Two-way	1,296	119	115	124
Four-way	1,296	119	115	141
Two-way	2,320	67	63	72
Four-way	2,320	67	63	89

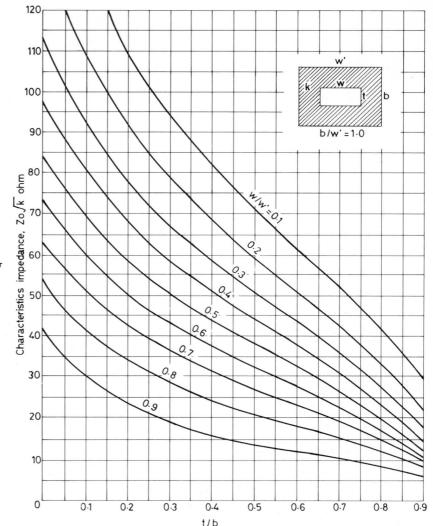

Fig 4.20. Impedance of strip conductor in square outer

thin flat centre conductor. This version eases the problem imposed by standard-size materials. The width required is established using Fig 4.20 and may be cut from sheet copper or brass. In this case the inner should be extended by 4mm to allow for soldering to the connector spills. Examples are given in Table 4.4.

A prototype four-way combiner/splitter, using an outer of 25.4mm square with 16swg or 1.6mm walls, required the centre conductor width to be 17.5mm and used copper strip for a 50Ω centre conductor impedance. The result obtained was good and a return loss of 40dB was measured. This performance is very close to optimum for this design.

When the strip width is 17.5mm, the gaps either side are just enough to accommodate the N-type connectors but this is only satisfactory for power levels up to around 25W. If higher-power operation is required then the line should be filed to leave a larger gap near to the connector body. Alternatively, trim the connector body so that only the ptfe protrudes in the vicinity of the inner line. The areas to be joined were pre-tinned. The end connectors were joined using the soldering iron in the normal way, as access is easy. With the 1.6mm thick outer wall, the two-way (71Ω) inner's width should be 13mm. The outer can be virtually the same without the extra connector mounting holes drilled.

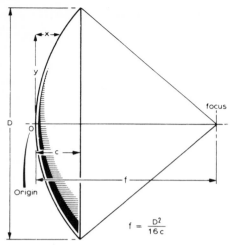

$$f = \frac{D^2}{16\,c}$$

Fig 4.22. Basic geometry of a paraboloid

4.4 PARABOLIC DISHES

Antennas based on paraboloidal reflectors are the most important type for the bands above 5.7GHz. Their main advantages are that, in principle, they can be made to have as large a gain as is required, they can operate at any frequency and they should require little setting up. Disadvantages are that they are not the easiest things to make accurately (which limits the frequency at which a given dish can be used), large dishes are difficult to mount and are likely to have a high windage.

The basic property of a perfect paraboloidal reflector is that it converts a spherical wave emanating from a point source placed at the focus into a plane wave, ie the image of the source is focused at an infinite distance from the dish. Conversely, all the energy received by the dish from a distant source is reflected to a single point at the focus of the dish.

4.4.1 The geometry of the paraboloid

A paraboloid is generated by rotating a parabola about a line joining its origin and focus. Two methods for

constructing a parabola are given below and the geometry of a paraboloid is given in Fig 4.22.

4.4.2 Constructing a parabola by calculation

Convenient forms of the equations of a parabola are, using the notation of Fig 4.22:

$$y^2 = 4 \times f \times x \qquad (1)$$
$$y^2 = 4 \times D \times x \times (f/D) \qquad (2)$$

where
$$f = \frac{D^2}{16 \times c}$$

y has both negative and positive values
D = diameter of corresponding dish
f = focal length
c = depth of parabola at its centre.

Suppose we wish to construct the profile of a dish 0.914m (36in) in diameter having a f/D ratio of 0.6. The procedure is as follows:

Using metric units

(a) From equation (2)
$$x = \frac{y^2}{4 \times D \times (F/D)}$$
$$= \frac{y^2}{4 \times 0.913 \times 0.6}$$
$$= 0.000456 \times y^2$$

(b) Tabulate the calculations for as many points as accuracy requires in the form shown in Table 4.5.

A plot of y from −457 to +457 against the values of x will produce the required curve (both x and y in millimetres).

Using imperial units

(c) From equation (2)
$$x = \frac{y^2}{4 \times D \times (f/D)}$$
$$= \frac{y^2}{4 \times 36 \times 0.6}$$
$$= 0.01157 \times y^2$$

Table 4.5

y (mm)	y^2	$0.000456 \times y^2 = x$ (mm)
0	0	0
50	2.5E02	1.14
100	10.0E05	4.56
150	22.5E05	10.26
200	40.0E05	18.24
250	62.5E05	28.50
300	90.0E05	41.04
350	12.3E06	55.86
400	16.0E06	72.96
450	20.3E06	92.34
457	20.9E06	95.24

Table 4.6

y (in)	y^2	$0.01157 \times y^2 = x$ (in)
0	0	0
2	4	0.05
4	16	0.18
6	36	0.42
8	64	0.74
10	100	1.16
12	144	1.67
14	196	2.27
16	256	2.96
18	324	3.75

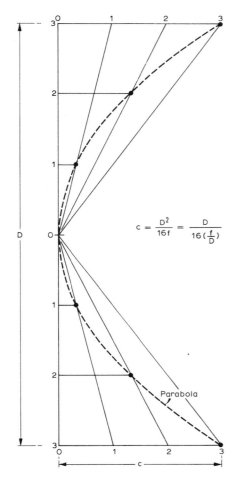

$$c = \frac{D^2}{16f} = \frac{D}{16(\frac{f}{D})}$$

Parabola

Fig 4.23. Simple graphical construction for a parabola

(d) Tabulate the calculations for as many points as accuracy requires in the form shown in Table 4.6.

A plot of y from −18 to +18 against the values of x calculated will produce the required curve (both x and y in inches).

4.4.3 Graphical method

A simple graphical method for constructing a parabola is shown in Fig 4.23. The value of c is calculated from:

$$c = \frac{D^2}{16 \times f} \quad \text{or} \quad c = \frac{D}{16 \times (f/D)}$$

Both axes are divided into the same number of equal parts in the way shown and numbered. Points where corresponding lines intercept describe the required parabola.

4.5 FACTORS AFFECTING PRACTICAL DISH DESIGN AND USE

4.5.1 Size

This is the most important factor since it determines the maximum gain that can be achieved at a given frequency and the beamwidth resulting. The actual gain obtained is given by:

$$G = \frac{4 \times \pi \times A}{\lambda^2} \times n \quad \text{or} \quad \frac{(\pi \times D)^2}{\lambda} \times n$$

where A is the projected area of the dish and n is the efficiency, which is determined mainly by the effectiveness of illumination of the dish by the feed, but also by other factors which are discussed.

Each time the diameter of a dish is doubled, its gain is quadrupled, ie increased by 6dB. If both stations double the size of their antennas, signal strengths can be increased by 12dB, a very substantial gain. A given dish used at twice the frequency also quadruples its gain if other factors do not intervene: accuracy and mesh size etc.

The relationship between the diameter of a dish and its gain at frequencies of amateur interest is shown in Fig 4.24. An efficiency of 50 per cent is assumed, which seems to be typical of better amateur practice. Antennas with a diameter less than 10 wavelengths will generally have a significantly lower efficiency than this value. The corresponding beamwidths are also given in Fig 4.24.

Two factors tend to limit the maximum gain that can be achieved. On the lower microwave bands (1.3, 2.3 and 3.4GHz) the physical size of the antenna is the limiting factor. Thus a 30dB antenna on 1,296MHz will have a diameter of just over 3.2m (10ft), which could well cause problems in fabrication and mounting. This gain can be achieved using four 50-element loopquad antennas with booms at 18λ long, properly constructed and combined. On the higher microwave bands (5.7GHz and above) the physical size of the antenna is less of a problem. Instead, the narrowness of the beamwidth tends to be the limiting factor. For example, a dish 0.9m (3ft) in diameter used at 24GHz will have a gain of up to 44dB and a beamwidth of 1°. Considerable skill is required in effectively handling such a directional antenna.

4.5.2 The ratio of the focal length of the dish to its diameter

This ratio f/D, using the notation of Fig 4.22, is the fundamental factor governing the design of the feed for a dish. The ratio is, of course, directly related to the angle subtended by the rim of the dish at its focus, and also therefore to the beamwidth of the feed necessary to illuminate the dish effectively. Two dishes of the same diameter but different focal lengths require different designs of feed if both are to be illuminated efficiently.

Practical values for the f/D ratio range from about 0.2 to 1.0. The value of 0.25 corresponds to the common focal-plane dish in which the focus is in the same plane as the rim of the dish. However, values of the f/D ratio which produce a deeper dish are frequently used commercially where it may be important to minimise sidelobe response. With such dishes, the unwanted interaction between antennas is reduced, albeit at the expense of antenna gain and extra difficulty in designing efficient feeds. Such considerations are unimportant in an amateur context. Indeed, the greater the sidelobe response the better, provided overall gain does not suffer.

As will be seen, there are a number of factors which influence the choice of the f/D ratio. For most amateur applications the range 0.5 to 0.75 would appear to be optimum, although satisfactory feeds for dishes outside this range can be constructed. There are difficulties associated with shallower dishes, both mechanical and electrical blockage (shadowing). The shallow dish requires a higher gain and therefore a larger feed horn. Also, this horn must be mounted at a greater distance, resulting in a heavier and unbalanced mechanical structure.

4.5.3 Changing the geometry of a dish

As a given dish is reduced in size, so its f/D ratio is reduced proportionately. Thus, if a focal-plane dish for which f/D = 0.25 is trimmed to half its original diameter (or a half-size moulding is made from an existing dish),

then the smaller dish will have a f/D of 0.5. This approach has been used to convert a virtually unusable dish into a more easily illuminated and efficient dish. As would be expected, the reverse is also the case but does not find so much favour as the f/D is reduced, and extending is not as simple.

4.5.4 The effect of dish accuracy on performance

An understanding of the degree of accuracy required in a dish is important for two reasons. It enables the maximum frequency for efficient operation of a given dish to be determined. It also enables an estimate to be made of how construction tolerances influence the gain and hence the ease with which dishes may be constructed. The reduction in gain due to surface irregularities depends upon two factors:

(a) The amount by which the surface deviates from a true paraboloid. This will be expressed as the mean value of the deviation as a factor related to wavelength.

(b) The ratio of any such deviation to the wavelength of operation. In this way a distinction is made between short-range and long-range irregularities. Short-range irregularities correspond to a bumpy surface on a good average shape. This limitation may be due to a mesh surface, for example, or a rough finish. Both will limit the upper frequency of operation.

The relationship between loss in gain, the peak deviation and the periodicity is shown in Fig 4.25. This assumes that the deviations occur uniformly over the

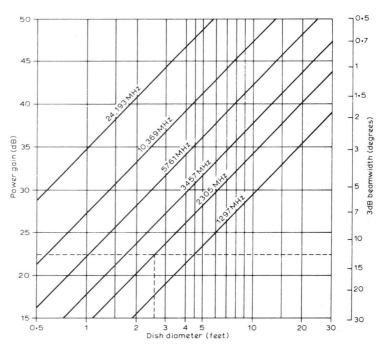

Fig 4.24. Relationship between the size of a dish, its gain and bandwidth as a function of frequency. An overall efficiency of 50 per cent is assumed. As an example, a dish 2.5ft in diameter at 2,305MHz will have a gain of 22dB and a beamwidth of about 22°

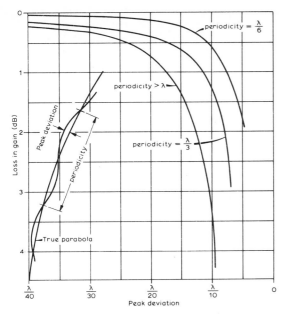

Fig 4.25. The effect of dish accuracy on performance

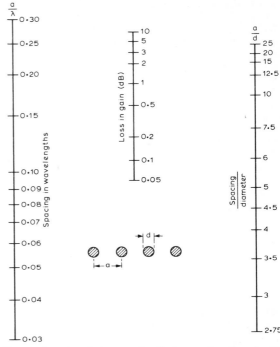

Fig 4.26. Loss in gain for a mesh reflector as a function of mesh size

surface of the dish. If they are restricted to a limited area, then the loss will be proportionately lower. It can be seen that when the periodicity of the irregularities is a small fraction of the wavelength, the irregularities can be fairly large before the gain falls off too much. Checking the long-range accuracy requires a well-made template. When checking remember that perhaps the parabola used is not quite that intended. This may show up as a steady deviation from the template. If the space is in the centre then the dish has a greater f/D than the template. Similarly, if the gap is at or near the rim then the dish has a smaller f/D. It is therefore reasonable to try a slight variation in the template and retest until a satisfactory conclusion is reached.

4.5.5 Materials of construction

Dishes up to about a metre are usually made from solid material. Aluminium is frequently preferred for construction due to its weight advantage. It also has the added advantages of its durability and good electrical characteristics. Obviously, windage increases rapidly with dish size and soon becomes quite a severe problem. For example, at a wind speed of 50mph the force on a flat surface will be about 44kg/sq m (9lb/sq ft). The structure supporting a 1.2m (4ft) dish would be subjected to a wind loading force of 45kg (100lb). Good engineering practice requires that a safety factor of five should be used. The result of this is that a structure which can survive a loading of 227kg (500lb) is required.

Fortunately, amateurs can use dishes which have a reflecting surface that uses an open mesh. The resulting poorer front-to-back ratio is unavoidable but it is a small price to pay for safety or continued operation. The loss in gain as a function of mesh size is illustrated in Fig 4.26. For example, if the mesh-to-wire ratio is 10:1 and the square size (or wire spacing if only in one plane) is at 0.1 wavelength a gain loss of 0.2dB or 5 per cent power loss will occur. Please note that if polarisation in *one plane* is satisfactory then the spacing between any supporting members need only satisfy mechanical requirements for stability of shape. It is unfortunate that as the velocity of the wind increases the loading will approach the value of a solid surface. This should be borne in mind.

Copper, aluminium, brass, galvanised (zinc-plated) or tinned steel and iron are suitable mesh materials. Unplated materials (iron and steel) are likely to corrode and perhaps become more lossy. Practical dishes can be made from a number of shaped pieces (petals) of solid metal or mesh. It is not essential that there be good electrical contact between sections but it is advisable to overlap or keep the gap small and insulated, as intermittent contact can introduce unwanted noises. Keep the joins parallel to the major plane of polarisation.

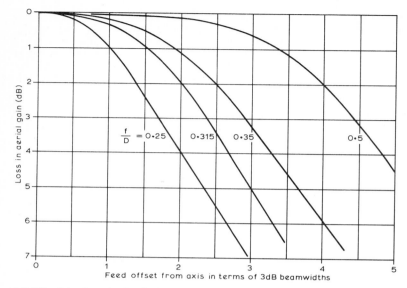

Fig 4.27. Loss in gain due to positioning feed off the axis of the dish

4.5.6 Positioning the feed off the axis of the dish

Fig 4.27 shows the loss of gain of dishes having several f/D ratios plotted against the amount of feed offset. Two important points are easily seen from this plot:

(a) The effect of construction errors on gain is not very great. For example, a focal-plane dish 1.5m (5ft) diameter, having a focal length of 380mm (15in) and used at 2.3GHz, will have a 3dB beamwidth of 7°. If the feed is offset by 51mm (2in), which is a large constructional error, then the offset angle is about 7° or one 3dB beamwidth. The resulting gain loss will be about 1dB. However, note that if the f/D was 0.5 this loss would be very much lower. This offset will result in an angular error equal to, but in the opposite direction to, the resulting beam. The practical effect of an offset error on the horizontal plane would be compensated for by pointing the dish for maximum signal. Unless elevation control is available, an error in the other plane would not be correctable. When the gain is high and thus the 3dB beamwidth even less, then this loss may become very serious.

(b) For a dish with high f/D, the feed may be offset by a large number of beamwidths before a significant loss of gain occurs. This effect can be used to advantage, as several feeds may be mounted side by side, providing the offset is compensated for by the appropriate angle of rotation. It is also, perhaps, a useful fine-search method for large dishes when used on the bands at 10GHz and above.

4.5.7 Dish obstruction

Fitting a feed in front of the dish inevitably obscures part of the dish and therefore causes some loss in gain. For example, when the diameter of the obstruction is one third of the diameter of the dish the gain loss is about 1dB or a 26 per cent power loss. Most practical feeds (except perhaps those based on the Cassegrain system) are usually much smaller and therefore will have a negligible effect.

4.5.8 The optimum ratio of focal length to diameter of a dish

The main parameters of interest, of course, are gain and efficiency. However, the effects of deficiencies in the design, adjustment or construction of both the dish and the feed are also very important. Sidelobe level and front-to-back ratio are of less importance to most amateur operation. This is very dependent on the intended application of the system under construction. The main advantage that favours the use of a low f/D ratio is the compactness of the antenna. This is because the feed is placed effectively at the focus, and the smaller f/D ratio results in a shorter focal length and therefore a less-bulky antenna.

An important factor favouring a high f/D ratio may be the ease of construction. It seems a fair assumption that the errors involved in making a curved surface are related to the degree of curvature. However, this only applies to some methods of construction as, for example, a moulding taken from another dish should not suffer in this way. The flatter the dish (ie the higher its f/D ratio), probably the more accurately it can be made when using a mesh covering. As has already been shown, the higher the f/D ratio the less critical also is the positioning of the feed. For dishes which are approximations to paraboloids, there is a clear relationship favouring a high f/D ratio.

A more important factor may be the ease of feeding. As is shown by Fig 4.28, the beamwidth of the feed required to illuminate a dish efficiently increases rapidly as the f/D ratio of the dish is decreased. However, producing this beamwidth becomes more difficult. The predictability of a wide-beamwidth feed is poorer as its beamwidth increases, which tends to compound the difficulties. As can be seen from Fig 4.28, most of the advantages in this respect are achieved when the f/D ratio is around 0.5 to 0.6.

The use of a long focal length for the reflector minimises the losses due to differences in the position of the phase centres of a feed in the horizontal and vertical planes. Similarly, the shift with frequency of the phase centre of multiband feeds such as log-periodic arrays is less important. It also allows the siting of feeds alongside one another as an alternative to the latter form of multiband feed.

Finally, for a short focal length dish, there is a relatively large space loss. For a focal-plane dish, for example, only the power contained within the 4dB beamwidth of the feed is reflected by the dish if an edge illumination of −10dB is specified. For a dish of 0.7, the power contained within a 9dB beamwidth is reflected by the dish, which is rather more efficient.

This statement suggests that the larger the f/D ratio the better, but the mechanical problems in supporting a feed for a long focal length dish becomes the main disadvantage. Practically, the obstruction of the aperture caused by the feed is only significant when small dishes are used on the lower microwave bands. For most amateur purposes the optimum f/D ratio, therefore, would appear to be in the range 0.5 to 0.75. One case where this mechanical problem is not so important is when the dish in question is being used to feed a flyswatter antenna.

4.6 PRACTICAL DISH CONSTRUCTION

4.6.1 Glassfibre reflectors

Perhaps the simplest dish construction method available to amateurs makes use of glassfibre faced with aluminium kitchen foil or fine wire mesh. This form of construction offers a practical method for making dishes with sufficient accuracy for use on the bands up to 24GHz. Some form of mould is required; this can be an existing solid dish, sand or a modern filler (substitute for plaster) cast taken from it. A method of making a mould is illustrated in Fig 4.29.

A template of the desired shape is rotated about a central pivot to shape the filler which then is left to set very hard so it will have a reasonable surface finish. The template can be used as a checking jig after setting. Smooth off with fine sandpaper where necessary. To assist with the releasing of the glassfibre from the mould, prepare it with a wax or silicone polish. Allow this release agent to harden, then paint on a thin "gel" coat, which is a resin mixed with a coloured filler. Follow this by applying strips or shaped pieces of aluminium kitchen foil. Ensure the foil closely follows the contours

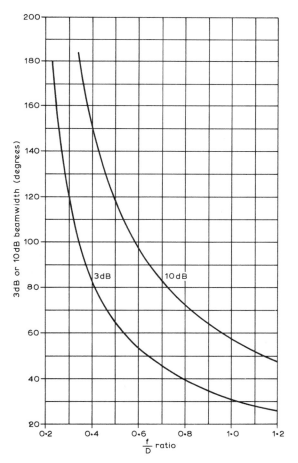

Fig 4.28. Beamwidths of feeds for efficient illumination of dishes as a function of their f/D ratio. An edge illumination 10dB down compared with the centre is assumed

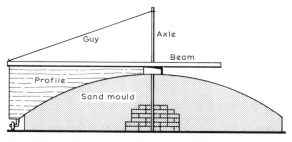

Fig 4.29. Preparation of a mould for constructing a glassfibre dish

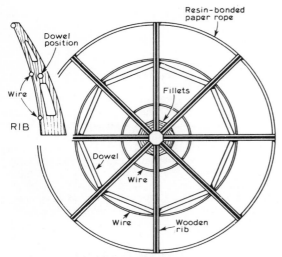

Fig 4.30. Framework for a mesh dish

of the mould. A further layer of gel or clear resin should then be applied. Layers of glassfibre impregnated with resin are laid on until the required thickness is built up. This is typically 6mm for a dish 1.2m in diameter. During the build-up, plywood or aluminium stiffeners cut to shape may be incorporated into the structure as may any mounting fixtures required. The glassfibre should be allowed at least a week to harden before it is removed from the mould. After removal trim the edges and remove any excess resin. This time can be reduced if a large, *low-temperature* (80°C) oven is available.

A modified version of this technique is to use glassfibre as the main material, but to leave large holes which are later filled with a fine wire mesh. This method significantly reduces the windage compared with a solid dish but unless a suitable mesh is available the advantage may be lost. A suitable mesh is one with a thin wire and holes as big as possible determined by the wavelength in use. Yet another method is to make two thinner mouldings 2–3mm thick which are then joined together using stiffeners between them (as before, include mounting bushes inside). This form requires more preparation but results in a more rigid structure and perhaps a lighter dish. See [9] for further ideas on glassfibre reflectors.

4.6.2 For the adventurous
Make your own long-focus dish from aluminium alloy sheet. Blank discs of suitable size are available from most non-ferrous metal suppliers up to 0.6m (2ft) diameter. The softer alloys should be chosen for use. Due to the work hardening that occurs during hammering to shape, it will be necessary to soften the workpiece by heating regularly. This may be by using an oven set to just less than 600°C, or (with much more care) a flame

or hotplate. Rub soap onto the cold metal surface as this will act as an indicator that the desired temperature has been reached by changing colour to a brown or dark shade. Decide on the f/D that is to be aimed for and calculate the central depth from:

$$C = \frac{D^2}{16 \times f}$$

where   c is the depth
              D is the diameter
              f is the focal length

Mark and cut out a template for later use. It is useful to make or be prepared to make another template to one side of the chosen f/D. G3JVL made a dish with a 0.8 f/D and a diameter of 0.46m (18in) and it is used to illuminate a flyswatter on 10GHz.

A sand-filled, robust bag is essential to the constructor, as is a large helping of patience! Begin by hammering in the centre and while slowly rotating, increase the working diameter. Do not expect the result at this early stage to look very attractive. Continue in the described fashion, softening at regular intervals when progress slows. When the rough, distorted shape of the dish has a slightly greater depth at the centre than required, it is the time to work from the other side and hammer onto the outer surface of the dish. Place the roughly shaped dish face down on a paving stone or other suitable firm, flat area. Now, using the template previously made, compare the shape achieved. This is a much more rewarding time, as progress appears to be faster. By hammering radially from the centre and comparing frequently with the template, obtain a reasonable approximation, rotate a small amount and repeat. Remember to soften frequently to speed progress.

When the dish has a reasonable average shape, determined using the template, the final stage where the finer details are dealt with may begin. It is likely that some work will be required from both sides of the dish but only the minimum force should be used. When working on the inside surface, use a ball-paned hammer and a flat one from the outside. Remember to keep the surface of the hammer pane free from scratches. Work only from the inside surface to remove bumps. Progress slowly round the dish with the template and hammer until you have a satisfactory match. The quality of finish required depends on the upper frequency of intended use.

Although this project is laborious it is rewarding if you can see it through. The skill acquired will also be useful and will also enable the repair of quite badly damaged dishes to be undertaken.

4.6.3 Construction of a mesh dish
Figs 4.30 and 4.31 show a method of constructing dishes from shaped ribs covered with mesh. In the original version, which was 1.83m (6ft) in diameter, the dish was

made in two halves to facilitate transportation. Eight ribs cut from waterproof (marine) plywood define the main shape of the dish, and inner circles of wire help in making the mesh conform to a near-paraboloidal shape. The perimeter is made from paper rope impregnated with resin. Ordinary rope should suffice but the resin must be well worked in. Shaped sections of chicken wire are clipped to the spider with 22swg tinned copper wire and the final structure is protected by paint.

4.6.4 Construction of a large eme dish antenna

In this first edition, there has been no attempt to include a chapter specifically devoted to eme operating.

This section describes the construction of a large dish antenna specifically designed for this mode. It is included here because the materials and methods of construction are applicable to the manufacture of skeleton dishes of any size. For smaller dishes, the materials specifications (sizes) may be scaled down in proportion. What follows is GW3XYW's description of his practical experiences while constructing a large dish for eme work.

For many amateurs a diameter of 6m (20ft) is a practical limit, although there are exceptions. For a good eme performance, as it is a marginal mode, the greater the diameter (gain) the better. However, other considerations govern the limit of maximum practical size, eg cost, weight, windage and neighbours' tolerance!

The ratio of focus to diameter (f/D) must be chosen with great care because, once the dish is constructed, there is no way that it can be altered. Factors which govern the choice of f/D ratio are:

(a) The geometry and type of feed.

(b) The application.

For eme receive-only, a deeper dish (f/D = 0.3) is quieter because it picks up less ground noise and also man-made noises. For eme at 1.3GHz (transmit and receive) an f/D of 0.55 gives optimum forward gain.

Having chosen the dish parameters f/D = 0.55 and D = 6.1m (20ft) in this case, the next step forward is to calculate the dimensions for a template. This may then be constructed using suitable materials such as wood, faced with hardboard and painted matt white. This is done so that a graph of the rib contour can be drawn by plotting x against y (where x is the radial distance from the centre of the dish and y is the curvature of the parabola) as derived from the following formula:

$$y^2 = 4 \times f \times x = 4 \times (f/D) \times D \times x$$

$$f/D = 0.55 \qquad D = 6.1m$$

therefore $f = 3.355m$

thus $y^2 = 4 \times 0.55 \times 20 \times x = 13.42 \times x$

therefore $x = \dfrac{y^2}{13.42}$ metres

Fig 4.31. A completed mesh dish with circular horn feed

From this, Table 4.7 is then drawn up, continuing out to 3.05m. The template is shown in Fig 4.32.

Central hub

The central hub (Fig 4.33) is the unit which has to support the completed dish and subsequently is the component which takes the full weight of the completed antenna.

Two 610mm (24in) diameter discs are required. The top one uses 10swg or 3.15mm (1/8in) aluminium and the bottom one uses 10swg 3.15mm (1/8in) mild steel. These are braced at 305mm (1ft) apart by a mild-steel angle structure 3.15 by 38.1mm (1/8in by 1.5in).

Preparation of the ribs

The central portion of the dish to a radius of 0.305m (1ft) is the hub. The radius from 0.30 to 3.05m (1 to 10ft) is continued by the rib, making the length of the rib 2.286m (9ft) plus an extra 2.286m (9ft) to allow for the curve. The rib is shaped by bending it while held in a modified carpenter's vice (Fig 4.34) and then matching it against the template. The ribs are made from 25.4mm (1in) "T" section aluminium.

Table 4.7

Radius y (m)	y^2 (m)	x (mm)
0.25	0.0625	4.7
0.50	0.25	18.6
0.75	0.5625	41.9
1.00	1.00	74.5
1.25	1.5625	116.4
(and so on..)		

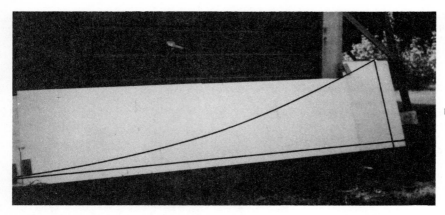

Fig 4.32. Template for a large dish

Bending is achieved by fixing the rib in the vice, gently stressing, moving the rib along about 152mm (6in), and repeating the process, checking periodically against the template until the whole rib is bent. If any part of the curve is too great, then the "T" section is reversed in the vice and stressed in the opposite direction.

The number of ribs was decided after reference to a number of eme dish designs in use by amateurs throughout the world. This design uses 16 and represents the lowest number generally found.

The next stage is to fully construct the cross-bracing on the first rib. It is useful to make as large a scale drawing as possible on squared paper 0.6 by 1m. Plot the parabolic curve and draw in the details of the bracing structure (Fig 4.35). This should be used as the reference when cutting the various lengths.

Assemble the first rib and check that it fits onto the central hub. Fit a temporary tube into the hub to define its centre axis and use this to check the dish radius to the outer tip of the rib (see Fig 4.36).

All the component parts are identified using coloured adhesive tape and then the unit dismantled. The marked component parts are used as templates for the 15 other rib sets. The tape ensures that the same components are used every time when measuring, thus avoiding any cumulative errors. Fig 4.37 shows assembled ribs.

Outer rim

The outer rim consists of 19mm (3/4in) aluminium tube bent to a radius of 3.05m (10ft), using the same modified vice. Before bending, it is advisable to draw a line along the full length of tube using an indelible fibre-tipped pen. This will show any twist introduced during the bending process: this would result in a spiral rather than an arc.

An arc of 3.05m (10ft) radius can be drawn onto the original hardboard template for comparison. The sections may be joined together with 150mm (6in) lengths of tube fitted inside and secured by M5 or 2BA screws. The rim is then test-assembled on a flat surface and its diameter checked at several points.

Fig 4.33. Central hub for large dish

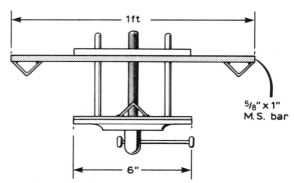

Fig 4.34. Modified carpenter's vice for forming dish ribs

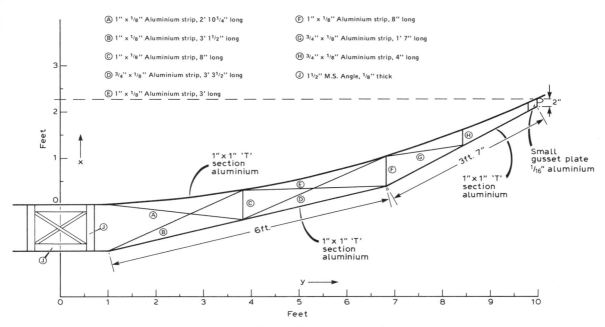

Ⓐ 1" x ⅛" Aluminium strip, 2' 10¼" long
Ⓑ 1" x ⅛" Aluminium strip, 3' 1½" long
Ⓒ 1" x ⅛" Aluminium strip, 8" long
Ⓓ ¾" x ⅛" Aluminium strip, 3' 3½" long
Ⓔ 1" x ⅛" Aluminium strip, 3' long
Ⓕ 1" x ⅛" Aluminium strip, 8" long
Ⓖ ¾" x ⅛" Aluminium strip, 1' 7" long
Ⓗ ¾" x ⅛" Aluminium strip, 4" long
Ⓙ 1½" M.S. Angle, ⅛" thick

Fig 4.35. Parts making up a complete rib

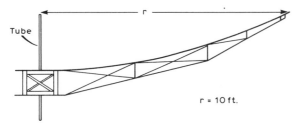

Fig 4.36. Checking the dish radius

Two inner rings with radii of 1.83m and 2.44m (6ft and 8ft) are made up using 19mm by 3.15mm (3/4in by 1/8in) flat aluminium bar. Calculate the circumference of these rings ($\pi \times D$), divide by 16 and add 19mm (3/4in) to give the length of an individual section. These are joined through the "T" section ribs as shown in Fig 4.38.

Test assembly

At this stage it is useful to assemble all the parts already prepared to test for dimensional accuracy. The ribs are

Fig 4.37. Assembled ribs

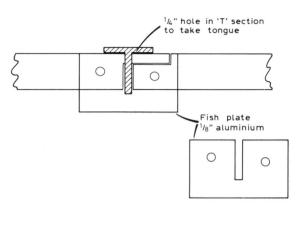

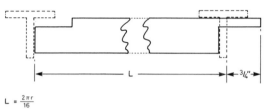

$$L = \frac{2\pi r}{16}$$

r = 6ft. or 8ft.

Fig 4.38. Method of interlinking ring sections

fixed onto the hub in pairs, diametrically opposite each other.

Using a tube through the central axis (as in Fig 4.36), check the radius is correct by measuring the diameter.

Identify each rib (by marking) and allocating to a specific hub position.

The assembled outer rim should spring over the ribs and be tight enough to hold in position under its own tension. Before fixing it to the ribs, make sure that the 16 segments are equal in size. Fig 4.39 shows the part-assembled dish and Fig 4.40 shows detail of the inner ring.

At this point there are two options open to the constructor:

(a) Dismantle and reassemble *in situ* on the mast

(b) If plenty of helpers and a large winch are to hand, bodily lift the unit up to its final position.

The former option is the easier and what follows assumes this to be the method chosen.

Accuracy of construction

The dimensional accuracy must be better than $\lambda/10$, otherwise loss of gain will start to be significant (refer to Fig 4.25).

The main supporting mast

The mast needs to be a fairly substantial structure in order to support the weight and lateral forces created by the dish in high winds. One advantage is that this support need not be very high for eme work, eg the pivot point of a dish of diameter D can be at a height of D/2 (see Fig 4.41). If activity down to the horizon (and neighbours' tv antennas) is required, then the pivot height would have to be increased. Obviously this is dependent on the local surroundings. Fortunately, most eme activity takes place at elevations above 30°. The only time when operation close to the horizon needs to

Fig 4.39. Part-assembled dish

Fig 4.40. Detail of inner ring

be considered is for working stations near the An-tipodes. If there is a choice of site, a good take-off either east or west is very desirable.

In the installation described the mast was surface mounted and held in place by large concrete blocks with mild-steel rods hammered into the ground to prevent twisting (see Fig 4.42).

Having cut the component parts, this unit is best as-sembled *in situ*. The central hub is bolted onto this assembly using four high-tensile bolts (Fig 4.43).

The 75mm (3in) pipe which makes up the azimuth axis is supported on a car clutch thrust-bearing which rests on the platform within the mast. This platform can be fixed at different heights. During dish construction the lowest position is used to facilitate access. After final completion the whole assembly is jacked up to its work-ing height using a good vehicle (heavy-duty) jack (Fig 4.44).

Feed support

An old bicycle wheel of 660mm (26in) diameter may be dismantled and the rim salvaged. Four 228.6mm (9in) pieces of 22.2mm (7/8in) diameter mild-steel tube are then brazed onto it at 90° intervals, and inclined at 45°. The outside of these tubes should be a sliding fit with the 25mm (1in) diameter aluminium tubes which make up the four legs of the feed support structure. Cut slots at the end of these legs so that jubilee clips can be used to tighten up onto the mild-steel tubes. Small brackets are used to connect the bottom of these legs to the ribs (Fig 4.45).

At this stage it is useful to tilt the antenna. In order to do this safely, some counterweighting should be applied. The final amount of counterweight required is best found by trial and error and must be slowly increased as assembly proceeds. Counterweights are made by melt-ing scrap lead (old water pipes, flashing etc) and pouring into a suitable mould. Concrete blocks may make ade-quate counterweights but are rather bulky.

Meshing the dish

The reflecting surface of the dish may now be applied. Chicken-wire mesh is best used for this purpose, with due regard to the operation frequency when choosing the size of the mesh. The mesh size should be less than $\lambda/10$ at the highest operating frequency (refer to Fig 4.25).

Aluminium strips 12.7mm by 3.15mm (1/2in by 1/8in) are laid across the dish and the mesh is then laid across in bands with its ends loosely tied to prevent recoiling (see Fig 4.46). Since the mesh has been rolled off a cylindrical coil and has to lie on a surface which is curved in two dimensions, a lot of time and effort is required, stretching and contracting (Fig 4.47) until it can be per-suaded to take up the parabolic curve. As it is "tamed", it is permanently fixed onto the antenna structure using 20 or 22swg (0.9 or 0.8mm) galvanised wire.

When mounting the feed system the dish elevation axis should be clamped or tied to prevent the antenna tipping over with the extra weight until the counter-weighting is adjusted.

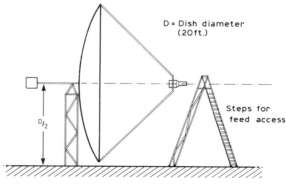

Fig 4.41. Dish mounting geometry

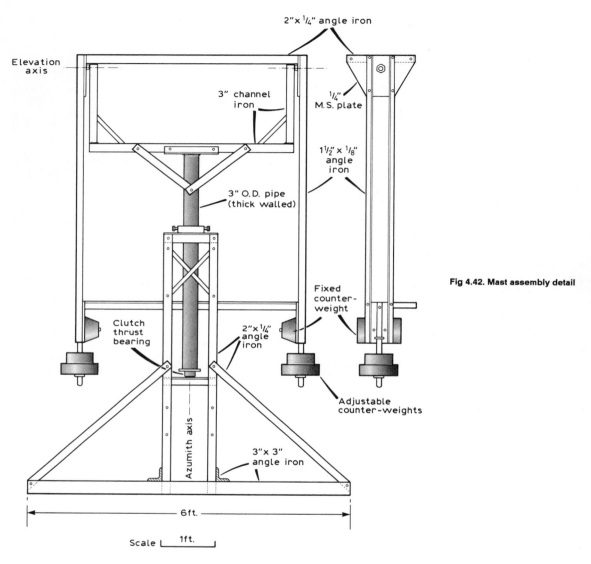

2"x ¼" angle iron

Elevation axis

3" channel iron

¼" M.S. plate

1½" x ⅛" angle iron

3" O.D. pipe (thick walled)

Fixed counter-weight

Clutch thrust bearing

2"x ¼" angle iron

Azumith axis

Adjustable counter-weights

3"x 3" angle iron

6ft.

Scale ⊢ 1ft. ⊣

Fig 4.42. Mast assembly detail

Fig 4.48 shows the antenna mesh and feeder run; Fig 4.49 shows the final assembly.

Forward gain

The forward gain attainable with such a dish depends on the accuracy of construction, size of the mesh and feed illumination. However, assuming an efficiency of 50 per cent, the gain at 1.3GHz will be in excess of 35dBi and at 432MHz will be around 25dBi. This performance will permit successful eme activity on both bands within the current amateur transmitter power limits.

4.7 THE DESIGN OF FEEDS FOR DISHES

In a perfect feed system for a parabolic dish, all the energy would appear to emerge from a point source placed at the focus, and would be contained within a cone which just intercepts the rim of the dish. All the energy would then be reflected by the dish in the form of a plane wave. This ideal picture is complicated by several factors:

(a) Practical feeds do not cut off very sharply. Generally the power density is at a maximum on the axis of the feed and then falls off on either side. Clearly there is no

Fig 4.43. Central hub mounted on mast

Fig 4.44. Final assembly in situ

Fig 4.45. Feed support structure

absolute value for the beamwidth of the feed. However, what can be specified is the beamwidth at which the power density is either a half or a tenth of the maximum value. There is therefore a judgement to be made on what the optimum beamwidth for the feed should be for a given dish. If too low, as is illustrated by Fig 4.50(a), most of the energy radiated by the feed is reflected by the dish but, since the energy is concentrated at the centre of the dish, the overall gain of the antenna suffers. The pattern produced is very clean with the minimum of sidelobe amplitude. If the beamwidth of the feed is too high, as illustrated by Fig 4.50(b), much of the energy radiated by the feed is not reflected by the dish and is lost. This may result in large sidelobes. There is clearly an optimum feed beamwidth that results in a fairly uniform illumination of the dish. This is achieved when the illumination at the edge of the dish is approximately 10dB down on that at the centre. This value will be assumed throughout this section.

(b) Because the rim of any parabolic dish is further from the feed than is the centre, there is already some loss

built in the system. This loss is called the "space loss", and it varies according to the f/D ratio of the dish. For a focal-plane dish, it is 6dB. Therefore, to produce an

Fig 4.46. Laying the mesh

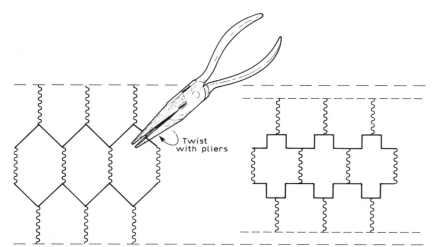

Twist
with pliers

Fig 4.47. Method of contracting the
wire mesh area

illumination at the edge of the dish 10dB down on that at the centre, the feed must have a 4dB beamwidth equal to the angle subtended by the rim of the dish, which is 180° in this example. For a dish of longer focal length, the space loss is smaller. For example, a dish having a f/D ratio equal to 0.6 has a space loss of 1.5dB at the rim. Therefore a suitable feed should have a 8.5dB (10 – 1.5dB) beamwidth at 88° to optimally illuminate this dish. This is obviously an easier task.

(c) To achieve high efficiency, the dish must be illuminated evenly over its surface, and it is therefore desirable to control the beamwidth of the feed in both the horizontal and vertical planes. Unfortunately, the commonly used dipole and reflector and tin-can feeds are generally not very good in this respect. Pyramidal horns are much more satisfactory and their use will be described in a later section.

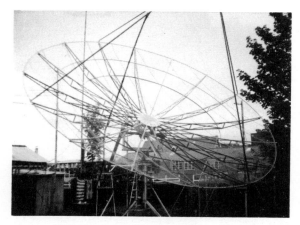

Fig 4.48. Antenna with wire mesh and cable run

(d) The phase centre of a feed is defined as the point from which the energy appears to emanate. In practical feeds the phase centre is rarely a point since the size of the feed is always significant in wavelength terms. The situation is further complicated by the fact that the phase centre in the horizontal (E) plane may differ from that in the vertical (H) plane. Multiband feeds such as log-periodic arrays suffer the additional disadvantage that the phase centres will move significantly as the frequency of operation is changed. The reduction in antenna gain due to variations in the position of the phase centres are likely to be significant, especially so for dishes of short focal length since the effect will be proportionally greater. This is yet another factor favouring the use of dishes with a relatively high f/D ratio.

4.8 PRACTICAL FEED SYSTEMS

4.8.1 Direct feed

In this method, which is illustrated by Fig 4.51, the phase centre of the feed is placed at the focus of the dish. Power radiated by the feed as a spherical wave is converted by reflection at the paraboloidal reflector into a plane wave.

The characteristics of the feed required to illuminate the dish correctly are determined by measuring the f/D ratio by the methods described earlier, and determining the beamwidth of the feed from Fig 4.28. Thus the feed for a focal-plane dish for which f/D = 0.25 should have a 3dB beamwidth of 155°. For a dish having a f/D ratio of 0.7, the 3dB beamwidth should be 46°. Alternatively, the 10dB beamwidth may be specified, and the corresponding value is 83°. Fig 4.28 was derived assuming an edge illumination 10dB down on that at the centre of the dish. Due allowance has been made for space loss. It will be noted that the beamwidth required changes very rapidly as the f/D ratio is reduced, which makes the

Fig 4.49. Final assembly with 1.3GHz feedhorn in position

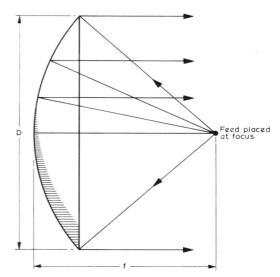

Fig 4.51. Geometry of direct feed system

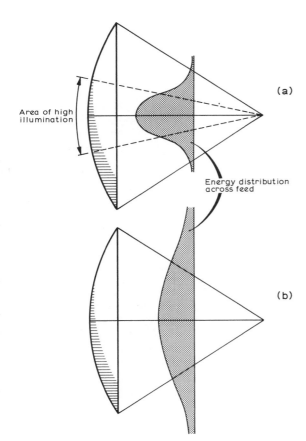

Fig 4.50. Non-optimum dish illumination. (a) Under-illuminated. (b) Over-illuminated.

design of suitable feeds for short focal length dishes rather more difficult. In practice, under-illumination is the result.

The main advantage of this method of mounting the feed is its simplicity in conception and construction. It can have a high overall efficiency, and it leaves the back of the dish clear for mounting on the mast or tripod. Its main disadvantage is that with dishes of long focal length, the feed support structure becomes quite bulky. Fig 4.52 shows a practical antenna system of this type.

Fig 4.52. A dish with 10GHz direct feed

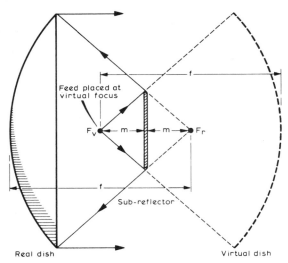

Fig 4.53. Geometry of indirect feed system

4.8.2 Indirect feed

Fig 4.53 illustrates the geometry of this method. Power radiated by the feed is reflected by a plane sub-reflector onto the main reflector. A spherical wave generated by the feed is converted by the sub-reflector into a spherical wave of the same radius of curvature but moving towards the dish. This, in turn, is converted by the dish into a plane wave.

The sub-reflector should preferably be a minimum of a few wavelengths in diameter, but should not exceed a third of the diameter of the main dish in order not to incur more than 1dB loss of performance. Once the size of the sub-reflector is chosen, then its position is fixed.

It must just intercept lines drawn from the real focus of the dish, F_r, to its rim. The position of the feed is also fixed. It is set at the virtual focus, F_v, which is as far in front of the sub-reflector as the real focus is behind, meaning that the lengths m are equal. Because the sub-reflector is planar, the virtual dish has the same focal length as the real dish, and therefore the design of the feed is the same as if the direct-feed method were used.

The sub-reflector is usually made from solid material since it is so small, but mesh or wires running parallel to the plane of polarisation and spaced by about a tenth of a wavelength offer a suitable alternative construction.

The main advantages of this method are that the feed can be supported from the centre of the dish (although this may complicate mounting the dish), and only a relatively light structure is needed to support the sub-reflector. The disadvantages of the method are that an extra component, the sub-reflector, needs to be aligned accurately, and that extra losses are involved compared with the direct feed method due to diffraction around the sub-reflector.

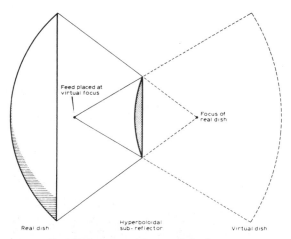

Fig 4.54. Geometry of Cassegrain feed system

Fig 4.55. A Cassegrain-fed dish

4.8.3 Cassegrain feed

The geometry of a Cassegrain system is shown in Fig 4.54. It is similar to the indirect feed method already described, the essential differences being that the planar sub-reflector is replaced by a shaped reflector in the form of a hyperboloid. The main result of this change is that the virtual dish seen by the feed has a longer focal length than the real dish. Thus a dish of short focal length which can be difficult to illuminate efficiently can be converted into one of longer apparent focal length. A second feature is that there is more flexibility in the positioning of the feed. The feed may be mounted behind the dish firing through a suitable hole. This form has a great mechanical advantage, and is commonly used on optical telescopes.

A completed antenna using this type of feed is shown in Fig 4.55.

4.8.4 BASIC Cassegrain reflector design program

This is a computer program, written in BBC BASIC by G8AGN, to assist in the design of Cassegrain antenna feeds.

```
10 CLS
20 PRINT"Cassegrain Antenna Design Program"
30 PRINT"_____":PRINT:PRINT
40 PRINT:INPUT "Do you want a printed copy (Y/N?) " ans$
50 IF ans$="Y" THEN VDU2:CLS
60 IF ans$<>"Y" THEN CLS
70 @%=131850
80 REM Set print format
90 DIM X(1000)
100 PRINT"Cassegrain Antenna Design Program"
110 PRINT"_____":PRINT:PRINT
120 INPUT"Enter frequency in GHz    " F
130 WL=30/(2.54*F)
140 INPUT "Enter dish diameter (in.)    " D
150 INPUT "Enter actual dish f/D    " frd
160 INPUT "Enter Required virtual f/D   " fvd
170 fr=frd*D
180 cr=D*D/(16*fr)
190 th0=2*ATN(1/(4*fvd))
200 ph0=2*ATN(1/(4*frd))
210 d=D*(COS(0.5*th0)^4*0.1*WL/(16*PI*PI*SIN(ph0)*D))^0.2
220 PRINT:PRINT "Optimum sub-reflector diameter = ";d;"  in."
230 fv=D*fvd
240 cv=D*D/(16*fv)
250 m=d*(fr-cr)/D
260 l=d*(fv-cv)/D
270 PRINT:PRINT"Feed phase- centre should be positioned"
280 PRINT fr-(1+m);" in. from back of dish"
290 REM subreflector profile
300 a=0.5*(1+m)*(fv-fr)/(fv+fr)
310 e=0.5*(1+m)/a
320 PRINT:INPUT "Enter Y increment in thou.in.:   " inc
330 inc=inc*0.001
340 y=0.000
350 i=0
360 REPEAT
370 X(i)=SQR(a*a+y*y/(e*e-1))
380 y=y+inc:i=i+1
390 UNTIL y>0.5*d
400 X(i)=SQR(a*a+0.25*d*d/(e*e-1))
410 PRINT:PRINT"Sub-reflector profile: ":PRINT
420 PRINT"      Y (in.)      X (in.)           Y (mm)      X (mm)"
430 PRINT"_____"
440 FOR j=0 TO i-1
450 PRINT j*inc,X(j)-X(0)," ",j*inc*25.4,(X(j)-X(0))*25.4
460 NEXT
470 PRINT d*0.5,X(i)-X(0)," ",d*0.5*25.4,(X(i)-X(0))*25.4
480 PRINT:INPUT "Do you wish to calculate another virtual focus
    (Y/N) " ans$
490 IF ans$="Y" THEN RESTORE:GOTO 160
500 IF ans$<>"Y" THEN PRINT:PRINT "End of program":VDU3:END
```

4.8.5 Pyramidal horn feeds

Pyramidal horns have significant advantages over most other types of feeds which makes them especially suitable for use by amateurs. First, they offer a virtually perfect match over a wide range of frequencies and are therefore uncritical in their design and construction. Even quite large dimensional errors do not affect the

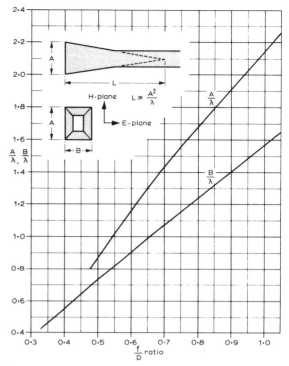

Fig 4.56. Form of horn antenna to feed dish and dimensions as a function of dish f/D ratio

quality of this match, but only the efficiency of illumination of the dish. A second advantage is that these horns are designed to produce optimum illumination of the dish in both planes. With other types of feed, there may be little or no control of the ratio of beamwidths in each plane.

The form of a horn is shown in Fig 4.56. It consists of a length of waveguide which is flared in one or both planes to produce the beamwidth required. At the higher microwave frequencies, the horn will normally be fed by waveguide. The body of the feed horn will therefore usually consist of a length of waveguide which matches the rest of the system. On the lower microwave bands (1.3, 2.3 and 3.4GHz) the horn is often fed by using coaxial cable. A waveguide-to-coaxial-cable transition will be needed to serve as the method of launch. The horn design method is otherwise exactly the same. It is not necessary in this case to use a standard waveguide.

The dimensions of the pyramidal horn as a function of the f/D ratio of the dish to be illuminated are given in Fig 4.56. They are based on an edge illumination of 10dB down on that at the centre of the dish. Due allowance has been made for space loss. The dimensions are given in terms of wavelength, so enabling

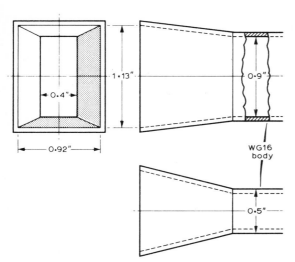

Fig 4.57. A typical pyramidal horn feed designed for a dish having f/D ratio of 0.53, for use at 10GHz

any frequency of operation to be catered for. The actual dimensions are, of course, determined by multiplying the values of A/λ and B/λ by the wavelength in air at the design frequency.

It can be seen from Fig 4.56 that the aperture of the horn decreases as the f/D ratio of the dish is reduced. The limit of the design data is reached first with the "A" dimension at a value of A/λ equal to 0.8, which corresponds to a minimum f/D ratio of 0.48. To feed dishes of smaller f/D ratio, the Cassegrain system may be used.

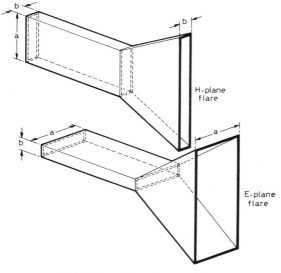

Fig 4.58. General form of sectoral horn

Alternatively, the end of the waveguide may be suitably shaped to increase its beamwidth but, as this shaping has to be determined experimentally, much of the advantage of horn feeds is lost.

As an example of the design of a horn for a specific dish, consider a dish of diameter D of 0.914m (36in), which has a depth at its centre of c or 108mm (4.26in). It is to be fed at 10,400MHz, for which λ is 28.846mm (1.136in). The focal length of the dish is given by $D^2/16c$ = 0.483m (19in), and the f/D ratio therefore is 0.53. From Fig 4.56, the values corresponding to this ratio are:

H-plane aperture = A/λ   = 0.96 (ratio)
A is broad wall = 28.846×0.96   = 27.69mm (1.09")
E-plane aperture = B/λ   = 0.78 (ratio)
B is narrow wall = 28.846×0.78 = 22.50mm (0.886")
L = A×A/λ = 27.69×27.69/28.846 = 26.58mm (1.046")

At this frequency a convenient waveguide is WG16, so a practical horn would have an aperture of 27.69 by 22.50mm (1.091in by 0.886in), tapering to 22.86 by 10.16mm (0.9in by 0.4in). This design is shown in Fig 4.57.

The same design procedure is applicable to any dish with the same f/D ratio. For example, the feed horn at 1,296MHz would have an aperture of 222 by 180mm (8.74in by 7.10in), tapering to 165 by 82.5mm (6.5in by 3.25in), if WG6 were used. Similarly, one for use at 24GHz would have an aperture of 11.99 by 9.8mm (0.472in by 0.384in), tapering to 10.67 by 4.32mm (0.42in by 0.17in) for WG20.

4.8.6 Sectoral horns

The sectoral horn is a form of pyramidal horn but flares in only one plane. The result of this is that a wider beamwidth is formed in the unflared plane. Fig 4.58 shows the general form of this type of antenna.

A small horn with dimension B fixed at the width of the narrow wall of the waveguide would give a symmetrical polar pattern and low gain when it uses the ratios described above. However, if the broad wall is flared to form a long rectangular mouth, a very non-symmetrical but higher-gain pattern will result.

It should be possible to achieve a little wider coverage by tapering the narrow wall dimension to a narrower aperture than that of the waveguide. The length must still be close to that which would be required for a normal pyramidal horn with the broad wall dimension suggested.

If this form of horn is to produce a horizontally polarised wave, then the broad wall should be vertical. The result will be better coverage around the horizon and the beamwidth will be quite wide at perhaps several tens of degrees. The extra gain is achieved by compressing the vertical pattern. The gain achieved will appear to be rather moderate when compared to a dish but will give extra coverage in the favoured sector.

Fig 4.59. Biconical horns for 10GHz

This is particularly useful where an omnidirectional pattern would waste power in directions of no particular interest, eg when a beacon or repeater is located on a site which has some badly screened directions, or maybe when located at an extreme of activity geographically. But remember that, just because it has not been achieved before, this does not mean that under some circumstances there may not be a path to open. (There must be activity though!)

4.8.7 Biconical horns

This form of omnidirectional antenna is rather more difficult to construct and to feed. However there is a form of launch called the "Alford loop" that should prove satisfactory at least up to 10GHz. It may be rather difficult to construct for the higher bands.

The bicone is self-explanatory in form, but the points of the cones must be truncated by enough to allow the launch to be fitted in the gap. Some examples for 10GHz are shown in Fig 4.59.

As with the Alford slot (see section 4.9.1), a coaxial cable will be needed to energise the launching loop. The form of this loop is shown in Fig 4.60.

4.8.8 Circular horn feeds

This type of feed is quite common on the lower microwave bands, its main advantage being that it can be made from readily available materials. Its efficiency is fairly high, but it does require some setting up. As is shown in Fig 4.61, the feed consists of a length of short-circuited, circular waveguide, often made from tin cans. A simple form of coaxial-cable-to-waveguide transition generally used consists of a probe just less than a quarter of a wavelength long, spaced approximately a quarter of a guide wavelength from the closed end. The

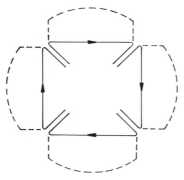

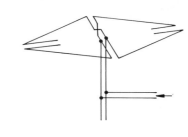

Fig 4.60. Launching loop for biconical horn (from Antenna Theory and Design, Vol 2, 2nd edn, H P Williams, Pitman, 1966)

(a) Principle of loop (Dotted lines indicate relative current distribution.)

(b) Method of feeding

(c) Loop of 2 half wave elements.

(d) Loop of 1 half wave element.

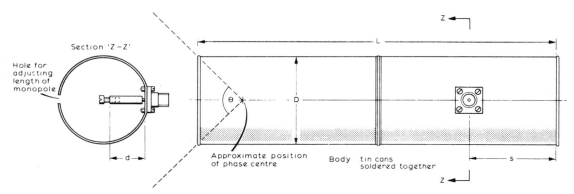

Fig 4.61. Circular horn feed

exact distance and length should be established experimentally, and remember that the required length will alter with the diameter of the probe.

The design factors are as follows:

(a) The diameter of the feed D must exceed 0.58 wavelength in air at the design frequency. If it is smaller, the waveguide is then operating in its cut-off region and proper operation will be difficult. A reasonable practical value for D is between 0.65 to 0.7 wavelength.

(b) The length of the horn L preferably should exceed a guide wavelength, λ_g, where

$$\lambda_g = L/\sqrt{(1-(\lambda/1.706\times D)\times 2)}$$

For $D = 0.65\times\lambda_g$, L should be greater than $2.4\times\lambda_g$.
For $D = 0.70\times\lambda_g$, L should be greater than $1.8\times\lambda_g$.

Note that as the diameter of the feed approaches $0.586\times\lambda_g$, the length of the horn required increases very rapidly. At cut-off it would be infinitely long!

(c) The correct spacing between the probe and the short-circuit should be determined experimentally. The spacing required is around a quarter of a waveguide wavelength, so the position of either the probe or the short-circuit can be made adjustable.

(d) The E-plane (horizontal) and H-plane (vertical) 3dB beamwidth, θ degrees, is given by the values of 29.4 L/D and 50 L/D respectively. That these differ significantly is the main disadvantage of this type of feed since it results in an uneven illumination of the dish. When the value

suggested for D is 0.65L the respective beamwidths are 46 and 78°. Reference to Fig 4.28 shows that these values would optimally illuminate a dish with a f/D of 0.69 and 0.43 respectively. The mean value of 0.56 represents, perhaps, the minimum f/D ratio of the dish that can be illuminated with reasonable efficiency. However, a real compromise will depend on the application. This is because one plane would be over-illuminated and the other under-illuminated.

There is very little flexibility of design. If the diameter of the horn is increased, then its length may be reduced, but the beamwidth of the horn will also decrease. By using an elliptical waveguide perhaps better symmetry can be obtained. The amount of "distortion" may be adjusted to optimally illuminate the dish. Typical dimensions of horns for the lower microwave bands based on D = 0.65L are given in Table 4.8. The equivalent phase centre of the feed will be just inside the mouth and this should be adjusted to coincide with the focus of the dish.

4.8.9 BASIC horn design program

This computer program, in BBC BASIC, is a "universal" horn design program for optimum-gain pyramidal or conical horns and sectoral horns for any bands, using WG6 to WG28 as the transmission line.

Table 4.8

Frequency (MHz)	D (mm)	D (in)	L (mm)	L (in)	d (mm)	d (in)	s (mm)	s (in)
1,297	150	5.9	560	22.0	46	1.8	140	5.5
2,320	84	3.3	312	12.3	25	1.0	76	3.0
3,457	56	2.2	208	8.2	18	0.7	51	2.0
5,760	34	1.3	125	4.9	11	0.4	31	1.2
10,400	12.5	0.5	69	2.7	6	0.24	17	0.7

```
10 REM ------------------------------
20 REM
30 REM      HORN DESIGN PACKAGE
40 REM
50 REM      B. CHAMBERS G8AGN
60 REM
70 REM ------------------------------
80 REM
90 REM
100 DEF FNL(X)=LOG(X)/LOG(10)
110 DEF FNR(X)=.01*INT(100*X+.5)
120 DEF FNA(X)=10^(.1*X)
130 GOTO 1090
140 ER=(SQR(2*LE/LA)-B/LA)^2*(2*LE/LA-1)-(SQR(3*K*LA/LE)-A/LA)^2
     *(4*K*LA/(3*LE)-1)
150 RETURN
160 RESTORE
170 FOR T=1 TO 12
180 READ WG,A,B,FL,FH
190 IF F>=1E3*FL AND F<=1E3*FH THEN 230
200 NEXT T
210 PRINT
220 PRINT:PRINT"Waveguide data is";CHR$(136)"NOT";
     CHR$(137)"available for":PRINT"this frequency":GOTO 1170
230 PRINT:PRINT:PRINT"Recommended waveguide size is WG ";WG
240 PRINT:PRINT"Frequency range is ";FL;" to ";FH;" GHz"
250 PRINT:PRINT"Internal dimensions are: A = ";A;" ins."
```

```
260 PRINT:PRINT"                              B = ";B;" ins.":PRINT
270 PRINT:INPUT"Is this choice OK ";P$
280 IF LEFT$(P$,1)="Y" THEN 360
290 PRINT:PRINT"Which waveguide size is to be used ?":INPUT W
300 RESTORE
310 FOR T= 1 TO 12
320 READ WG,A,B,FL,FH
330 IF W=WG THEN T=12:NEXT:GOTO 360
340 NEXT
350 PRINT:PRINT"Waveguide data";CHR$(136)"NOT";
    CHR$(137)"available":GOTO 290
360 A=.0254*A:B=.0254*B
370 RETURN
380 Z2=Z/2
390 C=0:S=0
400 FOR I=1 TO 20
410 Y1=Z2*X(I)+Z2
420 Y2=-Z2*X(I)+Z2
430 C1=COS(P2*Y1*Y1)
440 C2=COS(P2*Y2*Y2)
450 S1=SIN(P2*Y1*Y1)
460 S2=SIN(P2*Y2*Y2)
470 C=C+W(I)*(C1+C2)
480 S=S+W(I)*(S1+S2)
490 NEXT
500 C=Z2*C:S=Z2*S
510 RETURN
520 RESTORE
530 FOR T=1 TO 12
540 READ Z,Z,Z,Z,Z
550 NEXT
560 FOR I=1 TO 20
570 READ X(I),W(I)
580 NEXT
590 RETURN
1090 CLS:P2=.5*PI
1095 DIM X(20),W(20)
1100 PRINT"GENERAL HORN DESIGN PACKAGE"
1110 PRINT"---------------------------":PRINT
1120 PRINT"Options are: ":PRINT
1130 PRINT"1        Optimum gain horns":PRINT
1140 PRINT"2        Sectoral horns":PRINT
1150 INPUT" Choice    ";C
1160 PRINT
1170 PRINT:INPUT "Frequency (MHz)   ";F:LA=300/F
1180 PRINT:INPUT "Required gain (dB)    ";GD
1190 ON C GOTO 1210,2000
1200 END
1210 CLS
1220 PRINT"OPTIMUM GAIN HORN DESIGN"
1230 PRINT"------------------------":PRINT
1240 PRINT:INPUT "Horn type (P) pyramidal or (C) conical    ";T$
1250 IF T$<>"C" AND T$<>"P" THEN 1240
1260 G=10^(0.1*GD)
1270 K=(G/15.7497)^2
1280 IF T$="C" THEN 1860
1290 GOSUB 160
1300 S=.1:LS=0:LE=1E-3:GOSUB 140:ES=ER:E=ER
1310 FOR L=1 TO 50
1320 LE=S*L+LS
1330 GOSUB 140
1340 IF (ES*ER)<0 THEN L=50:GOTO 1360
1350 ES=ER
1360 NEXT L
1370 IF S<1E-6 THEN 1400
1380 LE=LE-S:S=0.1*S:LS=LE:ES=E
1390 GOTO 1310
1400 LH=K*LA*LA/LE
1410 HA=SQR(3*LH*LA)
1420 HB=SQR(2*LE*LA)
1430 PRINT:PRINT"Horn mouth dimensions are:"
1440 PRINT:PRINT"   A = ";FNR(100*HA);" cm"
1450 PRINT:PRINT"   B = ";FNR(100*HB);" cm"
1460 AX=SQR(LH*LH-.25*HA*HA)
1470 AX=AX-AX*A/HA
1480 PRINT:PRINT"Horn axial length = ";FNR(100*AX);" cm"
1490 TE=LE-LE*B/HB:TH=LH-LH*A/HA
1500 PRINT "E-plane flare slant length =";FNR(100*TE);" cm"
1510 PRINT "H-plane flare slant length =";FNR(100*TH);" cm"
1520 GC=8.08+10*FNL(HA*HB/LA^2)
1530 PRINT:PRINT"Calculated optimum gain is ";FNR(GC);" dB"
1540 PRINT:PRINT"Approximate 3dB beamwidths are:":PRINT
1550 E3=54*LA/HB:H3=79*LA/HA
1560 PRINT"E-plane = ";INT(E3+.5);" deg.":PRINT
1570 PRINT"H-plane = ";INT(H3+.5);" deg.":PRINT:PRINT
1580 PRINT:INPUT "Is gain-frequency data required   Y/N ";T$
1590 IF LEFT$(T$,1)<>"Y" THEN END
1600 PRINT:INPUT "Lower frequency limit (MHz)      ";BL
1610 IF BL>= 1E3*FL THEN 1640
1620 PRINT"Waveguide operating";CHR$(136)"BELOW";
    CHR$(137)"recommended"
1630 PRINT"frequency limit ( ";1E3*FL;" MHz )."
1635 PRINT:INPUT"Is this OK ";T$:IF T$<>"Y" THEN 1600
1640 PRINT:INPUT"Upper frequency limit (MHz)      ";BH
1650 IF BH<=1E3*FH THEN 1680
1660 PRINT"Waveguide operating";CHR$(136)"ABOVE";
    CHR$(137)"recommended"
1670 PRINT"frequency limit ( ";1E3*FH;" MHz )."
1675 PRINT:INPUT"Is this OK ";T$:IF T$<>"Y" THEN 1640
1680 BL=50*INT(BL/50)
1690 BH=50*INT(BH/50)+50
1700 PRINT:PRINT"Rounded frequency limits are :"
1710 PRINT:PRINT BL;" TO ";BH;" MHz"
1720 PRINT:PRINT TAB(5)" MHz";SPC7;" dB"
1730 PRINT TAB(5)" ---";SPC7;" --":PRINT
1740 GOSUB 520
1750 FOR F=BL TO BH STEP 50
1760 LA=300/F
1770 U1=SQR(LA*LH)/HA:U2=1/SQR(2)
1780 Z=(U1+1/U1)*U2:GOSUB 380
```

```
1790 CU=C:SU=S
1800 Z=(U1-1/U1)*U2:GOSUB 380:CV=C:SV=S
1810 Z=HB/SQR(2*LA*LE):GOSUB 380
1820 G=8*PI*LE*LH*(C*C+S*S)*((CU-CV)^2+(SU-SV)^2)/(HA*HB)
1830 PRINT F,FNR(10*FNL(G))
1840 NEXT F
1850 END
1860 LA=LA*10^(.05*(GD+2.82))
1870 D=C/PI
1880 L=D*D/(3*LA)
1890 CLS
1900 PRINT"Optimum gain conical horn design"
1910 PRINT"--------------------------------":PRINT:PRINT
1920 PRINT:PRINT"Aperture diameter = ";FNR(100*D);" cm"
1930 PRINT:PRINT"Flare slant length = ";FNR(100*L);" cm"
1940 E3=INT(60*LA/D+.5)
1950 H3=INT(70*LA/D+.5)
1960 PRINT:PRINT"Approximate 3dB beamwidths are:":PRINT
1970 PRINT"E-plane = ";E3;" deg.":PRINT
1980 PRINT"H-plane = ";H3;" deg.":PRINT:PRINT
1990 END
2000 CLS
2010 PRINT"SECTORAL HORN DESIGN"
2020 PRINT"--------------------":PRINT
2030 PRINT"   Options are: ":PRINT
2040 PRINT"1      E-plane flare":PRINT
2050 PRINT"2      H-plane flare":PRINT
2060 INPUT "Choice    ";C
2070 IF C<1 OR C>2 THEN 2060
2080 GOSUB 160
2090 ON C GOTO 2100,2270
2100 HB=LA*LA*FNA(GD-9.08)/A
2110 HA=A
2120 LE=SQR(.5*HB*HB/LA)
2130 PRINT:PRINT"Horn mouth dimensions are: "
2140 PRINT:PRINT"   A = ";FNR(100*HA);" cm"
2150 PRINT:PRINT"   B = ";FNR(100*HB);" cm"
2160 AX=SQR(LE*LE-.25*HB*HB)
2170 AX=AX-AX*B/HB
2180 PRINT:PRINT"Horn axial length = ";FNR(100*AX);" cm"
2190 TE=LE-LE*B/HB:TH=AX
2200 PRINT:PRINT"E-plane flare slant length = ";FNR(100*TE);" cm"
2210 PRINT:PRINT"H-plane length = ";FNR(100*TH);" cm"
2220 GOSUB 520
2230 Z=HB/SQR(2*LA*LE):GOSUB 380
2240 GC=64*HA*LE*(C*C+S*S)/(PI*LA*HB)
2250 PRINT:PRINT"Calculated gain is ";FNR(10*FNL(GC));" dB"
2260 END
2270 HA=LA*LA*FNA(GD-9.08)/B
2280 HB=B
2290 LH=SQR(.333333333*HA*HA/LA)
2300 PRINT:PRINT"Horn mouth dimensions are: "
2310 PRINT:PRINT"   A = ";FNR(100*HA);" cm"
2320 PRINT:PRINT"   B = ";FNR(100*HB);" cm"
2330 AX=SQR(LH*LH-.25*HA*HA)
2340 AX=AX-AX*A/HA
2350 PRINT:PRINT"Horn axial length = ";FNR(100*AX);" cm"
2360 TE=AX:TH=LH-LH*A/HA
2370 PRINT:PRINT"H-plane flare slant length = ";FNR(100*TH);" cm"
2380 PRINT:PRINT"E-plane length = ";FNR(100*TE);" cm"
2390 GOSUB 520:U1=SQR(LA*LH)/HA:U2=1/SQR(2)
2400 Z=(U1+1/U1)*U2:GOSUB 380
2410 CU=C:SU=S
2420 Z=(U1-1/U1)*U2:GOSUB 380
2430 GC=4*PI*HB*LH*((CU-C)^2+(SU-S)^2)
2440 GC=GC/(LA*HA)
2450 PRINT:PRINT"Calculated gain is ";FNR(10*FNL(GC));" dB"
2460 END
2470 REM WAVEGUIDE DATA
2480 DATA 6,6.5,3.25,1.12,1.7
2490 DATA 8,4.3,2.15,1.7,2.6
2500 DATA 10,2.84,1.34,2.6,3.95
2510 DATA 12,1.872,0.872,3.95,5.85
2520 DATA 14,1.372,0.622,5.85,8.2
2530 DATA 16,0.9,0.4,8.2,12.4
2540 DATA 18,0.622,0.311,12.4,18.0
2550 DATA 20,.42,.17,18,26.5
2560 DATA 22,.28,.14,26.5,40
2570 DATA 24,.188,.094,40,60
2580 DATA 26,.122,.061,60,90
2590 DATA 28,.08,.04,90,140
2600 REM FRESNEL INTEGRALS BY GAUSS INTEG.
3000 DATA 0.038770605,0.077505948
3010 DATA 0.116084071,0.077039818
3020 DATA 0.192697581,0.076110362
3030 DATA 0.268152185,0.074723169
3040 DATA 0.341994091,0.072886582
3050 DATA 0.413779204,0.070611647
3060 DATA 0.483075802,0.067912046
3070 DATA 0.549467125,0.064804013
3080 DATA 0.612553890,0.061306242
3090 DATA 0.671956685,0.057439769
3100 DATA 0.727318255,0.053227847
3110 DATA 0.778305651,0.048695808
3120 DATA 0.824612231,0.043870908
3130 DATA 0.865959503,0.038782168
3140 DATA 0.902098807,0.033460195
3150 DATA 0.932812808,0.027937007
3160 DATA 0.957916819,0.022245849
3170 DATA 0.977259950,0.016421058
3180 DATA 0.990726239,0.010498285
3190 DATA 0.998237710,0.004521277
```

4.8.10 Dipole and reflector feeds

This type of feed is shown in Figs 4.62 and 4.63. The radiation pattern makes it suitable for feeding a dish with an f/D ratio of 0.25 to 0.35. The feeds are built around a length of fabricated rigid coaxial line; the ratio of the inside dimension of the outer to the diameter of the inner must be 2.3:1 to produce an impedance of 50Ω. or 3.3:1 to produce an impedance of 72Ω. The dipole-to-reflector spacing should be increased to return to a good match at 72Ω. It is also possible to obtain a good match to 72Ω by using a ptfe "slug" as a transforming section within the airline coaxial cable.

4.8.11 Balance-to-unbalance devices

The slot in the outer shown in Figs 4.62 and 4.63 is used to provide the balance-to-unbalance (balun) action required. Associated with this form of balun is an impedance transformation of 4:1. It behaves in exactly the same manner as the one used and described in the Alford slot section (see section 4.9.1) but this one is twice the length and provides a convenient method of mounting a dipole and reflector feed. It may be considered as two quarter-wave sections end to end. This permits the inner to be physically joined to the outer at the dipole as shown. The impedance transformation in this case is 2:1 as there are two baluns in parallel.

This form of balun is analogous to the type that uses a half-wavelength of coaxial cable on the lower frequencies. The form used with this feed produces the balancing and transforming action at the outer rather than the inner, as does the flexible coaxial cable form. The outer is split and one side is energised by connection to the inner. The other half of the outer is thus forced to have an equal voltage, but of opposite phase, imposed on it. In this way double the voltage is present across the two halves and this explains the transformation.

The same explanation may be used when the standard coaxial cable type is considered, but read "inner" for

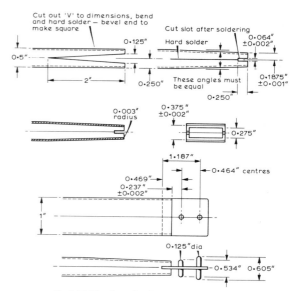

Fig 4.63. Dipole and reflector feed for 10GHz

"outer". Of course in both cases this action occurs totally within the cable. Due to the skin depth being very small, none of this current flows on the outside. The radiation from the slots is extremely small providing they are narrow. A heat-shrink sleeve should be used to strengthen this form of balun when made from semi-rigid cable.

4.8.12 Waveguide feed for 2,320MHz

This feed for use with a dish of short focal length is shown in Fig 4.64. By the use of a scatter pin, and by cutting the waveguide in the way shown, the angle of radiation has been increased significantly when compared with a plain aperture. The feed may be tuned by adjusting the position of the rf short which is then firmly bolted or soldered in place. The plane of polarisation is parallel to the scatter pin. Suitable materials for construction for the body are brass, copper or tinplate.

4.8.13 The "penny" feed – a simple waveguide feed for short focal length dishes

Most dishes that amateurs inherit have a short focal length, which means that the ratio of the focal length to the diameter of the dish is typically within the range 0.25–0.3. The polar diagram of an example of this feed has been measured and had a double humped main lobe in the horizontal plane: see Fig 4.65.

It is suggested that the spacing between the two dipoles can be used to produce a beam shape to suit other f/Ds. This will require either flaring or narrowing the waveguide. In the vertical plane, the pattern is that of a single dipole. The advantage of this is as explained in section 4.8.10. This feed could, perhaps,

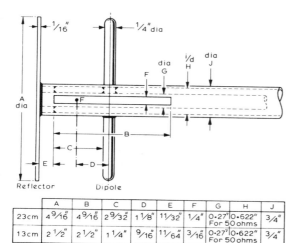

	A	B	C	D	E	F	G	H	J
23cm	4 9/16"	4 9/16"	2 9/32"	1 1/8"	11/32"	1/4"	0·27" For 50 ohms	0·622"	3/4"
13cm	2 1/2"	2 1/2"	1 1/4"	9/16"	11/64"	3/16"	0·27" For 50 ohms	0·622"	3/4"

Fig 4.62. Dipole and reflector feeds for 1.3 and 2.3GHz. The feed is mounted so that point F coincides with the focus of the dish

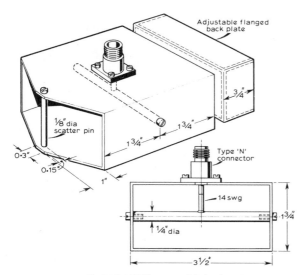

Fig 4.64. 2.3GHz waveguide feed

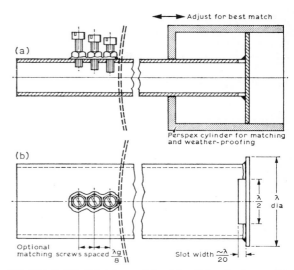

Fig 4.66. Detail of the "penny" feed for dishes having an f/D ratio of 0.25-3. Matching can be done either by matching screws as shown or as in (a) by using a Perspex matching (and weatherproofing) sleeve. (b) Side view of feed

better illuminate a dish if this effect also occurred in the vertical plane. To achieve this a further pair of slots in the same plane are required (above or below).

The feed described is shown in Fig 4.66. It is constructed by cutting two slots at the end of a length of waveguide of suitable size, then soldering on a circular disc. The length and width of the slot formed alter the vswr so they are quite critical. Obviously, care should therefore be taken when cutting and filing the slots to size. It is easy to get a reasonable match over a fairly narrow bandwidth, and it is possible to cover the whole of the 10GHz allocation for example. However, it is recommended that the important area between 10.35 and 10.45GHz is optimised to a very good match.

Values for λ_0 and λ_g at the frequency of interest are given in Table 4.9. Horizontal polarisation is produced when the broad faces of the waveguide are mounted vertically.

A method by which both weatherproofing and matching can be achieved is shown in Fig 4.66. This uses a Perspex sleeve which is a sliding fit on both the disc and the waveguide. By adjusting its position, a proportion of the power may be reflected in the correct phase to cancel the mismatch. The sleeve-to-waveguide gap should then be sealed using a silicone-rubber sealant.

Another method of weatherproofing uses small scrap pieces of Duroid or Cu-Clad printed circuit board, with the copper removed, glued to the waveguide over the slots. In this case the slot length should be reduced by approximately 1mm, depending on the thickness of the pcb. A good match will be obtained if the slot length and the board thickness are chosen correctly. Any plastic material can be used but common plastics generally require to be very thin due to their higher dielectric constant and losses.

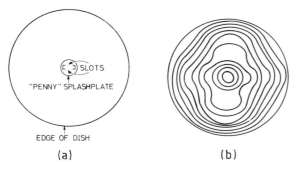

Fig 4.65. Polar diagram of the "penny" feed

Table 4.9

Centre frequency (MHz)	Suitable waveguide	λ_0 (mm)	λ_g (mm)
1,297	WG6	231	324
2,305	WG8	130	162
3,457	WG10	86.7	109
5,761	WG14	52.0	78.2
10,050	WG16	29.8	39.4
10,369	WG16	28.9	37.3
24,193	WG20	12.4	15.2

4.8.14 Periscope or flyswatter antennas

Operating microwave equipment from domestic locations gives rise to new problems especially when mounting the antenna. Waterproofing, feeding to, and receiving power from, the antenna are problematical. Both waveguide and good coaxial cable are very expensive, and even good-quality coaxial is quite lossy (up to 3dB/m at 10GHz) so it should not be used in long lengths for serious operation. Even the better Andrews cable may result in many decibels loss and will be quite hard to handle due to its size and weight. One method for avoiding feeder problems is simply to mount the essential equipment at the top of the mast and feed the dc, af and i.f supplies instead. This approach can still present problems, of course. If the equipment is to be mounted semi-permanently, then weatherproofing will need careful attention. On the other hand, if it is fitted to the mast only when it is to be used, then some ingenious engineering will be required to ensure that this can be done speedily and reliably as a matter of routine. An alternative approach is the "periscope" or "flyswatter" antenna, as it has been dubbed.

An example is shown schematically in Fig 4.67. Although this antenna type is widely used professionally, it had received little attention from amateurs until G3JVL began using one in 1979. In this system, the feed is usually a parabolic dish (although not necessarily so), and this directs a signal upward at a reflector mounted so as to reflect it toward the horizon. The area of the reflector illuminated normally is an ellipse which will ideally have the ratio of the major to minor axes of 1.414:1 if the reflector is set at 45°. An elliptical reflector could obviously be used, but a rectangular one is to be preferred for ease of manufacture and actually produces a little extra gain. However, the shape is unimportant and the dimensions should be chosen to suit available materials. If a non-ideal ratio is used then a non-symmetrical beam shape will be the result. If a longer, narrower reflector is used the vertical beam will narrow and similarly vice versa, if in the other plane.

The reflector may be planar or parabolically shaped, the former case being that most likely to meet home station requirements. Detail of the expected performance is indicated by reference to Fig 4.68. Although interest in this antenna stems from 10GHz operation, it works equally well on other frequencies if the guidelines are adhered to. Fig 4.69 shows the gain of a specified system as a function of frequency.

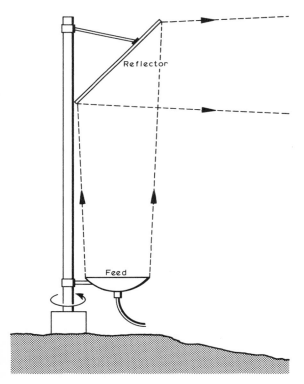

Fig 4.67. Schematic of the "flyswatter" or "periscope" antenna

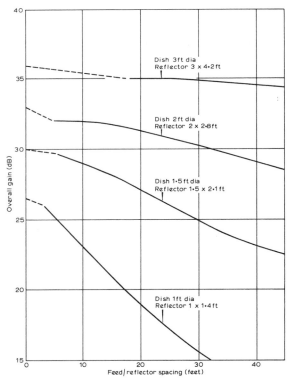

Fig 4.68. Overall gain at 10GHz as a function of dish size, plane reflector same size as dish

It should be considered also for use at some portable sites in order to avoid obstacles like trees or shrubs. A system for portable use may be very much simpler than a home-based version. A standard length of mast at 6m (20ft) with a reflector using flat sheet and stiffened by a bracing structure could be quite useful. The feed dish mounted at the base of the mast may be inside a tent or just above the car roof.

Design data

The generalised data from which the performance can be determined are given in Figs 4.70 and 4.71 for the flat or curved forms. The gain over and above the feed's gain when used with a parabolically shaped reflector is very hard won, and is not worth the trouble that will be needed to get it.

The overall system gain is the important factor and is dependent on the size of reflector used only, when considered at the simplest level. As can be seen from Fig 4.68, the choice to be made after deciding on the size of reflector to be used is what to feed it with.

The parabolic reflector will return a good gain with a small feed antenna but the distance between them is quite critical and rather close. This form of reflector is very much harder to make (Fig 4.72).

The flat reflector, however, can be fed with a dish that has a diameter of around 80 per cent of the reflector's width and will be much less critical as to spacing.

It is, however, possible to get a higher gain from a reflector by using a larger dish to illuminate it. Obviously, it may be impossible to use a larger dish as the feed for mechanical reasons.

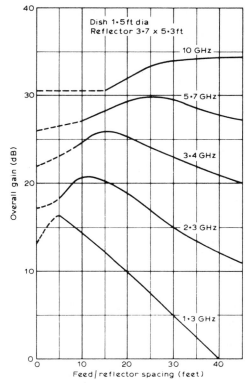

Fig 4.69. Gain of flyswatter as a function of frequency

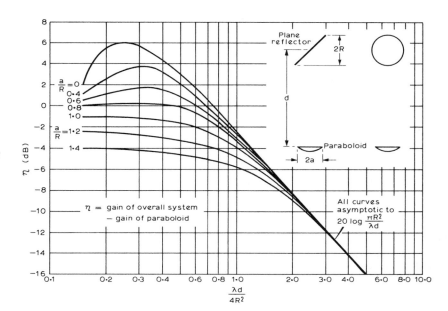

Fig 4.70. Relative gain with planar reflector

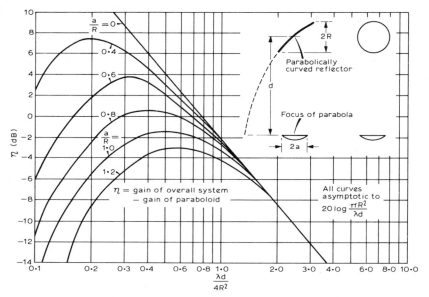

Fig 4.71. Relative gain with a parabolically shaped reflector

4.9 PRACTICAL OMNIDIRECTIONAL ANTENNAS

4.9.1 Omnidirectional horizontally polarised antennas

The slot antenna that has become known in the amateur world as the "Alford slot" actually derives from work by Alan D Blumlein of London and is detailed in his patent number 515684 dated 7 March 1938. The work by Andrew Alford was carried out during the mid-'forties and 'fifties, and not applied to microwave bands but to vhf/uhf broadcasting transmitters in the USA.

G3JVL's development was carried out during 1978 when designs for the GB3IOW 1.3GHz beacon were being investigated. The initial experiment was carried out at 10GHz as the testing was found to be much easier, especially when conducted in a relatively confined space. A rolled copper-foil cylinder produced results close to those suggested in the reference. The work published to date has been confined to the solid cylinder with a slot cut along its length. Models for 0.9, 1.3, 2.3, 3.4, 5.7 and 10GHz have been constructed and performed as expected.

Initially, it was thought that the skeleton version would be best used at the lower frequencies only. However, several models for use on 144MHz have been constructed and performed very well, but the design was at the time not regarded by G3JVL as being of interest. Further developments have resulted in working models being constructed for the 50MHz, 432MHz, 900MHz and 1.3GHz bands. However, some aspects were not easy to explain and valuable assistance was provided by G3YGF. This assistance provided more than just an

explanation for the fact that early skeleton versions worked at a lower-than-designed frequency. A working

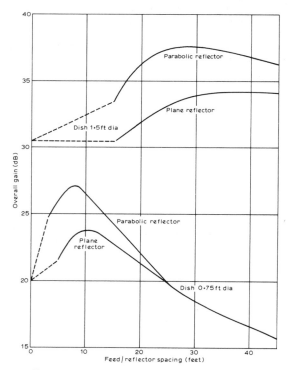

Fig 4.72. Comparison of plane and parabolic reflectors

operational theory was developed as a direct result, along with a better understanding of the strange effects that were observed.

Propagation advantages influenced the RSGB Microwave Committee's decision when insisting on the use of horizontal polarisation. There was a genuine desire to avoid the conflict, experienced at the lower frequencies, while still at the proposal stage of narrow-band microwave beacons and repeaters. The Alford slot was offered as a solution to the objections voiced about the lack of a suitable omnidirectional antenna.

The use of these slots has been further fostered by the current worldwide and rapidly growing interest in atv where the standard polarisation is also horizontal. For mobile use the skeleton version presents lower windage without losing performance, thus having a great appeal. This type does require a little more care during construction and final adjustment, as it has a narrower bandwidth.

Operation

As explained, these antennas are not new. It is well known that a vertical slot in an infinite plate produces a magnetic dipole and has the opposite polarisation to that expected from the physical appearance. It is also true for this type of slot but with the advantage that more gain can be obtained with only small physical differences. This novel feature is due to the ability to make the wave appear to travel along the slot faster than the speed of light.

This results in a field distribution over the slot's length which has the appearance of a dipole but may be many times longer than the free-space half-wavelength value. In this way a net gain, equivalent to that obtained by feeding several dipoles in phase, is obtained but without the need for a complicated phasing harness. The gain obtained is directly proportional to the length of the slot in free-space half-wavelengths. The idea that waves are travelling faster than light would at first sight seem to be impossible, but in fact it is only a standing wave pattern that appears to travel at this speed; the actual wave travels at a lower velocity than that of light. The velocity of the wave along the slot varies with frequency as shown in Fig 4.73.

This is very similar to the effect which occurs in waveguide near its cut-off frequency (F_{co}). The slot behaves like a transmission line shunted by inductive loops (the solid cylinder is equivalent to an infinite number of closely spaced loops). Cut-off occurs when the shunt inductance resonates with the capacitance of the slot. Below the cut-off frequency, waves cannot propagate at all. However, above the cut-off frequency limit, the wavelength eventually returns to the free-space value.

In principle, any velocity factor could be used but the higher the velocity factor, the more critical are the dimensions. Velocity factors of much greater than 10 are impractical for this reason and the normal operating

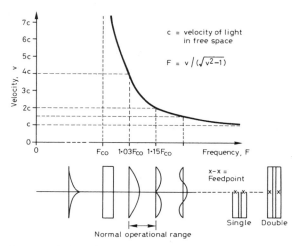

Fig 4.73. Velocity of the wave along a slot antenna as a function of frequency

range is around three per cent to 15 per cent above cut-off, resulting in a velocity factor of between two and six. In the designs previously published the velocity factor has been up to around four. The gain achieved for these dimensions will be about 6dBi for the end-fed version and 8dBi for the centre-fed version. The dimensions are quite interdependent. The velocity factor will be increased by decreasing the tube diameter, or by increasing the slot width. However, the range of tube sizes is rather limited, especially when a high velocity factor is to be obtained. Reference to Fig 4.73 shows the usable range as $1.03 \times F_{co}$ to $1.15 \times F_{co}$, or between the point where the distribution is one or two dipoles across the length of the slot. However, note that the velocity factors indicated are true only when the physical length of the slot is two wavelengths for the double-length version.

It is equally practical to obtain more gain with a longer slot arranged to be within the equivalent limits of one or two dipoles (electrical), but this requires the normal range to move to the left where it is seen that the curve rises steeply, thus limiting the useful frequency range. As the velocity factor increases this range gets narrower. Designs are included which make use of these factors, thus permitting more gain to be obtained, but at the expense of bandwidth and ease of construction. Departure from the recommended dimensions means that to achieve the desired results careful adjustment is essential.

A further limit to the range of overall dimensions permissible is imposed when the deviation from the perfect "omni" pattern is required. The best pattern is obtained when the tube diameter is the smallest but the slot width is then becoming perhaps too small to control. Conversely it becomes much easier to produce the

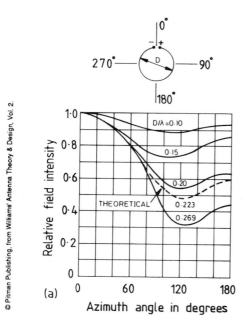

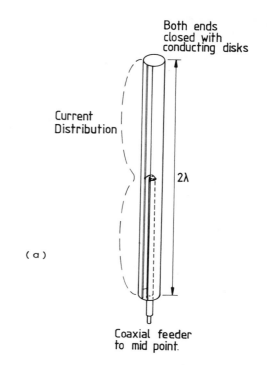

(a)

Both ends
closed with
conducting disks

Current
Distribution

2λ

Coaxial feeder
to mid point.

Vertical Polar Diagram

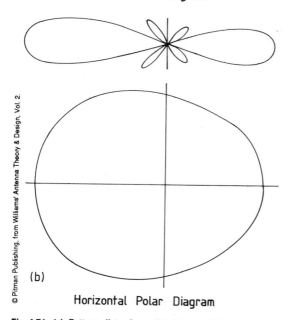

(b)

Horizontal Polar Diagram

Fig 4.74. (a) Pattern distortion related to an Alford slot antenna diameter and slot width (from Antenna Theory and Design, Vol 2, 2nd edn, H P Williams, Pitman, 1966). (b) Polar diagram of an Alford slot antenna

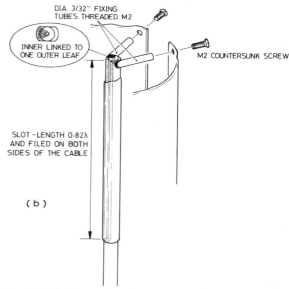

Fig 4.75. (a) Construction of Alford slot antenna using a dual slotted cylinder. The impedance at the feedpoint is 200Ω. Dimensions for 1,296MHz are: slot length 510mm, slot width 4mm, tube diam 31.75mm by 18swg (1.25in). Dimensions for 2,320MHz are: slot length 280mm, slot width 3mm, tube diam 19mm by 18swg (0.75in). (b) Construction of suitable balun

required conditions when the tube is larger and the slot wider. The disadvantage is that the pattern becomes distorted in a manner related to this increase. Fig 4.74 shows the form this distortion takes. It may be that for some applications the less-than-perfect omni pattern will actually be that desired!

When performance is being assessed it must be stressed that vswr and radiation characteristics are not closely related in quite the way that is expected. In practice, primary importance should be placed upon the distribution of the power along the slot and thus the radiation pattern. Then, finally, ensure that a good vswr is presented by some means of matching. For example, the solid-cylinder version normally proves to have a good match to 200Ω (4:1 balun), but the skeleton versions have needed a short matching section. In practice this has been achieved by using two short parallel wires from the slot feed point to the coaxial balun (see Fig 4.75). The wire diameter, length and spacing are used as the final trimming method.

Blumlein pointed out long ago that as the length of an *end*-fed vertically mounted slot is increased, the angle at which the wave is radiated will be increasingly above the horizon. This is due to the power distribution being unequal. Power is radiated as it progresses along the structure. Unless some means of restricting radiation initially is employed, the far end does not receive enough. This problem is avoided by centre-feeding the structure. (Using this method, this effect is thereby compensated for). This is also very likely to be one of the limiting factors in waveguide slot arrays. Centre-feeding the reduced-height waveguide section may prove to be impossible. This may be explained as being due to the reduced power arriving at the more distant slots or slot position.

4.9.2 Slotted-waveguide antennas

This type of antenna [10] is made from rectangular waveguide and consists of a series of resonators (slots) cut into one or both broad faces (see Fig 4.76). If an omnidirectional pattern is essential, reduced-height waveguide is a must: see Fig 4.77(b). The slots or dipoles are required to be parallel with, but alternately offset from, the centre line of the broad face of the guide. This ensures that the phase relationship between adjacent slots is correct. Horizontally polarised radiation is obtained when the slots are vertical. If standard waveguide is used then the pattern shown in Fig 4.77(a) is obtained, having nulls adjacent to the narrow faces. In either case a narrow beam is formed in the vertical plane with the radiation concentrated on the horizon, making this antenna ideally suited to general-coverage beacons. On the lower bands the Alford slot is perhaps more manageable.

Departure from truly circular coverage is mainly dependent on the following factors.

(a) The internal height of the waveguide.

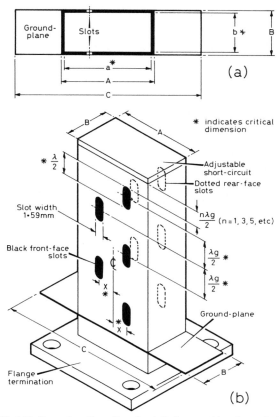

Fig 4.76. General configuration of a slotted waveguide antenna (not to scale). A ground plane is shown in the diagram; this is only needed if the antenna is made from full-height waveguide. If dimension b is 0.1λ or less, the ground plane is omitted but a tapered section (at least 3λ long) from standard-height guide to the reduced section will be required

(b) The thickness of the broad wall material.

(c) Whether the slots are machined in one or both broad faces of the guide.

(d) The accuracy and the relative positioning of the resonators.

The resonator length is related to its width. A convenient ratio is when the width is approximately 1/20th of the waveguide wavelength. The length will then be about $0.85 \times \lambda_0$, the free-space wavelength.

Gain is dependent on the *total* number of slots used on the antenna and also on how the power is distributed between them. An array using 16 slots (ie N = 16) is likely to produce a gain in the region of 10 to 12dB.

Reduced-height waveguide

When both broad faces contain slots the pattern will approach optimum when the height is minimum. The

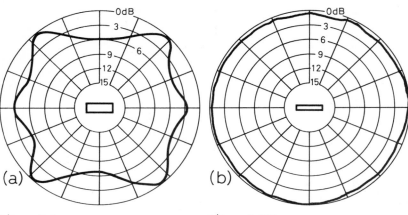

Fig 4.77. Approximate radiation patterns for slotted-waveguide antennas. (a) Full-height waveguide. (b) Reduced-height waveguide

C/λ = 2·0
b/λ = 0·397   Circularity = 6dB

C/λ = 0·794
b/λ = 0·1   Circularity = 1dB

height that can be used is perhaps dictated by the ease of feeding the slots. A value of around 0.1λ is recommended as minimum. Due to power being progressively radiated from each slot the ideal situation is departed from along the length of the array. It would be preferable if the power could be introduced to the slots centrally so as to obtain the best symmetrical pattern. See the discussion at the end of the next section which applies generally.

Standard waveguide

In this case, when both broad faces have slots the pattern is bidirectional, producing a four-leaf clover shaped pattern but with the side nulls being very deep and the front less so.

In practice the perfect field pattern is never achieved even in an amateur installation. The tolerances for instance may be as high as 0.2mm (8/1,000in) and still give an acceptable pattern. In the design example given (for 10GHz), the width used is 1.6mm (1/16in). In practice, the use of a 1.6mm end-mill or slotting drill has yielded acceptable results both at 10 and 24GHz, when combined with the somewhat wider tolerances mentioned.

The gain of an antenna using a total of 16 slots (as in the sample calculation) is 10 to 12dB. In order to benefit from a longer array some steps must be taken to ensure that the power arriving at the furthest elements is still sufficient to allow them to contribute in the correct manner. A possible explanation for this requirement is linked to the findings of Blumlein which show that a long structure, when end-fed, radiates power progressively (exponentially). This causes the angle of the radiated wave to shift away from the perpendicular axis of the slots. To avoid this disadvantage centre-feeding the array is suggested. By combining two half-length sections the problem is greatly reduced by introducing equal but opposite angle shifts on each half. One practical way of achieving this may be to construct

two practical-length arrays and combine them with a two-way power-splitting device. Then with the slot arrays mounted one up and one down. The resulting array will have both increased gain due to using more better-fed slots and also due to the radiation being maintained on the horizon.

Matching from standard waveguide to reduced-height waveguide is achieved by using a tapered section, the length of which is as long as possible, with three waveguide wavelengths being recommended. An alternative would be to include a matching iris or screws. This will produce the same result but over a much-restricted bandwidth. The remote end of the antenna is closed by means of a sliding short-circuit positioned $\lambda/4$ away from the end of the uppermost resonator. The final position may be adjusted on test for best vswr (minimum return loss). It may be advantageous to fit three or four matching screws, spaced approximately $\lambda_g/8$ apart, near the base of the antenna. A combination of adjustment to these screws and the sliding short should then result in a good match. However, please note a good match is *not* a sign of a good performance. A poorly made array is likely to be capable of a good match! The variation in vswr when an object is moved parallel to the polarisation plane will indicate approximately where the power is being radiated.

Design formulae

   N = total number of slots

ie twice the number of slots in one face of the guide, and

$$g = g_1 \times \sin^2(\pi \times x/a)$$

where $g = 1/N$ and x = displacement of slots from centre-line, in millimetres.

   L_0 = free-space wavelength
   L_g = waveguide wavelength
   a = internal dimension of broad face of guide (mm)

b = internal dimension of narrow face of guide (mm)

Note that angular functions are in radians.

Then $g_1 = 2.09 \times (L_g/L_0) \times (a/b) \times \cos^2(\pi \times L_0/2 \times L_g)$

Worked example for 10GHz

L_g (at 10,368MHz)   = 37.322mm
L_0 (at 10,368MHz)   = 28.911mm
N = 16
a = 22.86mm
b = 3.0mm
Slot width = 1.59mm

$$g_1 = 2.09 \times (\frac{37.322}{28.911}) \times (\frac{22.86}{3}) \times \cos^2(\pi \times \frac{28.911}{2} \times 37.322)$$

$$= 2.47$$

Then $1/16 = g_1 \times \sin^2(\pi \times x/a)$

$$= 2.47 \times \sin^2(\pi \times x/22.86)$$

$\sin^2(\pi \times x/22.86) = 0.025$ and $\sin(\pi \times x/22.86) = 0.159$

giving x = 1.16mm (slot displacement).

Slot length = $L_0/2$ = 28.911/2 = 14.46mm
Slot spacing = $L_g/2$ = 37.322/2 = 18.66mm
Spacing of top slot from end of antenna = 45mm (min)

The formulae and calculations given are directly applicable to other waveguide sizes, and antennas for other frequencies and bands can be designed along the same principles. Such an antenna can be mounted within a thin plastic or glassfibre tube for weather protection, and it has been found that such housings have little effect on the radiation pattern of the antenna but do cause vswr changes. This may be compensated for experimentally by either resetting the matching screws or perhaps by altering the design a little to return to optimum performance when the radome or housing is present. Thus the simplest 10GHz beacon could consist of a Gunn or dielectric tuned oscillator coupled directly to a stacked, slotted-waveguide antenna, with both items of equipment housed within the one protective tube and the modulated supply voltage being fed to the oscillator via an ordinary coaxial cable of any convenient length. See the "Beacons and repeaters" chapter in Volume 2.

PCB material version

This will behave in exactly the same manner but ought to be easily reproduced once the exact pattern is determined. A single artwork will be needed to allow the slots to be etched on both sides of a thin double-sided board. The negative can be reversed to provide the other side's pattern. The edges may be connected using copper foil soldered along the edges in the same manner as is used to join ground planes together. The width of the broad face will be reduced by the square root of the dielectric constant as it forms a filled waveguide, and thus will

have the same cut-off with a narrower broad-face dimension.

4.9.3 Slotted waveguide design program

The following program, written in BBC BASIC, enables easy design of slotted-waveguide antennas of the type described in the preceding section and is due to G8AGN.

```
10 REM SLOTTED WG ARRAY DESIGN
20 REM
30 REM C. 1987 B.Chambers G8AGN
40 REM Modified 1987 M.Dixon G3PFR
50 REM
60 @%=&20309:REM set print format to F9.3
100 MODE0
110 PRINT"Slotted waveguide array design program"
120 PRINT"---------------------------------------":PRINT
130 INPUT"Enter centre frequency in GHz ";F
140 RESTORE
150 FOR T=1 TO 6
160 READ WG$,A,B,FL,FH
170 IF F>FL AND F<FH THEN 200
180 NEXT
190 PRINT:PRINT"WAVEGUIDE DATA NOT AVAILABLE FOR THIS FREQUENCY":
      GOTO 310
200 PRINT:PRINT"Recommended waveguide size is WG";WG$
210 PRINT:PRINT"Internal dimensions are :    a = ";A;" ins"
220 PRINT"                                    b = ";B;" ins"
230 PRINT:INPUT"Is this OK ";P$
240 IF LEFT$(P$,1)="Y" THEN T=6:NEXT:GOTO 320
250 PRINT:INPUT"Which size is to be used ";W$
260 RESTORE
270 FOR T= 1 TO 6
280 READ WG$,A,B,FL,FH
290 IF WG$=W$ THEN T=6:NEXT:GOTO320
300 PRINT:PRINT"WAVEGUIDE DATA NOT AVAILABLE"
310 PRINT:INPUT"Enter a and b in inches";A,B
320 A=25.4*A:B=25.4*B
330 L=300/F:LC=2*A
340 LG=L/SQR(1-L*L/(LC*LC))
350 L2=0.5*L:LG2=0.5*LG
360 PRINT:
      INPUT"Enter value for reduced waveguide dimension b in inches
                     (default value is 0.25 of original b)
            ";b$
380 IF b$="" THEN B=0.25*B:ELSE B=25.4*VAL(b$)
385 VDU11:@%=&20409:PRINT"Enter value for reduced waveguide
      dimension b in inches        (default value is 0.25 of
      original b)              ?";B/25.4
390 PRINT:INPUT
      "Enter slot width in inches (default value is 0.0625in.) ";w$
395 IF w$="" THEN W=0.0625 ELSE W=VAL(w$)
400 W=25.4*W:W2=0.5*W
405 VDU11:@%=&20409:PRINT"Enter slot width in inches (default value
      is 0.0625in.) ?";W/25.4:@%=&20309
410 PRINT:
      INPUT"Enter desired vertical 3dB beamwidth in degrees ";BW
412 IF BW=0 THEN VDU11:VDU11:GOTO 410
420 NS=102/BW:NL=INT(NS):BWH=102/NL:NH=NL+1:BWL=102/NH
430 @%=&10:PRINT:PRINT:NL;" slots will give a beamwidth of approx.
      ";INT(BWH);" degs."
440 PRINT:PRINT:NH;" slots will give a beamwidth of approx. ";
      INT(BWL);" degs."
450 @%=&20309:PRINT:INPUT"Enter number of slots ";NS
460 PRINT:INPUT"Is antenna to be semi-omni (1) or omni-directional
      (2) ";NF
470 N=NS*NF
480 G=1/N
490 PRINT:PRINT"Normalised slot conductance = ";G
500 AA=COS(PI*L*0.5/LG)
510 BB=G*L*B/(2.09*LG*A*AA*AA)
520 SD=ASN(SQR(BB))*A/PI
530 PRINT:PRINT"Slot displacement = ";SD;" mm"
540 IF SD<W2 THEN PRINT:PRINT"SLOT DISPLACEMENT TOO SMALL. REDUCE
      NUMBER OF SLOTS";GOTO 410
550 PRINT:PRINT"Slot length = ";L2;" mm"
560 PRINT:PRINT"Centre to centre slot spacing = ";LG2;" mm"
570 PRINT:PRINT"Waveguide internal dimensions are a = ";A;" mm"
580 PRINT:PRINT"                                    b = ";B;" mm"
590 PRINT:PRINT"Nominal bandwidth = +/- ";50/N;" %"
800 @%=&10:REM Reset print format
4990 REM Waveguide data
5000 DATA 10,2.84,1.34,2.6,3.95
5010 DATA 12,1.872,0.872,3.95,5.85
5020 DATA 14,1.372,0.662,5.85,8.2
5030 DATA 16,0.9,0.4,8.2,12.4
5040 DATA 18,0.622,0.311,12.4,18.0
5050 DATA 20,0.42,0.17,18,26.5
5060 END
```

4.10 ALIGNING AND CHECKING ANTENNAS

An antenna may be aligned by using some form of power detector, field-strength meter or receiver, and maximising its output from signals received from a relatively distant transmitter. There are several ways in which this apparently simple task is made difficult. Try to ensure that the antenna responds only to the direct signal from the transmitter, and not to any signals reflected from intermediate objects such as the earth's surface. The choice of the test site is of great importance when trying to avoid this problem. The risk of receiving reflections usually increases as the test antennas are spaced further apart, but also there is a minimum spacing that can be accepted: each antenna should be operating outside their "near field" or within their "far field". This is determined by twice the diameter of the dish (D), squared, divided by λ, ie $2 \times D^2/\lambda$.

When the antenna is of the Yagi type, D should be determined by assuming a value for its gain and converting this to an equivalent dish size by reference to Fig 4.24.

A good test site is one where the test antenna is located on one side of a valley with the transmitter located at a similar height on the other side at less than a mile away, with the valley between broken up by trees, houses or rough ground. When testing high-gain antennas, the transmitting antenna should have at least a comparable performance to minimise unwanted reflections. The effect of reflections is to make the performance appear to be inferior, due to the non-uniform illumination of the test antenna. Ideally the signal received at the test antenna should not change by more than 1dB over more than its capture area. This is true in both planes and is the reason for the suggestion that the valley bottom should be cluttered to prevent or reduce ground reflections causing a vertical pattern of peaks and troughs. If these conditions cannot be realised, then the requirements are altered and the path length should be reduced to the smallest permitted, determined using the equation in [11].

In order to reduce the effect of ground reflections causing changes over the capture area, the signal source should be mounted close to the ground. This ensures that the reflected signal cancels well up from the ground at the test end. Also, if possible, alter the aim of the transmitting antenna, both elevation and azimuth and also the height, to ensure the signal is the greatest possible.

If large antennas and a moderately powerful signal source is used over a short range a diode detector can be used with a sensitive meter. This can be a conventional mixer or detector mount at the higher frequencies. The best indicator to use is a sensitive power meter, as the readings can be taken directly in decibels with good accuracy. However, the results with a diode detector used as described should include an attenuator between the antenna and the detector to minimise the effects of any mismatch. Over longer paths it may be necessary to use a receiver as the detector. Remember that the receiver needs to have a *linear* response, so if an fm receiver is to be used reduce its gain so that limiting does not occur. For a dish, the operations needed to return the optimum gain differ in detail from that required by a Yagi type of antenna.

The dish operations are as follows:

(a) The adjustment of the feed with respect to the dish. This is necessary because there is always some uncertainty as to the precise position of the phase centre of the feed, and possibly that of the focus of the dish. The feed should be adjusted by altering its distance from the dish surface to optimise the received signal and then clamped or soldered in place.

(b) It is not safe to assume that the antenna is free from squint, however accurately it has been made. It must be remembered that the vertical beamwidth of even a small dish may only be very small when used at the higher frequencies. Whereas squint in the horizontal plane (azimuth) is relatively unimportant, a squint in the vertical (elevation) plane will result in a permanent loss. An azimuth error just means the direction to point the dish differs from the mechanically obvious one. On the other hand, an elevation error not observed and corrected may considerably degrade the performance unless a means of controlling its elevation is provided.

Also, it is important to recognise that the axis of rotation should be truly vertical, otherwise the antenna will be tilted with respect to the horizon in some directions of rotation. If a tripod is being used on the higher frequencies the use of a spirit level is recommended to ensure that this problem does not occur.

(c) When checking the gain of an antenna the use of a calibrated attenuator or a power meter is recommended. It is possible to provide a direct measurement of antenna gain by substituting a second antenna of *known* gain and adjusting the attenuator to produce the same detected signal or reading on the power meter. For an antenna of this type, an efficiency of 50–60 per cent of the theoretical value is the normal practical limit. This may be calculated for a dish by using $(\pi \times D/\lambda)^2$. The gain of a conventional pyramidal horn determined from Fig 4.59 can be predicted with sufficient accuracy to be used as a standard. A horn used as a reference antenna is not too large, even at 1.3GHz where a horn with a gain of 10–13dB may be quite easily constructed for this purpose. Horns normally exhibit gains well within a decibel or so of design and across a range of frequencies without the need for matching devices. This can be shown by running the horn design program given earlier.

(d) An invaluable facility is an optical sighting method which may be aligned by sighting the signal source after optimising the received signal. A suitable device can be made using a small-diameter tube which should have cross-wires fitted. With a Yagi array the sighting may be by use of the boom direction. If the signal source cannot be seen directly, use a landmark determined from a map. When this has been done and the sighting device is fixed firmly, then on arriving at a new site the same method may be used and checked by the use of a sighting compass. It is also of very great value to use a fairly local beacon to give a reference direction. If the site is not clear in the direction of the beacon do not be fooled by false headings or even by the broadening effect of a range of hills. It is likely the best signal will be coming from a reflection or just be broadly spread by knife-edge refraction over the top. For this reason it is essential that as many directions as possible be used to check the heading reference. Especially if several beacons are available, the headings to them from a portable location can be determined prior to being on site. But do not ignore the fact that the best signal or even the only signal may be on a wrong heading due to the direct path being blocked.

When this method is employed and an apparently broad heading is observed, the first thoughts are that the high-gain antenna is no better, or it is not working. This is common and it becomes more obvious as the frequency rises due, in part, to the narrower beamwidths obtained with the same physically sized antenna. Also, the objects reflecting signals are bigger in terms of wavelengths and are therefore likely to be more effective. When it is possible to separate these individual sources of reflection, it is perhaps easier to comprehend why gain measurements attempted on this type of signal source produce doubtful results. A high-gain antenna has a narrower beamwidth and therefore sees only part of the "spread out" signal that a wider-beamwidth antenna would receive. The result is that when the two antennas' received signal strengths are compared there may be very little difference. This concept is rather difficult to accept at times.

The way to avoid this is to choose a test site carefully and use it with these difficulties in mind. A short distance of 1 to 2km (around a mile) across a fairly steep-sided valley would be satisfactory.

4.11 ROPES

Rope comes in a wide variety of sizes, materials and forms of construction (known as "lay"). The most popular form is the traditional three-strand variety with a right-hand thread because it is the strongest. It is given a right-hand twist because most people are right-handed and it is their natural tendency to coil the rope in a clockwise direction. Other types include a plaited or braided sheath covering parallel filament cores, the latter being known as "kernmantel" ropes. These have been developed for specific applications, eg rope climbing and abseiling. They do not kink, and the parallel cores give a very low stretch. Before discussing the multiplicity of materials let us be quite clear about its size. In Britain, rope is – or was – traditionally measured by its circumference in inches. This confuses most engineers, who are more used to considering something of round section by its diameter. Very roughly, the diameter of rope is about one third its circumference. So a 3/4in rope is about 1/4in in diameter. Under metrication, however, all this has changed and rope is now measured by its diameter in millimetres, and so a 3/4in rope has become a 6mm rope.

Until comparatively recently, all rope was made of one of several vegetable fibres such as hemp, manilla, cotton or sisal etc. Although these fibres have different characteristics, they all have one failing in common – they absorb water, swelling in both length and diameter in the process, and they are attacked by bacteria and fungi, and therefore rot. For this reason rope was never very popular for use as permanent mast guys as it required continual adjustment and frequent replacement. Guys were therefore invariably made of galvanised wire, although this also eventually corroded, and they also had to be split up into short lengths by insulators to reduce the absorption of rf by resonance.

Modern ropes made from synthetic fibres offer a tremendous advantage in that they do not swell when wet. Also, they resist petrol, oil, acids and alkalis reasonably well and, above all, do not rot. Synthetic ropes are generally much stronger than natural-fibre ropes and are therefore ideally suited for use as guys. However, some modern ropes are degraded by the action of ultra-violet light, and so do eventually rot or lose their strength.

Basically, the principles of ropemaking have not altered for hundreds of years. Threads of the fibre are first twisted into yarns which are then laid together in a spiral twist to form the strand. Finally, the strands (usually three) are laid around each other to complete the rope. This method puts an even load on all parts since all the threads run more or less straight along the direction of the load. Look at a rope and see.

With synthetic fibres, however, there is one important difference. Natural fibres, which make up the basic yarn, occur only in short lengths called "staple" fibre. It is the loose ends of these fibres sticking out of the side of the rope which gives it the familiar "hairy" finish. Synthetic fibre, however, comes in a continuous filament – each one as long as the rope itself. This contributes to the greater strength of synthetic rope and also gives it a much smoother, shinier finish. This can make the rope slippery and difficult to grip, so sometimes the continuous filament is cut into short lengths to resemble staple fibre, thereby giving it the traditional hairy finish. This does weaken it a little, however. The continuous filament also allows the yarns to be plaited or braided. This makes for a kink-free rope (very popular with water skiers and climbers) but it is not as strong as the conventional three-strand construction and it is much harder to splice.

One undesirable feature common to all synthetic rope is the fact that it melts. This is of little significance for most general purposes but it has to be watched very carefully by a seaman when easing a rope round bitts or cleats, or by cavers and climbers on a long abseil. This feature can be turned to advantage, however, as it obviates the necessity of whipping the ends to prevent fraying: a quicker method is to fuse the end in a clean flame, then round off with wet fingers (to prevent it sticking). This is best done before cutting; rotate a 25mm section of rope in a clean flame until fused all round then cut through with a sharp knife when cool. The two jobs can be done in one by using a hot soldering iron (professionals use an electrically-heated knife).

4.11.1 Polyamide

Polyamide filament, of which Nylon is typical, is derived from coal and oil. It was one of the first synthetic rope fibres and is still the strongest. For example, a dry Nylon rope of 8mm diameter (1in circumference) and of conventional three-strand construction (hawser-laid), will break at about 1.32 tonnes (1.3 tons). Commonly white in colour, it tends to be rather hard to handle unless plaited or braided. It absorbs a little moisture and loses about 10 per cent of its strength when saturated. It resists alkalis well but is expensive and is attacked by acids. It melts at around 210 to 260°C.

Nylon's most important characteristic is its very high elasticity, enabling it to stretch up to 20 per cent before breaking. This makes it ideal for use in situations where high shock loads occur and which would normally be unsuitable for supporting a mast; the guys could be tuned under tension like guitar strings but the mast would still wave about like a palm tree. Do not make the common error of referring to all synthetic rope as "nylon". If you ask for Nylon in a ship chandler's, Nylon is what you will get, but it may be useless for your purpose! Nylon is a trade name of Dupont.

4.11.2 Polyester

Polyester filament, of which Terylene is typical, is derived from oil. It is very similar in appearance to Nylon but not quite as strong; the same 8mm (1in circumference) three-strand rope breaks at about 1.016 tonnes (1 ton), but the strength is maintained when wet. In some respects Terylene is the converse of Nylon in that it resists acids well but is attacked by alkalis and stretches very little under load. The small amount of stretch can be reduced still further by a prestretching process during manufacture, making Terylene a virtually non-corrosive substitute for wire with the added advantage of also being non-conductive. Prestretched Terylene is, therefore, the ideal rope to use for mast guys and halyards, but it is also unfortunately the most expensive. It melts at about 250°C.

Terylene is the trade name of ICI. The same material is made in the USA and Germany, where it is called "Trevira", the trade name of Hoechst. To avoid confusion, many rope manufacturers now describe the material simply as "polyester".

4.11.3 Polyethylene

Also derived from oil, this was the first cheap, general-purpose, synthetic rope fibre and is often referred to as "Courlene", which is the trade name of the basic fibre.

In its early days it was always coloured bright orange but it is now available in a variety of colours, including black and white. The fibre, and therefore the rope, is hard, wiry and very smooth; the surface always feels greasy so this rope is easily recognised. It is about 50 per cent stronger than natural-fibre ropes but not as strong as Nylon or Terylene; the 8mm diameter (1in circumference) size will break at about 0.68 tonnes (1,500lb). Under load the stretch is a little less than Nylon but much greater than Terylene. It is very light in weight and floats in water.

When it was first introduced, polyethylene rope became very popular for general use on account of its low cost, the price being half that of Terylene. There are snags, however, the main one being the extreme difficulty in making knots and splices hold securely due to its springy and "greasy" nature. It is still surprisingly popular for use in the manufacture of fishing nets, but for the general purposes its popularity rapidly declined with the introduction of polypropylene.

4.11.4 Polypropylene

This is another oil-derived fibre and the latest introduction into the rope field. It is currently the most-popular, general-purpose rope on account of its excellent compromise with regard to performance and price. It has 90 per cent of the strength of Terylene – the 8mm diameter (1in circumference) size breaks at about 0.91 tonnes (2,000lb) – yet is only half the price. Under load it stretches slightly more than Terylene but nothing like as much as Nylon or polyethylene. It combines the acid resistance of Terylene with the alkali resistance of Nylon. The fibre is a little harder than Terylene or Nylon but not as hard or as slippery as polyethylene. It is light and floats in water. The melting point is low at 165°C, and it is susceptible to attack by ultra-violet light unless stabilisers are added.

When first introduced it was sold under the fibre's trade name Ulstron and coloured green, but it is now available in a wide variety of forms and colours. The basic fibre is commonly a continuous round-section filament about the thickness of a human hair, called "monofilament" in rope form. This form can be twisted into hawser-laid ropes or used to produce braided ropes with a straight-filament core (kernmantel). Cut to resemble staple fibre, this form of fibre is much softer and more flexible than monofilament but is more expensive, due to the extra work involved in its manufacture. The fibre may also be rectangular in section; this is obtained by slitting a flat sheet or film of the material which is then called "fibrefilm". This results in a coarse rope which tends to be rather rough on the hands, but it holds knots and splices much better than any other continuous-filament rope. Staple-fibre rope, produced as described above, has the traditional hairy appearance. Thus, this one basic material can be used to produce several very different types of rope, all with a similar strength.

4.11.5. Wire rope

Wire ropes are constructed in a similar manner to fibre or filament ropes, except that they are made from wire, usually stainless or galvanised steel. Size for size, they have much higher tensile and breaking strengths than ordinary ropes but do need more care and attention in use, and are less flexible and more difficult to handle than ordinary ropes. For permanent installations, use non-stretch types (aero-cable) as they are stronger and less likely to deteriorate if kept well oiled. Use a thick enough rope for guys which, on a typical amateur mast, should be 4mm, the exception being on a tower winch when 5mm or bigger will be required. This size cannot be knotted, so splices, eyes/thimbles or clamps/grips should be used. Beware of rf resonances.

The above are the current most popular ropemaking materials. For amateur use, pre-stretched Terylene, Dacron or Trevira makes ideal guys and halyards but is expensive. As this material suffers less from ultra-violet degradation than most other fibres, its use is especially recommended in those parts of the world which enjoy more than their fair share of sunshine. Nylon is un- suitable for guys but could be used for halyards, al- though this is also expensive. In the UK, Northern Europe and other places which would welcome some more sunshine, monofilament polypropylene is an excel- lent general-purpose rope, equally suitable for use as guys or halyards at a price which will give years of reli- able service at little cost.

4.11.6 Rope accessories

Thimbles

Whenever the end of the rope is formed into a loop to transfer strain to a metal fitting such as a hook, eye-bolt or pulley, it must be protected by a thimble to spread the load correctly and prevent chafe. This is especially important with polypropylene which seems to be par- ticularly susceptible to chafe. Thimbles are commonly pear-shaped troughs of suitable size to take a particular size of rope but they can also be circular for special purposes. They may be made of galvanised steel, stain- less steel or Nylon. The stainless ones are extremely strong and expensive and are usually reserved for use with stainless steel wire. The traditional galvanised ones are "cheap and cheerful"; the finish tends to be rough, which partly defeats their object, and they eventually corrode anyway. They can also set up a highly corrosive electrolytic action if used in contact with a dissimilar metal at sea or in coastal areas. For synthetic ropes, Nylon thimbles are preferred; they cost very little more than the galvanised ones but cannot corrode, cause electrolytic action or damage the fibres.

Thimbles are measured by their overall length but the "score" (width across the trough) is also taken into con- sideration as this must suit the size of rope it is to take. When a thimble is spliced into the end of a rope it is

known as a "hard eye"; without a thimble the spliced loop (eye-splice) is called a "soft eye".

Shackles

These are commonly D-shaped devices (although there are other shapes for special purposes) to link hard eyes, pulleys, eye-bolts, pickets etc. They have been referred to as "nautical safety-pins" and they may be made of galvanised steel, stainless steel, manganese bronze or even Nylon. Like chain, they are measured by the diameter of the bar from which they are formed and can range from 3mm to 50mm or more. In the smaller sizes the diameter of the screwed pin which forms the stroke of the "D" is usually the same as the rounded part but, in the larger sizes, the pin is often one size larger.

Stainless-steel shackles are very strong and last in- definitely, but are extremely expensive and are usually used where expense is no consideration. The galvanised ones are strong and cheap but eventually rust where the plating is worn through at the points of contact. The threaded parts, which cannot be galvanised, quickly seize due to rusting unless treated with a thick grease (preferably anhydrous lanolin) at frequent intervals. Shackles made of manganese bronze are not as strong as those of steel but have the advantage that they cost only a little more than the galvanised ones and do not corrode. Nylon shackles are usually reserved for use with Nylon chain which finds such light-duty applica- tions as mooring marker buoys or marking out exhibi- tion stands etc. The choice usually lies between galvanised or bronze.

The unthreaded end of the pin is flattened and has a small hole in it. It may be tightened by slipping it into the tapered slot in a special key or in the side check of a seaman's knife – not with pliers! Alternatively, the pin may be tightened by passing a thin, hard steel bar, such as a small Allen key, through the hole. However, the main purpose of the hole is to enable the pin to be "moused", ie locked, by twisting wire through the hole and round the bar. For long-term use, especially at sea or in coastal areas, the wire should be of similar material to the shackle to avoid electrolytic action, ie copper wire with bronze shackles and galvanised wire with gal- vanised shackles. Marine-grade stainless steel (EN 58 J) does not cause electrolytic action, so wire of this material may safely be used with any shackle or rigging screw. Any non-corrosive wire such as copper may be used with stainless shackles.

An alternative to conventional shackles is the oval (back-to-back double-D) shaped, screw-gate "maillon rapide", obtainable from climbing and caving shops.

Pulleys

For reliable service in any weather conditions, only genuine marine fittings should be used. They cost some- what more than cheap washing-line pulleys, but are a much better investment as they do not corrode, jam or seize, and need no lubrication or maintenance. Modern marine pulley blocks may be made with synthetic resin bonded fibre cheeks and sheaves and chromium-plated manganese-bronze bearings and straps, or with stainless-steel cheeks and Nylon sheaves. The stainless type costs fractionally more than the other type but there is little to choose between the two in terms of strength and reliability. There is a minimum diameter of sheave for every size of rope and there may be up to three sheaves in one block.

For a simple halyard pulley, a straightforward single-sheaved block will suffice to make up a tackle for raising a mast (or lifting out the car's engine). One of the pair of blocks must be provided with a becket. This is simply a point of attachment below the block for securing the fixed end of the rope. The apparent power gain varies directly as the number of ropes at the moving block. Thus, two single-sheaved blocks, one with becket, will give a 2:1 advantage in one direction and 3:1 in the other. A single and double gives 3:1 or 4:1, and a pair of doubles gives a 4:1 or 5:1 advantage, according to the direction of pull. The term "apparent power gain" is used because power is a function of time and, although a lifting tackle may be rigged to give a 4:1 advantage, it will take four times as long (and five times as much rope) to do the job. In fact about 25 per cent of the advantage will be lost through friction in the sheaves.

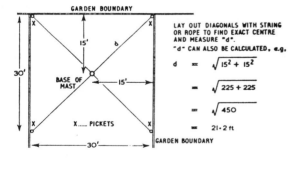

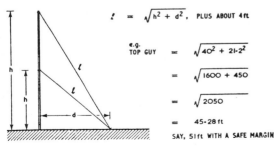

Fig 4.78. The geometry of guys. Above: determining guy layout for a four-guy system in a small garden, using Pythagoras' theorem or by direct measurement. Below: calculating the length of guys using Pythagoras' theorem. Note that the example given (for the longest guy for a 40ft mast) allows an extra 6ft or so for attachment to the picket

Guys

Non-rotting, non-stretching, non-shrinking, non-rf-absorbing Terylene or polypropylene make excellent guys for radio masts. For light masts such as the 30ft by 1in ex-Army type, the 6mm diameter (3/4in circumference) size, with a breaking load of 0.54 tonnes (1,200lb), will probably suffice but for anything heavier, or in case of doubt, the 8mm diameter (1in circumference) size is preferred. This latter size offers an 89 per cent increase in strength for only a 50 per cent increase in cost and is well worth the little extra to sleep peacefully through the winter storms instead of having numerous nightmares about the neighbour's greenhouse. Bear in mind that the Department of Trade and Industry recommends that the maximum working load of a fibre rope should not exceed one-sixth of its ultimate strength. In common with natural fibres, synthetics also suffer varying degrees of degradation from prolonged exposure to excessive ultra-violet radiation so it pays to err on the generous side regarding size and accept the increased strength as a bonus.

It is impossible to lay down any hard-and-fast rules regarding the number of sets of guys or the number of guys to a set, as so much depends on the characteristics of the particular mast and the ground area available. As a rough guide, three guys to a set on a pitch circle with a radius at least equal to one-third the height of the mast is a good basis on which to start where space permits. A thin flexible mast, such as the 30ft ex-Army type mentioned, will require guying every 15ft or so, whereas a sturdy flag-pole may manage with one set at the top only. In theory only three guys per set are necessary but it may be more convenient to use four; a mast at the end of the average rectangular garden can then be anchored to the corners and along the sides.

Guy lengths can be measured by drawing a scale diagram or calculated by courtesy of Pythagoras. As the guy forms the hypotenuse of a right-angled triangle, its length will be the square root of the mast height, squared, plus the distance from the base, squared. Then add about 1m extra for splices and hitches etc. See Fig 4.78.

Guys should not be set up too tightly; once the mast is held in position any further tension simply puts the mast under compression, which tends to make it buckle if it cannot be pushed into the ground. This is why high-stretch ropes like Nylon and polyethylene are unsuitable. As a general rule the guys should look tight but not feel tight. If the mast is to support a wire antenna it should be given a slight rake away from the direction of pull so that the antenna will tend to straighten it. This will obviously put a greater strain on the guys behind the mast, but it should not be possible to provide an accompaniment to the Beatles on them! If the mast is rigid enough to support itself without an antenna, it should only be necessary to use three guys, spaced about 120° apart, at or near the top. Only when the mast load (antenna plus rotator) is very high may it be necessary to

provide a second set near the middle to prevent buckling.

Pickets

Pickets depend a lot on the size and weight of the mast
and antenna, but also on the nature of the ground. As a
general guide, lengths of 50mm outside diameter galvanised pipe driven into the ground, angled away from
the mast and up to 1m deep, will make a good
anchorage. The guy may then be tied directly to the
picket using a round turn and two half-hitches, as the
strain is likely to be at right angles. When all is settled
the surplus rope should be bound to the guy to prevent
any possibility of slip and to tidy the loose end. In soft
ground it may be necessary to back up the picket with a
similar one close behind. Take a stout lashing from the
top of the first to the bottom of the second, or use a
longer picket – if it was easily driven in, then it will be
equally easy to pull out.

Lengths of 50 by 50mm angle-iron also make excellent pickets; a pair of old Vono bed rails can be obtained
cheaply from scrapyards. With the captive bolts cut off
and a 30° cut in the centre of each you have a matched
set of four pickets very quickly. The guys cannot be tied
directly to the angle-iron, unlike tube or rod. However,
in this case a hole should be drilled near the top (with
Vono rails it is already there) and a shackle fitted. If
8mm diameter (1in circumference) guys are being used,
the shackle should be fairly large – say, 8 to 12mm.

The guy is then cut a little shorter than required and a
hard eye spliced in. A lanyard comprised of 2m or so of
3 or 4mm diameter (3/8 or 1/2in circumference) pre-
stretched Terylene is then spliced to the eye and passed
two or three times through the shackle and eye to form
a simple tackle. To spread the load correctly and
prevent chafe, the diameter of the shackle should at
least equal the circumference of the lanyard. Three
turns will roughly equal the strength of the guy, and the
reduction ratio thus obtained will facilitate setting the
tension exactly. This system may look rather crude but it
was universally used for the rigging of sailing ships for
several hundred years (and occasionally still is), and has
proved to be extremely reliable as well as cheap.

Alternatively, if 6mm diameter (3/4in circumference)
guys are being used to support a light mast, the guy may
be passed round a suitable thimble and a smaller
shackle can be used. The loop should be formed with a
rolling hitch; if this is tied correctly with the second turn
jammed inside the first it should be possible to slide the
knot up or down the guy to set the length, but the knot
should not slide down by itself when left temporarily.
When the correct setting has been obtained, a seizing
should be applied close to the thimble to prevent any
possibility of slip.

Pickets can also be obtained in the form of a screw
made from 19 or 25mm (3/4in or 1in) bar. Although not
strong enough to be screwed into chalky or rocky

**Fig 4.79. The bowline is used to form a loop or "eye" near the end
of a rope. It is a very secure knot which tightens under load, after
which it is still easy to untie**

ground, they are easy to use in softer ground and are
ideal for temporary installations. The guys made fast to
an angle-iron picket should use a rolling hitch around a
thimble onto a shackle. An alternative method of securing a guy to an angle-iron picket is by means of a lanyard
and large shackle.

A rope under tension contains energy; if it snaps, this
energy is suddenly released and can cause the rope to
"whip up". If there is a chance that this might happen,
do not stand where the face or other exposed parts of
the body could be hit.

For further information on ropes the reader should
refer to manufacturers' literature and, for more detail
on rope accessories, terminology and rigging, to any
good nautical manual.

4.12 KNOTS

A wide variety of knots have been developed for a range
of applications. It is not often appreciated that each type
of knot has its limitations, and it is worth learning a
limited number of knots to cover the most common
applications. The very popular reef knot is *not* suitable
for most of the applications discussed here.

Knots can be considered to be of two basic types:
"bends" for joining rope to rope, and others for joining
a rope to a spar or eye. Splicing is the best method of
joining ropes which are hawser laid. It does not greatly
increase the diameter of the rope and does not reduce
the strength.

The *bowline* is a useful knot, especially for tying
around a post or eye. It is particularly easy to untie even
after carrying a heavy load. The bowline is shown in Fig
4.79.

The *Carrick bend* is essentially two bowlines, and is a
good method of joining ropes of similar diameter.

The *half-hitch and clove hitch* (Fig 4.80) is also a
simple secure knot for tying around a pole or post where
the strain is at a near right angle. It is simply two half-
hitches back to back.

Fig 4.80. The half-hitch (left) is a very simple "knot", usually used as a very temporary measure before tying a more reliable knot such as the clove hitch (right)

The *rolling hitch* (Fig 4.81) is a development of the clove hitch with two turns before the cross-over instead of one. It should be used when the strain is more-or-less in line with the pole against the two-turn end. If tied on to a rope (either itself or another rope) the second turn should be jammed inside the first on the right.

The *round turn and two half-hitches* (Fig 4.82) is the basic knot for making fast to a post where the strain is at a near right angle. It is very secure, quickly and easily tied and is one of the few knots which can be tied while there is a strain on the standing part. The two half-hitches actually form a clove hitch.

The *fisherman's bend* or *anchor bend* (Fig 4.83) is a variation in which the first half-hitch is taken inside the round turn. It is even more secure than the basic round turn and two half-hitches but it cannot be tied under load and is difficult to untie. It is ideal for permanently securing a pulley to the branch of a tree. For more details of these and other knots, splicing, whipping and other rope-management techniques, the reader is again referred to any good nautical manual.

4.13 HOW TO GET THE BEST FROM YOUR ROPES

Splicing man-made fibre cordage

Man-made fibre ropes may be satisfactorily spliced in the normal manner. However, owing to the larger number of filaments in each yarn and their smooth surface, particular care must be taken to maintain the form and lay of the strands. This can best be done by the use of light seaming twine applied in a series of temporary seizings around that part of each strand which has been unlaid for splicing. Five full tucks should be made.

Fig 4.81. The rolling hitch is a development of the clove hitch, with two turns before the crossover instead of one. It should be used when the strain is more-or-less in line with the pole against the two-turn end

Fig 4.82. The round turn and two half-hitches is the basic knot for making fast to a post where the strain is at a near right angle. It is very secure, quickly and easily tied, and one of the few knots which can be tied when there is strain on the standing part

Pulleys and sheaves

The radius of the groove of a pulley should always be slightly larger than that of the rope passing over it. The groove of the pulley or sheave should support a third of the rope's circumference. For the best effect, the pulley diameter to rope diameter ratio should be a minimum of 5:1 for fibre cordage and 12:1 for wire rope. Lubricate the bearings of sheaves at frequent intervals. A seized-up sheave can ruin a rope very quickly.

Keep them clean

Remove dirt, grit and any other sharp particles that may have become embedded in the rope. These could cause internal wear. Wash thoroughly with clean, fresh water and allow to dry in a natural atmosphere. Do not use detergents on ropes of, or containing, natural fibres, although mild detergent may be permissible with wholly synthetic ropes. If in doubt, refer to the manufacturer's recommendations.

Inspection of splices (water trap)

It is good practice periodically to remove the servings from wire rope splices to enable an inspection of the splice to be carried out, as water can be very easily trapped here. If the splice is sound and not corroded, re-grease, parcel and serve.

Abrasion/chafe

All cordage, both of natural and man-made fibres, will deteriorate rapidly if unduly abraded by rough surfaces. Fairleads, bitts, winch and capstan barrels should be regularly examined to ensure that their condition is satisfactory. At points where contact with rough surfaces cannot be prevented, the rope should be protected by parcelling or by the application of a leather sheath/plastic hose. Ordinary usage will cause polyester and Nylon ropes to acquire a slightly fluffy appearance. This is due to minor filamentation of the outer surface of the rope. It is not harmful to the main structure of the rope, in fact it provides additional protection against abrasion. It should be noted that ratchet blocks and winches with knurled surfaces will cause excessive wear.

Stow away from heat

Ropes and cordage should be stowed away from hot pipes, boilers and all forms of excessive heat. Man-made fibres are no exception to this rule – they can, however, be stowed wet as they are entirely water and rot proof. Take care not to damage the standing part when heat-sealing rope.

Uniform wear

In certain applications, some parts of a rope are subjected to more use and wear than others. In such cases it is often possible to change the position of the rope periodically, thus ensuring uniform wear. By having the rope a foot or two longer and changing position periodically, prolonged life may be obtained.

Keep away from chemicals

All types of ropes should be protected from chemicals. Although Nylon ropes are resistant to alkaline attack, they are subject to acid attack and it is far wiser to avoid contamination by *any* corrosive substance. Similarly, polyester rope is resistant to acid attack but susceptible to alkaline attack: the same rule applies.

Starting a rope on a drum

If choice permits, when starting a new rope on a smooth faced drum, start a right-hand lay rope from the right flange of an underwind drum or from the left flange of an overwind drum. (Directions are for a position behind the drum with the rope leading away from you.)

Kinking

If a rope develops kinks, it is an indication that it has been badly handled. In such cases, care should be taken to remove the cause of the trouble. This is usually associated with excess turn.

Uncoiling fibre rope

Avoid kinking when taking cordage from a coil. Most ropes are right-hand laid and should be uncoiled in a counter-clockwise direction. The starting end of a coil made by British Ropes Ltd is tagged with an appropriate label.

Fig 4.83. The fisherman's bend or anchor bend is a variation of the round turn and two half-hitches, in which the first half-hitch is taken inside the round turn. It is even more secure, but cannot be tied under load and is difficult to untie. It is ideal for securing a pulley to the branch of a tree, for example

Uncoiling wire rope

Treat it like a hose. A light coil of wire rope may be unrolled along the ground, but it should be kept under control. Under no circumstances should the end be drawn from a coil lying on the ground. If not handled correctly kinks will form.

Preventing distortion

When a tower is fully hoisted it is always the same portion of the halyard that bears on the masthead sheave/block. A tight serving, at this point, will prevent flattening and distortion.

Care of wire rope

Before being reeled or coiled for storage, wire ropes should be cleaned with a wire brush, and then given a coat of wire rope dressing, obtained from a chandlers' store.

Palm and needle whipping

It is advised that this method is used for all braided or plaited rope whipping. As a rope will reduce its circumference under load it is necessary to finish the whipping with over-stitches with a palm and needle to prevent the whipping from sliding out of position during load.

Whipping the braidline splice

The whipping should be made between the buried crossover point and the neck of the splice. If a thimble is fitted it should be as near the neck as possible.

1. Using a needle, sew through the rope to form an anchor for the tail of the whipping cord.

2. Bind the rope tightly for four or six turns.

3. Pass the needle through the rope close to the last turn.

4. Over-stitch three or four times and anchor end.

4.14 MECHANICAL ASPECTS OF MASTS

4.14.1 Loadings

There are basically three types of forces to be considered when designing masts:

1. Dead loading, which consists of the downward static forces on the mast, eg the weight of the poles and of antennas on it.

2. Wind loads, which are lateral forces due to wind drag on the structure. They are proportional to the cross-sectional area of the structure and the square of the wind speed. If any parts of the system can vibrate, these drag forces may excite such vibrations, eg halyards flapping on flag poles. The amount of energy transferred from the wind into such resonances can be sufficient to cause failures, eg vibration and eventually the fracture of Yagi booms.

3. Dynamic loads, which are caused by acceleration or deceleration of the structure – examples of these are suddenly stopping when raising or lowering a mast, and starting or stopping rotation of a beam. In another context, while towing a vehicle, if the slack is taken up very suddenly the load in the rope can be many times the weight of the towed vehicle.

The design must therefore cater for all three of these loads. For example, when a mast is being lowered and for some reason suddenly stopped, the forces to decelerate the mast also have to be absorbed by the guys.

4.14.2 Structural failure

Structural failure may be caused by tensile, brittle, fatigue or corrosive effects. Failures in structures such as amateur masts are unlikely to be due to direct stress.

A properly guyed mast is an extremely strong structure, and will probably fail due to something like pickets or guystakes pulling out, knots coming undone, shackle

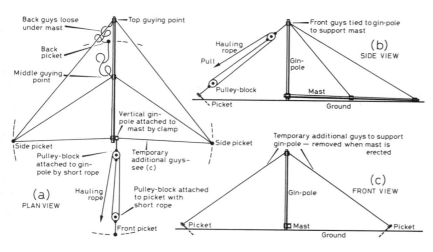

Fig 4.84. Use of a gin pole in erecting a mast. (a) Plan view of mast lying on ground, ready for hauling. The dotted lines show the approximate radius of guy pickets, the mast base being at the centre of the circle. More than two guying levels may be needed for a long mast. Note: back guys lie loose under the mast but attached to back picket. (b) Side view, showing front guys tied to gin pole to prevent mast sag. (c) Rear view

pins or bolts working loose, corrosion or chafing etc. Any such defect may allow excessive movement or bending, and that movement may lead to failure.

In such slender structures, the guys often carry very little load, but are essential to keep the geometry of the mast correct – the antenna's weight is carried almost entirely by the mast. The main forces the guys have to carry are horizontal forces due to wind loads, and the quite high loads during the erection.

Once the mast is up, there should be *just* sufficient tension in the guys to prevent the mast from swaying sideways – any further tension just increases the compressive load in the mast.

4.14.3 Buckling

This is a problem which occurs if the mast is not guyed at a sufficient number of points along its length.

Short masts are quite straightforward – they are anchored at the bottom and self-supporting. The main criteria are that the mast should be unable to sway sideways by much when subjected to wind loads and that, having swayed sideways, its dead weight should not make it bend any further.

For a taller or a free-standing mast, it is necessary to keep it vertical with guys near the top. Taller masts or those with greater dead weight at the top will show a tendency to bend out sideways and buckle. A small amount of bending is not serious but, if it becomes excessive, it can become catastrophic, as the load the mast can support will decrease as it bends into a U- or S-shape.

This effect is very noticeable with alloy scaffold poles, as they can bend considerably without deforming. They are also considerably lighter than steel scaffolding. However, steel scaffolding is much more rigid. It will suffer permanent deformation for fairly small amounts of bending but will require much more force to do so.

The weak points are close to the joints in a tubular mast assembly. Thus it is sensible to fit additional guy sets at or near these points. To determine whether the mast is guyed at a sufficient number of points to reduce sideways deformation, look up the mast after erection; any deformation should be immediately obvious.

In practice, the suitability of the guy spacing can be assessed during erection when using the gin-pole method, by subjecting the assembly to stress by shaking the mast when it is just beginning to lift. The stability of the assembly will become fairly obvious and the tendency to buckle will show when the assembly is deliberately subjected to these conditions. In this position, there is considerably more compressive load in the mast than when it is in the normal vertical position.

A gin pole is a mast section of about one-third the full height of the mast but mounted at right angles using a coupling device at the base as indicated in Fig 4.84. When the mast is on the ground the gin pole will be in a vertical position and held in position by the normal guys set to the correct final length. The gin pole is used to

raise the main mast, by ensuring that the hauling forces are applied at the correct angle.

The amount of bending depends on dead load, mast stiffness and the unguyed length. When a large load is to be raised (big antenna array) it is recommended that a multi-pulley reduction system is used or even a winch.

The number of guys per set can be three or four. Three are often used for simplicity and this is quite adequate. However, using four greatly simplifies and enhances safety during the process of erecting a mast but it does not protect against the failure of a guy rope.

4.14.4 Erecting a mast

The mast is usually at its most vulnerable when it is being raised or lowered. It is for this reason that the

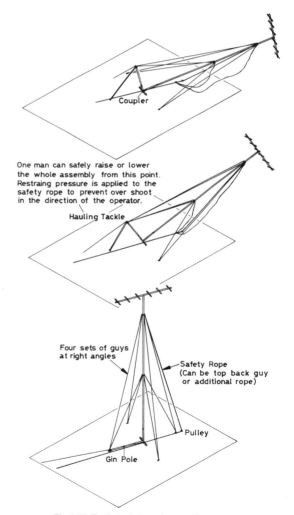

Fig 4.85. Basic technique for erecting a mast

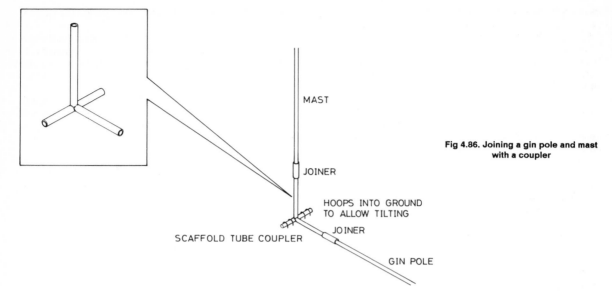

MAST

JOINER

HOOPS INTO GROUND
TO ALLOW TILTING

JOINER

SCAFFOLD TUBE COUPLER

GIN POLE

Fig 4.86. Joining a gin pole and mast
with a coupler

four-guy method is most strongly recommended, particularly for masts needing more than one set of guys. This will be borne out by anyone who has tried the method of having one person hold each of the three guys, and tried to co-ordinate them to prevent the mast from bowing.

The four-guy method allows the mast to be kept guyed straight at all times during its erection to prevent it bowing, and the mast can be left safely at any stage of the erection while any problems are sorted out. These are usually due to coaxial cables being caught or fitted wrongly. This method makes it quite possible for one person to safely raise and lower the system during assembly. The basic technique is shown in Fig 4.85.

The method works best on flat ground, so that all the stakes and the base of the mast are in the horizontal plane. However, it can still be used, provided that the mast is pivoted up in a plane that is perpendicular to the ground, so that the side guys are always tight. If the mast is to end up vertical, this means in practice that the mast must point straight up or down the steepest sloping direction.

Preparation

Prepare a scale drawing of the mast and antennas in plan and elevation. Draw in the guys so that they do not foul when the antenna is rotated through 360°. This provides a way of defining the radius required for the pickets or guy stakes.

Assembly

1. Choose the position for the base of the mast, then insert pickets or guy stakes at the predetermined positions. Their distance from the base of the mast can be

set by using a length of rope tied to the base to define the radius of the circle.

2. Ensure that the stakes are in line by sighting to a marker showing the position of the base of the mast.

3. Do this in both directions after ensuring that the second pair are at right-angles to the first pair.

4. Lay out the mast on the ground, along one of the guy lines.

5. If the ground is sloping in one direction, lay the mast pointing uphill.

6. Insert stakes at the base pivot to prevent it from moving.

7. Attach guys to the mast.

8. Attach the side and back guys to the stakes.

9. Lay the gin pole out along one side guy and attach its guys.

10. Attach the front guys to the gin pole.

11. Erect the gin pole and clamp it to the mast's base. It is highly recommended that a mast-coupling device is used for this purpose (see Fig 4.86).

12. Attach the gin pole side guys to the stakes.

13. Attach a pulley system to the front stake.

14. It is strongly recommended that the mast be raised at this stage to check all is well before mounting the antennas on it.

15. Use pulleys to lift mast a few feet off the ground, and secure the hauling rope.

16. Mount the antennas on the mast.

17. Check the balance; the mast should be straight, or slightly sagging.

18. Hoist up to vertical using a rope and pulley system. It is *very important* to keep the middle back guys in tension by pulling on them to prevent the mast bowing upwards. The gin pole will now be lying on the ground. This can be a serious problem if there is a heavy array on the mast, or if the gin pole is too short for the mast. Either results in very high compressive loads in the mast which increases the risk of it buckling upwards. The load is greatest when the mast is only a few degrees off the ground. The top guys should be as close as possible to the centre of mass of the antenna array to avoid introducing any additional bending forces in the mast.

19. Anchor the gin pole to its stake. If the gin pole is not the same length as the guy pitch circle radius it will be necessary to move the top guy out to its own picket or stake.

One of the great advantages of this method is that the structure is always under positive control, and so the process can be temporarily halted with the mast at any position and, provided the back guys are tied off, it can be left there quite safely. Lowering is just as simple as it is the reverse of this erecting process.

Using the procedure described here it is possible to put up quite large arrays at reasonable heights using aluminium scaffold poles.

For serious operation, the use of scaffold pole is strongly recommended as it is very robust, and a comprehensive range of couplers and fittings are available. However, if suitable joiners are available or can be made, the top section can use lighter gauge. This lowers the centre of gravity without weakening the structure. "D" shackles may be used on ropes which have to be released frequently, but whose length must remain the same.

If required, a rotator can be fitted a few feet from the bottom of the mast to keep the dead weight low down. This is necessary anyway if large antenna arrays are to be used. The only extra complexity is that rotating guy rings are then needed.

Bowlines are very strongly recommended for tying off to shackles etc, as they are easy to release even after carrying a load.

Clove or rolling hitches are fine for tying onto poles, provided there is something to stop the knot sliding along the pole. They are also good for tying guys to stakes, as it is quite easy to feed rope through them to adjust their length. It is probably a good idea to put a couple of half-hitches in the free end of the rope as a safety measure if it is to be left for a long period. If the array is permanent the use of multistrand steel wire is recommended. Avoid standing underneath the mast while it is being erected; the back guys can be fixed at the correct length to allow this. The front guy is attached to the gin pole so there is no need to be within the area marked by the stakes. Haul on the rope and pulley-set until the gin pole is lying on the ground, then secure the gin pole to the stake or take the front guy to the stake. (The best arrangement is when the gin pole length is the same as the stake-to-mast distance.)

If you must stand underneath, wear a hard hat. Keep a sharp eye and alert ear for anything unusual, and be prepared to take avoiding action.

4.14.5 Telescopic/tilting towers

These generally do not need guying, but one set of guys at the top will take a great deal of the wind-loading effects off the tower. The stress on the base will be considerably reduced when subjected to bending moments due to wind loading, which will be opposed by at least one guy and at a much smaller angle from horizontal (plane of the wind), thus reducing the internal stresses applied to the structure.

The forces involved in the winch cables when tilting the tower over are quite large, particularly with a large antenna array, and should be treated with due respect. Once up, most towers have some form of mechanical latch to carry the vertical load and to take the strain off the cable.

You should *never* climb the tower, relying solely on the winching cable to support it. As an additional precaution the latch and a short piece of angle iron or scaffold pole should be put through the tower just below the bottom of each section – this may also be used if you do not want the tower fully extended.

The winch wire used should be a flexible steel wire. It is similar in appearance to the guys but has many more strands of finer wire. These wire ropes are subject to severe loading, and should be inspected regularly for signs of fraying or broken strands. They sometimes pass over rough edges or round sharp bends – these are all sources of stress.

Winches with a removable ratchet for unwinding can present a hazard if the handle slips out of your hands while there is a load on the winch – the handle will spin round at high speed, and can do serious damage. You should use it very carefully, using both hands, and if you do let it slip, do not try to grab hold of it again. An emergency braking system is a wise investment to assist under such conditions. However the brake should not be the type that puts on a very sudden load. A system using a strong slipping clutch is to be favoured.

4.15 SUMMARY AND CONCLUSION

This chapter has tried to summarise the configuration and design principles of the most commonly used types of microwave antenna. Practical antennas for amateur use have been examined in some detail and microcomputer design programs given for most of the types discussed. Finally, some consideration has been given to masts and rigging used to support antennas.

It is stressed that a good antenna, ie one having high gain and a good radiation pattern, can make or break the performance of any microwave station. Use of such high gain with the associated narrow beamwidths leads to a need to point antennas accurately in the right direction. This aspect of antennas has been covered in Chapter 2.

4.16 REFERENCES

[1] "High performance long Yagis", Ian F White, G3SEK, *Radio Communication* April 1987, pp248–252.

[2] "Yagi antennas", Gunter Hoch, DL6WU, *VHF Communications* 9 (March 1977), pp157–166, UKW Berichte.

[3] "A new method of obtaining maximum gain from Yagi antennas", H W Ehrenspeck and H Poehler, *IRE Trans on Antennas and Propagation* October 1959, p379.

[4] "LONG long Yagis", Kmosko, W2NLY, and Johnson, W6KQI, *QST* January 1956.

[5] "Yagi antenna design", P P Viezebicke, *NBS Technical Note 688,* December 1976.

[6] "How to design Yagi antennas", J H Reisert, W1JR, *Ham Radio* August 1977, pp22–30.

[7] "Notes on the development of Yagi arrays", C Greenblum, *QST,* and other ARRL publications, edited by Ed Tilton, W1HDQ.

[8] "Extremely long Yagi antennas", G Hoch, DL6WU, *VHF Communications* 14 (March 1982), pp131–138. Also "More gain from Yagi antennas", *VHF Communications* 9 (April 1977), pp204–211.

[9] "Designing paraboloids", T C Jones, G3OAD, *Radio Communication* April 1971.

[10] "X-band omnidirectional double-slot array antenna", T Takeshima, *Electronic Engineering* October 1967, pp617–621.

[11] "Antenna performance measurements", R Turrin, W2IMU, *QST* November 1974.

[12] "Ropes and rigging for amateurs – a professional approach", J M Gale, G3JMG, Radio Communication March 1970, pp144–152.

CHAPTER 5

Transmission lines and components

5.1 INTRODUCTION

Probably the most fundamental distinguishing characteristic of microwave circuitry is that the dimensions of the components are of the same order as the wavelength of radiation. This means that transmission lines at microwave frequencies are used not just to carry signals to and from the antenna as at lower frequencies – the majority of components are actually made from, or built inside, sections of transmission line. The whole subject of transmission lines is therefore of great importance in understanding microwave components, devices and techniques.

In contrast to lower frequencies, where coaxial cable (and occasionally twin-wire transmission line) are the only common types of line used, there is a much wider

(a) Coaxial

Outer conductor (usually covered with protective jacket)

Inner conductor

Dielectric filling (eg Polythene)

(b) Waveguide

Hollow solid conductor (air dielectric)

(c) Stripline

Metallic ground planes

Conductor

Dielectric filling

(d) Microstrip

Dielectric insulator

Conductor

Conductive earthplane

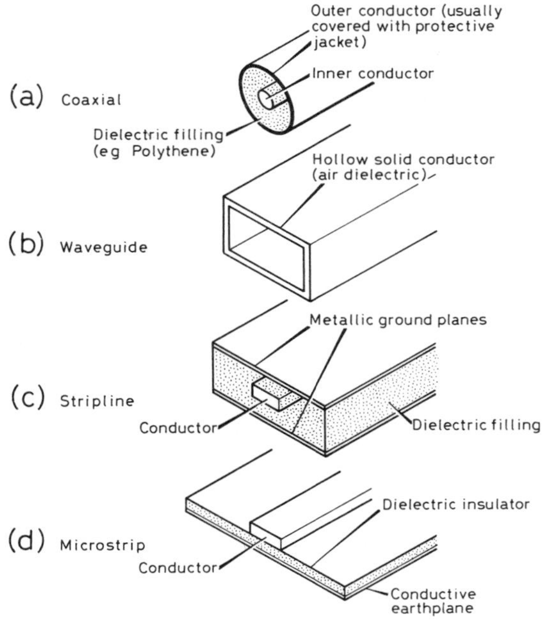

Fig 5.1. Common types of transmission lines

variety of transmission-line media used at microwave frequencies; certainly much more than the rectangular waveguide conventionally associated with microwave "plumbing"! These include certain types of coaxial line (usable to 18GHz and beyond), circular and elliptical waveguide, stripline and microstrip, and various millimetre-wave transmission lines including finline. Some common transmission lines are illustrated in Fig 5.1.

This chapter sets out to introduce the various types of lines and passive components used at microwave frequencies, and to give an explanation of how they work. Many of these are peculiar to microwaves and much of the fascination and challenge to the amateur is related to their exploitation. Indeed some microwave techniques are closer to optics than to rf. Antennas have already been covered in the last chapter, and filters are covered in a separate chapter in Volume 2. Semiconductor and valve devices are covered in the next chapter.

The treatment is at a fairly basic level with an emphasis on the practical aspects and a minimum of mathematics, though references are given where appropriate for those seeking a more complete treatment or further background reading. In addition, a considerable amount of practical advice on the use of different types of transmission lines and connectors is also given.

5.2 BASIC THEORY OF TRANSMISSION LINES

A transmission line is any structure which guides electromagnetic energy along itself, and in reality an enormous variety exists. It can be either conductive, eg coaxial, open-wire feeder and metallic waveguide, or dielectric, eg fibre-optic cables, dielectric rod and atmospheric ducts caused by temperature inversions.

In all cases, energy is carried by varying electric and magnetic fields which have instantaneous values, which are functions of both position and time. The most fundamental properties of a transmission line, common to all types, are the characteristic impedance, attenuation and velocity of propagation.

The characteristic impedance is a function of the geometry of the line and the dielectrics used within it. In

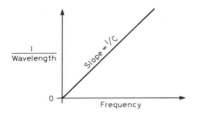

Fig 5.2. Wavelength against frequency for a non-dispersive line

the case of coaxial lines, it represents the ratio of the voltage across the line to the current in each conductor. In the case of a waveguide, it represents the ratio of E-field to H-field strengths. Its absolute value is often not important, but variations along a line are usually undesirable.

Losses in a line can occur either in the series resistance of the conductors or in the dielectric between them. In some types of line where the fields are not contained inside a metallic screen, eg open-wire feeder, losses can also occur due to the field radiating energy into space.

Fields in transmission lines, like those in free space, cannot travel faster than the velocity of light c, which is 3×10^8 m/s. In a simple coaxial line with air dielectric, the fields travel at this speed, but in practice most cables are filled with dielectric and consequently the fields travel more slowly. The velocity is about 0.7c for ptfe or polythene dielectric.

While it is simple to measure voltage and current on lines such as coaxial or twin wire, this is not really possible with either metallic or dielectric waveguides. For this reason, power is the simplest quantity to measure.

5.2.1 Modes

There are a number of ways that energy can propagate down any transmission line – these are referred to as "modes". A mode describes the pattern in which the field strength varies across the transmission line. Normally only one mode exists in a well-designed transmission line; this is known as the "dominant" mode. However, if the transverse dimensions of the line are large enough, usually greater than about a half-wavelength, a variety of patterns can exist. Common

modes are illustrated for each type of line later in this section. A more comprehensive set is included in the "Data" chapter in Volume 2.

Higher-order modes can be thought of as resulting from giving the wave room to propagate across as well as along the line. In general, if it is theoretically possible for more than one mode to exist, then the performance of the line may be unpredictable. This situation is best avoided as any discontinuities in the line may generate other modes.

Modes can be divided into two types – tem and non-tem. "TEM" stands for "transverse electric and magnetic wave", as both the electric and magnetic field components are always at right angles (transverse) to the direction of propagation. The tem mode requires at least two separate conductors and therefore cannot exist in waveguides. In general, tem lines are quite straightforward and simple to analyse. The properties of non-tem lines may be frequency dependent and so are much more complex. Examples of tem lines are coaxial and stripline; examples of non-tem lines are waveguide and microstrip.

In most microwave lines, there is usually only a possibility of one or two modes existing. However, in optical fibres whose dimensions can be many hundreds of wavelengths across, the mode pattern across the fibre might consist of a random "speckle" pattern of thousands of dots which change randomly with time or movement of the cable.

5.2.2 Dispersion

If the propagation velocity varies with frequency, then the line is said to be "dispersive". This means that if pulses of different frequency were simultaneously sent off down the line, after a while they would each have travelled different distances, or dispersed.

Most coaxial and twin-wire lines are examples of non-dispersive lines. Small amounts of dispersion can arise from changes in dielectric properties with frequency; much larger ones can be caused by resonant or periodic structures in the line. Waveguides are a good example of dispersive lines.

One way of illustrating these properties is to plot the wavelength against frequency, as shown in Fig 5.2. In this graph the vertical scale is the reciprocal of λ, being the number of cycles per metre, also known as the "wave number". In non-dispersive media, such as free-space propagation and most coaxial or twin-conductor lines, this graph is a straight line whose slope is related to the velocity of propagation, ie:

$$c = F \times \lambda$$

An example of this plot for a dispersive line such as waveguide is shown in Fig 5.3. This only propagates frequencies above a certain frequency, the "cut-off" frequency. At frequencies well above the cut-off, the graph is very similar to the previous diagram, ie the properties of the guide are similar to free space. However, as you

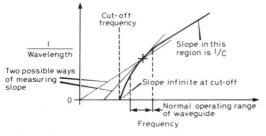

Fig 5.3. Wavelength against frequency for a dispersive line

approach the cut-off the wavelength is longer than before, and at the cut-off frequency the wavelength becomes infinite. The guide cannot propagate waves in the conventional sense at frequencies below this; the fields are then what is known as "evanescent". This is a non-propagating field which decays exponentially with distance, an effect used in piston attenuators and some special types of microwave filter.

The problem that now arises with a dispersive line is that there are two possible slopes on the graph at any point – one is the line from the origin to the point, and the other the tangent to the curve at the point. These two had the same value for the non-dispersive line, but are now different. What does this mean in practice? Well, it is possible to measure the velocity of propagation in two ways:

1. Measure the distance between adjacent peaks or troughs in the field at any instant. This could be said to be the distance that the wave has travelled during the period of one cycle. The time taken to travel this distance is one period of the frequency of the wave. Thus velocity = distance/time. This gives what is known as the "phase" velocity, since you are effectively observing a point at a particular phase on the sine wave, and seeing how far it travels in a known time.

2. Another approach is to produce a pulse of rf with a very fast rise time, and measure how long it takes to travel down a known length of cable. Again, velocity = distance/time. This is known as the "group" velocity, as you are taking a specific group of cycles of the wave, and timing them over a known distance.

The reason for these two velocities can be illustrated by considering how waves propagate in waveguide. Fig 5.4 shows three different frequencies being sent down a rectangular waveguide. In Fig 5.4(a) the frequency is much higher than cut-off, and the waves, being much shorter than the dimensions of the guide, travel in almost straight lines down its centre. The phase and group velocities are nearly equal to the free-space values.

If the frequency is, say, a factor of two above the cut-off frequency, the waves can be thought of as bouncing off the sides of the guide in a zig-zag course, as in Fig 5.4(b). The wave now has to travel further, along an oblique course, and so takes longer to make headway along the guide. The delay before it appears at the other end will therefore be longer than in the first case, so the group velocity is lower.

When the frequency is only a few per cent above the cut-off frequency (Fig 5.4(c)), the waves are launched across the guide, almost at right angles to it, and so travel to and fro across the guide, making very little progress along it. Here, they take a very long time to come out of the far end, corresponding to a very small group velocity.

Each time the wave crosses the centreline of the guide, it is almost exactly in the same phase as the last

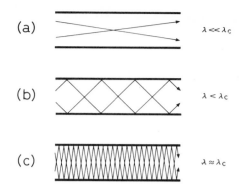

Fig 5.4. Illustration of dispersion in waveguide

time it crossed it. (The path from centre to edge is a quarter-wave long, and there is a 180° phase change at the reflection.) Thus the phase of the field in the centre of the guide changes only very slowly with distance along the guide, and so the phase velocity appears to be very large. The phase might change by a few degrees for every free-space wavelength travelled along the guide.

In the limit when the guide is exactly a half-wave across, the phase of the field does not change with distance along the guide, and the phase velocity appears to be infinite. The group velocity is then zero, as the wave will take an infinite time to come out at the far end – it is just bouncing to and fro across the guide at all points along the guide. The amplitude will still decay as the wave travels along the guide, but at a much greater rate than when operating well above the cut-off frequency.

This non-propagating wave, which consists of a field whose polarity will oscillate at the rf frequency, but whose oscillation is in phase over a large number of wavelengths, is called an "evanescent" wave. It is essentially a short-range effect, involving distances of a few wavelengths, and is often employed in filters and antennas. The piston attenuator works on this principle to give a linear increase in the number of decibels attenuation as two coupling loops are moved apart in a metal waveguide which is below cut-off.

The delay in the signal appearing at the end of the line also implies that energy is stored in the line, the amount corresponding to the power fed into it for the time the wave takes to travel through the line. There are many parallels between transmission lines and filters; in particular, energy storage – the signal has to be present for some time before an output is obtained. A filter operates by comparing the phase of the signal at several instants in time, and to do this it has to store energy.

If the velocity in the original straight line was the free-space velocity c, then we have just shown that the phase velocity V_p has gone faster than c, and the group velocity V_g slower than c. In fact this is a general principle, that the product of phase and group velocity in a line must always equal the square of the speed of light in that dielectric:

$$V_g \times V_p = c^2/\varepsilon_r$$

The phase velocity is thus generally used to predict the position of maxima and minima of the rf field on a line. The group velocity is used to predict how long changes in signal level will take to travel through a line or circuit.

When using highly dispersive lines, such as waveguides near their cut-off frequency, you must be careful to use the correct velocity for the type of calculation. Thus, to calculate the length of guide needed to produce a 90° phase shift when making a balanced mixer, you must use the phase velocity. However, to calculate the propagation delay down a guide, eg to calculate the time a pulse took to arrive at the end, as in a radar system, the group velocity would be needed.

All this talk of infinities and velocities greater than light may appear contradictory to the Theory of Relativity, which says that nothing can travel faster than the speed of light in a vacuum. However, the phase velocity is not the speed at which anything tangible travels – it is rather an abstract but useful concept to describe the wave pattern that has been set up. The fields and energy that form that pattern, and this includes any modulation waveforms, always travel slower than light, ie at the group velocity.

5.2.3 Model of a transmission line

The theoretical treatment of transmission lines is usually heavily mathematical. The exponential notation is commonly used because it is a very concise way of describing the wave's behaviour. This section attempts to explain the practical meaning of some of the more commonly used terms, without delving too deeply into the maths. The beginner should concentrate on the qualitative explanations rather than the maths in the first instance and perhaps skip this section on a first reading.

The basic properties of a line are:

1. The field at any point on the line varies with time at the frequency w, where $w = 2\pi \times F$, F being the frequency in hertz and w the frequency in radians per second.

$$V = V_o \times \sin(w \times t)$$

2. The wave is attenuated as it travels along the line. This is represented by the constant α, which defines the fraction by which the voltage decreases over a distance of one wavelength along the line. This is related to the familiar losses quoted in decibels per 10m.

$$V = V_o \times e^{\alpha \times l}$$

If α is zero, then V does not change with length – the line is lossless. If it is not zero, then V decreases exponentially with distance – another way of saying a number of decibels per metre. As will be seen later, the loss

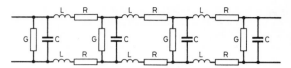

Fig 5.5. Equivalent circuit of a transmission line

of a cable can be used to predict the Q that will be obtained if is used as a resonator, eg a quarter-wave line.

3. The phase of the wave changes as it travels along the line. This is represented by the constant β, which determines the rate of change of phase with distance along the line, in radians per metre. The wavelength is the distance between two points where the phase is the same.

$$V = V_o \times e^{j \times \beta \times l}$$

These two are combined into one complex constant, γ, which describes how the amplitude and phase of the voltage vary with distance; it is known as the "propagation constant".

$$\gamma = \alpha + j\beta$$

When put together, the overall expression for the voltage on the line is:

$$V = e^{\alpha \times l} \times e^{j \times \beta \times l} \times e^{j \times w \times t}$$

The simplest line to consider is balanced twin-wire line, the equivalent circuit of which is shown in Fig 5.5. Each wire has a certain amount of self-inductance per unit length, which is represented by the series L in each wire. There is also distributed capacitance between the two wires, represented by C. There is a series resistance due to the resistance of the conductors, represented by R, and a shunt resistance due to dielectric losses, represented by G. Provided that a sufficiently large number of these elements are used, eg many per wavelength, this lumped-constant circuit is an accurate model of a transmission line.

A quick check can be made on this model by considering it at dc – at very low frequencies all the reactances can be ignored, so it simplifies to two wires. However, the model only applies up to the frequency where the line acts as a low-pass filter. It therefore only applies to the lowest mode on the line.

In terms of the constants shown in Fig 5.5,

$$\gamma = \sqrt{((R + jwL) \times (G + jwC))}$$

and $$Z_o = \sqrt{\left(\frac{R + jwL}{G + jwC}\right)}$$

So far, this may look quite heavy going. However, for a lossless line, G and R are zero, so these simplify considerably:

$$Z_o = \sqrt{(L/C)}$$

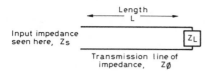

Fig 5.6. Transmission line as an impedance transformer

$$\gamma \quad = \quad j \times w \times \sqrt{(LC)}$$

$$\alpha \quad = \quad 0$$

$$\beta \quad = \quad w \times \sqrt{(LC)}$$

From β :

$$\lambda \quad = \quad -$$

$$V \quad = \quad$$

So the fundamental properties of a line – its characteristic impedance, velocity and wavelength – are all determined by the inductance of, and the capacitance between, the conductors.

In non-dispersive lines, the L and C are independent of frequency. Dispersion is caused by L or C varying with frequency.

The way in which a cut-off occurs in a line can now be seen – if the shunt capacitance can be made zero, eg by placing inductors across the shunt capacitors so that they form parallel-resonant circuits, the wavelength and phase velocity become infinite. From the previous section, this means that the group velocity must be zero. So the line does not propagate. This is described in more detail in the section on waveguide, which can in fact be thought of as a twin-wire line with shunt inductors across it.

Waves in free space can be thought of as being in a transmission line whose dielectric properties are determined by the permittivity, ε_o, and its magnetic properties by the permeability, μ_o, which correspond to the values of C and L in the twin line.

$$\varepsilon_o \quad = \quad 8.85 \times 10^{-12}$$

$$\mu_o \quad = \quad 4\pi \times 10^{-7}$$

$$Z_o \quad = \quad \sqrt{(\mu_o / \varepsilon_o)} \quad = \quad 377\Omega$$

$$V \quad = \quad \sqrt{(\mu_o \times \varepsilon_o)} \quad = \quad 3 \times 10^8 \text{ m/s}$$

For waves propagating in space filled with a dielectric, these can more usefully be expressed in terms of relative permeability and permittivity, where unity represents the free-space values:

$$Z_o \quad = \quad 377 \times \sqrt{(\mu_r / \varepsilon_r)}$$

$$V \quad = \quad c \times \sqrt{(\mu_r \times \varepsilon_r)}$$

where c is the free-space velocity, 3×10^8 m/s.

The ratio of V to the speed in free space, c, is known as the "velocity factor". Thus a block of dielectric can both slow down a wave and also reduce the impedance, just as it would if it were a dielectric in a coaxial line.

Transmission lines as impedance transformers

The input impedance of a length (l) of line whose characteristic impedance is Z_o, as shown in Fig 5.6, is given by:

$$Z_s \quad = \quad Z_o \times \frac{Z_l + Z_o \times \tanh(\gamma \times l)}{Z_o + Z_l \times \tanh(\gamma \times l)}$$

where Z_l is the terminating impedance and γ is the propagation constant defined earlier. For simplicity $\gamma \times l$ can be thought of as electrical length in degrees, ie 90° is equal to $\lambda/4$, 45° to $\lambda/8$ and so on.

This equation can be used to explain the operation of many components. For example, open-circuit and short-circuit stubs are simply lines where the terminating impedance is either infinity or zero. More information on these is given in section 5.12.

5.3 COAXIAL LINES

5.3.1 Theory of coaxial lines

Coaxial lines are the most familiar type of transmission line. They consist of concentric inner and outer conductors on a common axis, separated by a dielectric. Various types of cable are available – flexible cables, semi-rigid and Heliax, for example, and these are described later.

Coaxial lines are a simple form of transmission line where the electric and magnetic fields are always at right angles to the direction of propagation; they are thus known as "transverse electric and magnetic" lines or tem lines. They have no cut-off frequency and so theoretically operate from dc to infinity. The electric and magnetic fields in a circular coaxial line are shown in Fig 5.7 for the lowest tem mode.

However, higher-order, non-tem modes having more complicated field patterns can exist at sufficiently high frequencies. The first of these can appear when the mean circumference is greater than one wavelength. Thus, at high frequencies, there is a limit to the diameter of coaxial lines that can be used if overmoding is to be avoided. This is only likely to be a problem on the higher bands; for example at 10GHz the maximum diameter before overmoding occurs is about 9mm, so

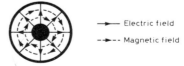

Fig 5.7. Fields in a circular coaxial line

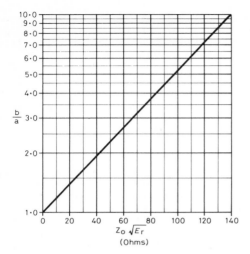

Fig 5.8. Characteristic impedance of a round coaxial line

the larger diameters of Heliax should be used with caution. However, 0.5in Heliax, FHJ4, has been used successfully at 10GHz with a measured loss of 4dB per 20ft.

Neglecting losses, the expression for the characteristic impedance Z_o simplifies to:

$$Z_o = \sqrt{(L/C)}$$

where L and C are the inductance and capacitance per unit length of the line. Similarly, the velocity of propagation is:

$$V = \sqrt{(LC)}$$

The inductance and capacitance depend upon the geometry of the line. The capacitance also depends upon the dielectric filling the cable; this is typically about 100pF/m. For a circular line, Z_o is:

$$Z_o = 138 \times \sqrt{\varepsilon_r} \times \log(b/a)$$

and the velocity V is:

$$V = C / \sqrt{\varepsilon_r}$$

Thus the wavelength in coaxial lines is simply that which would exist in space filled with a medium of the same dielectric constant as that filling the line:

$$\lambda_g = \frac{\lambda_{fs}}{\sqrt{\varepsilon_r}}$$

The characteristic impedance for a round line is plotted in Fig 5.8. See the "Data" chapter in Volume 2 for expressions and graphs of Z_o for other line cross-sections.

50Ω has evolved as standard impedance for coaxial lines, although several other values are still used. It is interesting to see why this is so. For coaxial transmission lines there are three main important properties:

1. Attenuation
2. Power-handling capability
3. Breakdown voltage

Of these, the attenuation and power capacity are the most important. The power capacity will be determined by the breakdown voltage at low frequencies (where the attenuation is low) and by the heating effect due to the losses at high frequencies (where the attenuation is higher).

Coaxial lines of the same material have higher conductor losses than waveguides and also have dielectric losses as well. The latter stem from the fact that, apart from short lengths of line for special components, the centre conductor needs supporting concentrically. For short lengths, spaced insulating beads can be used, but usually this support is provided by completely filling the line by a solid or foamed dielectric.

Loss occurs in the conductors due to their resistance (so-called "ohmic losses"). The current flows mainly within a thin layer on the surface of the conductor, known as the "skin depth", and defined as the depth where the field has decreased to 1/e of the surface value, ie –8.7dB.

$$\text{Skin depth} = \sqrt{\left(\frac{1}{\pi \times F \times \sigma \times \mu}\right)}$$

where σ is the conductivity, μ the permeability, and F the frequency.

This depth decreases as the square root of frequency, and so the loss increases as the square root. The losses in the dielectric are much smaller than the conductor losses at low frequencies, but usually increase directly with frequency. As a result the conductor loss dominates at low frequencies and the dielectric losses dominate at high frequencies. This means that at microwave frequencies, dielectric losses are the more significant and are prohibitively large for long lengths of line.

The following comparisons of properties apply to air-cored cylindrical coaxial cables. The dielectrics used in cables will probably stand quite high voltages (typically 50kV/mm for polythene, 40 to 80kV/mm for ptfe). However, in practice the breakdown in dry air (1.2kV/mm) will usually be the limiting factor as there are almost inevitably gaps in the dielectric at connectors. The following relations give the breakdown voltage V and the power-carrying capacity P:

$$V = \frac{E_{max} \times b \times \ln(b/a)}{1.414 \times (b/a)}$$

$$P = \frac{E_{max}^2 \times b^2 \times \ln(b/a)}{1,920 \times (b/a)^2}$$

where a is the diameter of the inner, b the inside diameter of the outer conductor and E_{max} the breakdown voltage of the dielectric (assumed to be air).

For a given cable outside diameter, properties vary as shown in Fig 5.9. From these:

Minimum attenuation occurs at $Z_o = 77\Omega$
Maximum breakdown voltage occurs at $Z_o = 60\Omega$
Maximum power handling occurs at $Z_o = 30\Omega$

As a reasonable compromise, 50Ω was chosen as a standard. The attenuation is 10 per cent higher than the minimum at 77Ω, the breakdown voltage 5 per cent lower than the maximum at 60Ω, and the power capacity is 20 per cent lower than the maximum at 30Ω. 75Ω cables are sometimes used where low attenuation is important, but the improvement obtained will be small, and will only be significant if the loss is high in the first place, eg a 3dB loss will reduce to 2.6dB but a 1dB loss will only reduce to 0.9dB. The 75Ω cable also happens to be closest to the input impedance of a half-wave dipole, which can thus be fed directly, although a balun should be used.

A number of cables are quoted as 52Ω impedance; the reason for this is that the impedance of a coaxial line changes slightly with frequency. As the frequency is increased from audio to hf/vhf, the current changes from flowing in all of the inner conductor to only the outer surface, due to the skin effect. This change alters the self-inductance of the inner and causes a small impedance change. There is about a 4 per cent decrease as the frequency is increased through the transition region. Theoretical expressions for the impedances of lines usually refer to the low-frequency value; this must be allowed for when using them at higher frequencies. The transition depends on the diameter of the inner, but usually occurs between 1MHz and 20MHz.

5.3.2 Flexible cables

Flexible cables are available in a variety of sizes, materials and characteristic impedances. The most common impedances are 50 and 75Ω, but others, eg 93Ω, are available.

The cheaper types use a polythene dielectric and a pvc outer sleeve; higher quality and more expensive types use ptfe for both the dielectric and sleeving, which is heat resistant and has a slightly lower loss. A few common types are listed in Table 5.1; for a more complete list plus graphs of loss versus frequency see the "Data" chapter in Volume 2.

The very small sizes are suitable for wiring up pcbs and relays inside equipment. The larger cables will be needed for connecting equipment, together or for feeders, although at microwave frequencies it will often be necessary to use semi-rigid coaxial cable and Heliax for these applications. PTFE types are recommended when the cable has to be soldered directly to circuitry so that the insulation does not melt. Other dielectrics such as polythene will melt but can be used with care.

Table 5.1. Flexible cables

Type	Impedance (ohms)	Diameter (mm)
RG178B/U	50	1.8
RG174A/U	50	2.8
UR43	50	5.0
RG58C/U	50	5.0
UR70	75	5.8
UR67	50	10.3
RG213/U	50	10.3

5.3.3 Semi-rigid cable

This consists of a solid inner conductor (usually copper or silver/copper-plated steel), a solid ptfe dielectric and a solid copper outer tube. Its characteristic impedance is usually 50Ω, although 10, 25 and 75Ω are also available. It is made in a wide variety of outer diameters, from 0.020 to 0.25in, 0.141in being the commonest (see Fig 5.10). It is widely used professionally, since it is sealed and its rigid construction means that it cannot flex and so alter its electrical length (it is phase stable). However, its loss is still relatively high because of its small diameter and it is therefore generally used for connections between modules inside equipment rather than as a feeder to an antenna.

5.3.4 Heliax

Heliax cables are basically larger-diameter flexible versions of semi-rigid cable, but have a corrugated solid outer conductor to enable them to flex more easily. They are available in diameters of up to 5in; see Fig 5.11. These cables are used for frequencies of up to several gigahertz, where their loss is not significantly

© Artech House, Inc, from Theodore S. Saad's Microwave Engineers Handbook, Vol. 1.

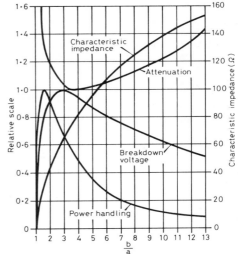

Fig 5.9. Attenuation, power handling and breakdown voltage of a coaxial line

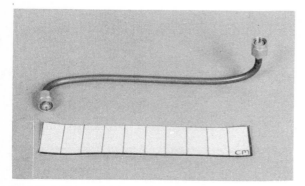

Fig 5.10. 0.141in semi-rigid coaxial "cable" fitted with SMA plugs. Note that the outer of the cable is solid copper. The inner is usually copper-plated steel and is used to form the connecting "pin" when used with this form of connector. The dielectric is solid ptfe

inferior to waveguide, and they are rather cheaper than long and heavy waveguide runs.

We have remarked that air is the least-lossy dielectric (unless you can evacuate the cable and have a vacuum). For this reason, air-spaced cable is the best way of achieving low loss. The problem remains of how to keep the centre conductor accurately in position since any sideways movement of it will alter the characteristic impedance of the line and cause a mismatch. The two common solutions to this used in Heliax are:

1. Use a helical supporting membrane
2. Use a foam dielectric

While the foam dielectric is slightly more lossy, the losses in the air-spaced cable can be greatly increased if water vapour leaks in. Professionally, the air-dielectric cables are pressurised with dry air so that any leakage lets dry air out rather than moist air in. Leaks are detected by monitoring the cable pressure. Such cables have valves on their connectors, which allow pumps or pressure gauges to be connected. When pumping them up, a silica-gel filter is used to dry the air entering.

Although special connectors are required for Heliax cable, it is possible to modify standard N-types to fit some of the smaller-diameter cables (see the "Common microwave equipment" chapter in Volume 2).

5.3.5 Coaxial connectors

The function of a connector is to provide a low-loss cable-to-equipment or cable-to-cable joint, whose performance does not deteriorate with time. For a lead which is in everyday use this means withstanding repeated connection and disconnection and flexure of the cable close to the connector. For a joint at the top of the mast, it is more important that the joint is waterproof. The choice of connector type depends on several factors, but is governed mainly by the size of cable to be used.

The mechanical aspect of the joint is extremely important. It cannot be stressed too highly that intermittent connections can cause all sorts of problems, and it is well worth spending time and trouble to make connectors up properly. Crimped connectors, where the cable braid is held to the connector body by a crimped sleeve, are recommended but need a special tool to make them up. Suhner make a particularly good crimped BNC connector. This has a tapered plastic sleeve which protects the cable/plug joint, and also prevents the cable flexing near the plug and fracturing the joint. A similar protection can be provided by taping the cable/plug joint and the first inch or two of the cable with several layers of self-amalgamating tape.

There are two separate aspects of outdoor connections which should be sealed against moisture. First, there is the joint between the cable and the connector. If this leaks, and moisture enters the cable, the cable loss rises rapidly. It is impossible to reclaim cable once this has happened, as the conductors will have become corroded. Some connectors (eg N-type, BNC) incorporate rubber sealing rings for this purpose. Second, there is the plug/socket joint. Screw-type connectors provide better protection than bayonet types and are to be preferred, but the whole joint should be protected with tape to be certain. For this purpose, self-amalgamating tape is highly recommended (available from RS Components in the UK, stock no 512-042). This chemically amalgamates to itself when applied, and produces a strong, waterproof joint with excellent insulation properties.

The use of a plug not designed for a particular cable will result in poor clamping and early mechanical failure of the connection. A frequent failure mode is that the braid or clamp loosens, which allows the whole cable to rotate in the plug body; the inner connection fails soon afterwards. To prevent this the cable clamp must be done up very tightly with spanners. Taping the plug/cable joint for a few inches also helps to avoid this

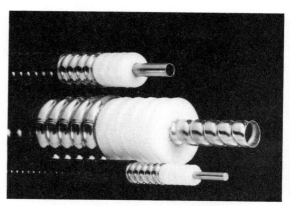

Fig 5.11. Heliax cables (courtesy Andrew Antennas)

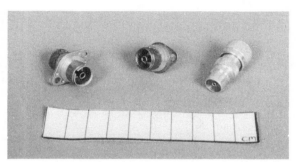

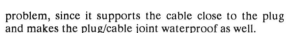

Fig 5.12. Various types of Belling-Lee connectors. Note that these are nominally 75Ω and are intended to work up to a few hundred megahertz

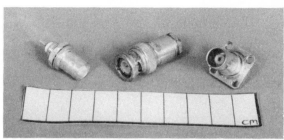

Fig 5.14. Various types of BNC connectors. These are obtainable as 50Ω or 75Ω types, offer constant impedance and are usable well into the gigahertz region. However, beware of overmoding and impedance changes caused by flexible cables!

problem, since it supports the cable close to the plug and makes the plug/cable joint waterproof as well.

The following list includes most types of connector likely to be encountered by amateurs:

Belling-Lee: a very simple, cheap, push-fit connector, much used on tv antenna cables which have an impedance of 75Ω. The plug is mechanically unreliable unless made up properly with the correct diameter cable; the inner must be soldered to the pin. These connectors are not waterproof and do not grip the cable well. Not really recommended. See Fig 5.12.

PL259/SO239 (uhf): a fairly common screw-locking connector. While their electrical performance is poor above 100MHz as they are not of constant impedance, they are quite useful at hf because they can accommodate UR67-sized cable. They are quite reliable mechanically as long as the plugs are correctly made up, but are not waterproof, and only really grip UR67-sized cable satisfactorily. They were originally used for video connections in radar (only a few megahertz). Not really recommended at uhf. See Fig 5.13.

BNC (bayonet Navy connector): a very common bayonet-locking connector, some makes being better than others. They are used primarily with UR43-sized

cable and their cable grip is quite adequate. The plug/cable joint is waterproof, but the plug/socket joint is not. Works well up to about 2GHz. Above that it can show intermittent tendencies and may radiate energy. Highly recommended for all but the most demanding applications. See Fig 5.14.

Miniature BNC: a bayonet-locking connector similar to the BNC, but about two-thirds of the size; intended for use with miniature cables (eg RG174/U) where the small size is important. Not very common. The electrical performance is similar to the BNC. See Fig 5.15.

N-type (Navy connector): these screw-locking connectors were originally developed during the second world war. Their specification varies from manufacturer to manufacturer, but more recent precision types are usable up to 18GHz. They are very common and are available for almost all types of cable. They provide an effective cable clamp and both the plug/cable and plug/socket joints are waterproof. Highly recommended. See Fig 5.16.

C-type: a bayonet-locking connector that looks rather like an N-sized BNC. Not particularly common. Their performance is roughly equivalent to BNC, but they can cope with larger-diameter cables. See Fig 5.17.

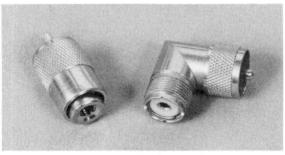

Fig 5.13. PL259/SO239 connectors

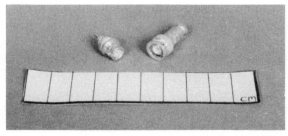

Fig 5.15. Miniature BNC connectors. These have similar characteristics to the standard BNC connector but are designed to be used with miniature flexible cables

Fig 5.16. N-type connectors. These are available in 50Ω or 75Ω impedance. Adaptors for different sizes of cable can be fitted. Special or modified N-type connectors are required for Heliax semi-rigid cables. Usable to 10GHz, they are probably the connector of choice for general microwave purposes

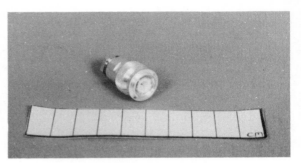

Fig 5.18. TNC connector

Fig 5.17. C-type connectors: a C-to-BNC adapter (left) and a C-to-N-type adapter (right). The C-type male and female fittings resemble large BNC connectors

TNC (threaded Navy connector): this is a screw-on version of the BNC connector and, though they are not particularly common, they are sound, both mechanically and electrically. They provide an effective cable clamp, and both the cable/plug and plug/socket joins are waterproof. They are usable up to 15GHz as the threaded clamp makes a more reliable joint than the bayonet connector and reduces stray radiation. See Fig 5.18.

SMA (sub-miniature A connector): the professional "standard" microwave connector, originally developed for use with 0.141in semi-rigid cable, although available for miniature flexible cables. Usually gold plated, occasionally stainless steel. Small size and high performance. Also known as OSM (Omni-Spectra miniature) and SRM by various manufacturers. Highly recommended. See Fig 5.19.

SMB (sub-miniature B connector): a miniature snap-on connector for use with miniature coaxial cable (RG188/U etc). They are gold plated and provide an effective cable clamp but are not waterproof. Not intended for frequent connection and disconnection. See Fig 5.20.

SMC (sub-miniature C connector): the screw-on version of the SMB connector. These are slightly more rugged with higher performance. In general the same comments as for SMB apply. See Fig 5.21.

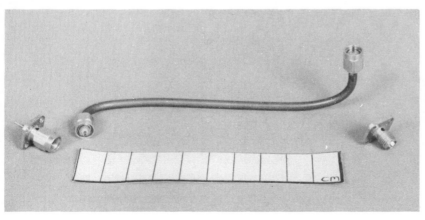

Fig 5.19. Various SMA connectors. These are the amateur's choice for use at any microwave frequency, up to and including 24GHz. Designed for use with semi-rigid cable

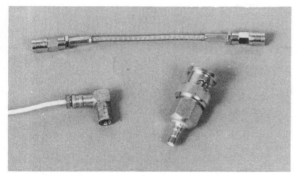

Fig 5.20. Various types of SMB connector. Bottom right is a SMB-to-BNC adaptor

Fig 5.22. General Radio-to-BNC adaptor

Fig 5.23. APC-7 connector

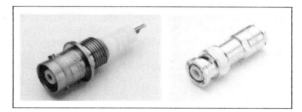

Fig 5.24. BNC-HT connectors

GR (General Radio connector): a rather old-fashioned type of hermaphrodite connector (ie plug and socket are identical), made by the General Radio Company and used mainly on their test equipment. Not very common. See Fig 5.22.

APC-7 (Amphenol precision connector, 7mm): a very high precision hermaphrodite connector used primarily on microwave test instruments. Very expensive and unlikely to be encountered by the amateur. See Fig 5.23.

BNC-HT: a connector made by Radiall which looks very similar to a BNC, but has a longer plug and a recessed pin. Both the plug and socket have extended ptfe insulation around the inner. It is intended for eht applications and is rated at 10kV test voltage, from dc to 2GHz. The plug takes UR43-sized cable. These connectors are recommended for taking eht supplies into high-power amplifiers, as the recessed pin cannot be touched accidentally. They are not compatible with ordinary BNC connectors. See Fig 5.24.

Fig 5.21. Various SMC connectors - somewhat similar to SMA but the frequency range is slightly more restricted. Ideal for interconnecting modules within equipment when using small-diameter cable

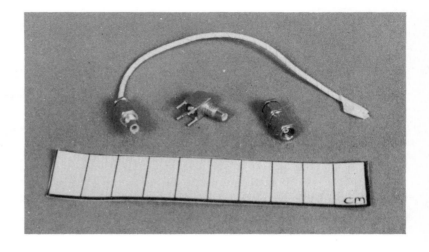

Fig 5.25. PET-100 connector. This is suitable for high-voltage and rf connections up to about 1.5GHz. Usually used in nucleonic equipment such as photomultipliers and Geiger detectors. Occasionally found on surplus microwave equipment, these connectors are very expensive

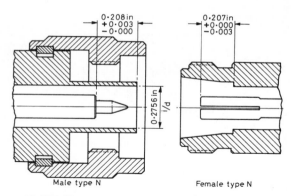

Fig 5.26. Dimensions of mating parts of N-type connectors

PET 100: a screw-on connector which is intended for the same sort of applications as the BNC-HT connector (mainly in instruments such as photomultiplier and Geiger counter tubes) but is rather more common. Rated to 3kV working voltage, 9kV proof, 2.5A rms, the plug takes UR43-sized cable. See Fig 5.25.

Some connectors are available in either 50 or 75Ω impedance, in particular N-types, BNCs and C-types. Be careful not to mix them, as this can cause damage to the connector as well as increasing the vswr. The impedance is usually stamped on the connector body, but for type N and C connectors, the difference in the diameter of the centre pin of the plug is also very obvious. For 50Ω plugs it is about 1.6mm, while for 75Ω ones it is about 1.0mm. The two different types will apparently fit together, but a 50Ω plug with a 75Ω socket splays out the inner contact of the socket, and a 75Ω plug with a 50Ω socket makes poor contact.

With BNC, the difference is less obvious, and the 50Ω and 75Ω versions do not damage each other when mixed. The difference is mainly in the socket; 50Ω sockets have a dielectric tube around the centre pin, while those of 75Ω ones have air dielectric. There is very little visible difference in the plugs, but the impedance is usually marked. The diameter that the cable clamping parts of the plug are designed to accommodate also differs in the two types.

Some N-type connectors allow a certain amount of choice in how far the centre pin protrudes. If one or other protrudes too far, the shoulder on the plug centre pin can damage the socket fingering when the plug is done up tightly (see Fig 5.26). A guide is that the pin in a plug should be positioned with the tip very slightly behind the outer fingering, but the critical distance is from the shoulder on the pin to the outer fingering which should be about 5.5mm. In a socket, the centre pin should be 4.5mm behind the open end of the outer body. Note that some precision N-type plugs do not have a rubber sealing ring and the fingering around the

centre pin is replaced by a solid tube. If you hear or feel a grating noise as the connector is done up the last turn, stop and check the centre pins are in the right place.

More detailed specifications for some of those connectors listed are given in Table 5.2.

These figures are taken from a connector catalogue by Omni Spectra, and refer to top-specification connectors. Secondhand ones may well not meet these specs, but the figures should serve as a good guide. It would seem to be worth standardising on BNC and N-connectors for all but the most-demanding applications, though above about 2GHz the more-specialised microwave connectors (eg SMA, TNC) should really be used.

5.4 STRIPLINE

Stripline is also known as "triplate" and can be thought of as a rectangular section of coaxial line with the side walls removed. Provided the open edges are not too close to the centre strip, its properties are similar to coaxial line. The dielectric can be air, but is more commonly a solid material and it can be made by sandwiching together a strip conductor between two pieces of single-sided pcb.

Table 5.2. Connector specifications

Connector	VSWR	Insertion loss (dB)
BNC	<1.12 + 0.007×F, dc to 2GHz	<0.1×F
N	<1.06 + 0.007×F, dc to 10GHz	<0.05×F
TNC	<1.07 + 0.007×F, dc to 15GHz	<0.05×F
SMA	<1.02 + 0.005×F, dc to 18GHz	<0.03×F
SMB	<1.08 + 0.017×F, dc to 4GHz	<0.12×F
SMC	<1.08 + 0.017×F, dc to 10GHz	<0.06×F
APC-7	<1.003 + 0.002×F, dc to 18GHz	
PET 100	<1.3, dc to 1.5GHz	

The frequency F is measured in gigahertz.

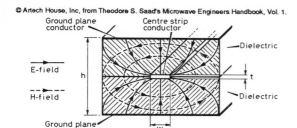

Fig 5.27. Field patterns in stripline

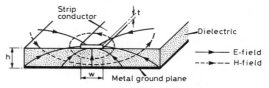

Fig 5.29. Fields in microstrip

Stripline is a transmission line where the wave propagates in a transverse electromagnetic (tem) manner. The electric and magnetic fields are shown in Fig 5.27. The most common dielectrics used are glassfibre, polythene or ptfe, or combinations of these. More-complicated stripline circuits can be produced by etching the required conductor pattern on one side of double-sided pcb, the other side being left as a ground plane. A sheet of single-sided, copper-clad pcb is then placed on top of this and the two pieces firmly clamped together.

The main advantage of stripline is that components and circuitry can be built in the same thickness of line. The circuit is essentially two-dimensional and most of the components are realised by altering the width of the line. This results in a considerable saving in volume over coaxial lines and waveguide, especially at the lower end of the microwave spectrum. However, the dielectric losses can be significant.

There are no simple expressions for the characteristic impedance. The thickness of the inner line is a parameter, and when this is particularly thick the line is often called "slabline". Very accurate expressions are complicated (see [4]), but for most amateur purposes the following approximation will suffice:

$$Z_0 = \frac{94.2}{\sqrt{e}} \times \ln\left(\frac{1 + W/b}{W/b + t/b}\right) \quad \text{(ohms)}$$

where W is the conductor width, t is the conductor thickness and b is the spacing between the ground planes. The accuracy of the formula is approximately one to two per cent for $W/b > 1$, and around five per cent for $W/b = 0.75$, provided that t/b is less than 0.2.

Results from more accurate equations are plotted in Fig 5.28 for W/b ranging from 0.1 to 10, for several values of t/b.

As with coaxial lines, if the frequency is sufficiently high, higher-order modes can propagate. This can occur when the distance between the ground planes is greater than a half-wavelength in the dielectric.

5.5 MICROSTRIP

The construction of microstrip is essentially like stripline but with only one ground plane (see Fig 5.29). It can easily be made by etching one side of double-sided pcb, and is more widely used than stripline.

Microstrip is a non-tem type of transmission line as the field is not entirely contained within the dielectric. The electric and magnetic fields are shown in Fig 5.29. Because not all of the electromagnetic field is confined within the dielectric, part of the wave travels in air and part in the dielectric, and consequently the effective dielectric constant is lower than that of the substrate. This constant is a function of both the substrate dielectric constant and the ratio of the conductor width to dielectric thickness. Thus velocity of propagation and hence the wavelength are functions of this ratio W/h. See Fig 5.30 for graphs of the wavelength against W/h for various dielectrics.

The line is also dispersive. It is therefore important to have accurate data on the substrate properties for any

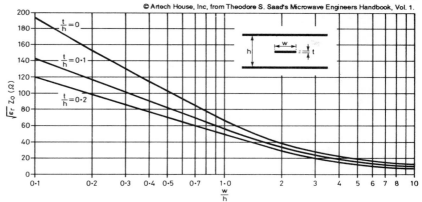

Fig 5.28. Impedance of stripline

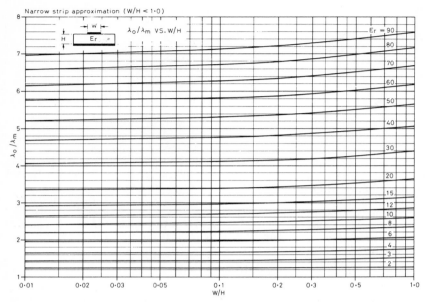

Fig 5.30. Velocity factor of microstrip

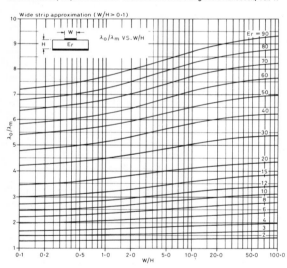

In order to confine most of the energy to the dielectric, and so to minimise the amount of stray radiation, a high dielectric constant is desirable. Professionally, such materials as alumina with a dielectric constant of 9.8 and a loss tangent of 0.0002 at 10GHz are used. However, these high dielectric constants also mean that the wavelength is much shorter and the line widths also become very narrow. Very high accuracy is therefore necessary in defining the line widths and a very smooth surface necessary on the substrate. These materials are not very suitable for amateur use and so lower-dielectric material is more suitable. Thus, be aware that there will be significant radiation from the lines.

As with stripline, accurate expressions for the impedance are very complicated. However, some approximations exist, and the most useful for amateur applications is one which is valid for dielectric constants between two and six:

$$Z_0 = \frac{60}{\sqrt{(0.475 + 0.67/e)}} \times \ln\left(\frac{h}{0.134W + 0.168t}\right)$$

where h is the dielectric height, e the dielectric constant, W is the conductor width and t the conductor thickness.

critical designs. These effects are relatively unimportant with most "microwave" dielectrics, but are more significant with glass epoxy board, where a typical permittivity of 4.55 at 1MHz may fall to 4.25 at 500MHz. Manufacturers' permittivity data tends to be unreliable as it is usually based on simple measurements on the capacitance of an area of board and it is difficult to take account of edge effects. The standard technique is to measure the resonant frequency of a ring resonator as shown in Fig 5.31, and to derive the effective value of the permittivity from that.

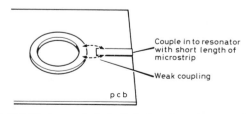

Couple in to resonator with short length of microstrip

Weak coupling

p c b

Fig 5.31. Measurement of velocity factor using a ring resonator

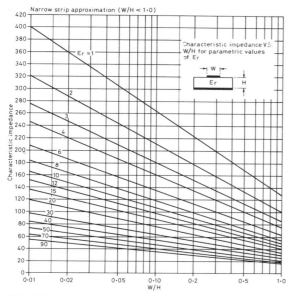

Narrow strip approximation (W/H < 1·0)

Characteristic impedance VS.
W/H for parametric values
of Er

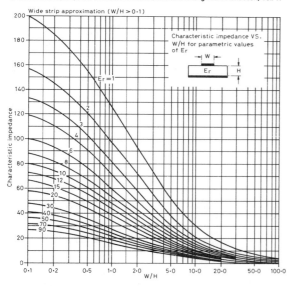

Wide strip approximation (W/H > 0·1)

Characteristic impedance VS.
W/H for parametric values
of Er

Fig 5.32. Characteristic impedance of microstrip

For W/h less than 1.25, a dielectric constant between 2.5 and 6.0, and t/W between 0.1 and 0.8, this formula will give results within five per cent.

The effective dielectric constant k for calculating the velocity factor for the transmission line is given approximately by:

$$k = 0.475e + 0.67$$

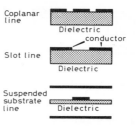

Fig 5.33. Coplanar, slot and suspended substrate lines

Again, this equation applies for e between 2.0 and 6.0.

See Fig 5.32 for graphs of the characteristic impedance against w/h for various dielectrics.

In addition to microstrip, there are other configurations which look similar and are useful in some applications. Some examples are the coplanar line, slot line and suspended-substrate line (see Fig 5.33).

5.6 WAVEGUIDE

Although all transmission lines are waveguides, since they guide waves, the term is generally used to describe hollow metal tubes with the field propagating down the middle. Four of the commonest types are illustrated in Fig 5.34.

When any electromagnetic field is confined in this way, its propagation characteristics are different from those in free space. The conducting boundaries only permit the field to exist if it conforms to specific patterns and there is no electric field along the surface of the metal. The properties of the waveguide are therefore related to its shape and size. Any discontinuities within the waveguide will alter its properties as a transmission line and this effect is used to produce inductive or capacitive reactances. This is the basis of many microwave components.

All waveguides of this type behave as high-pass filters, and will only carry frequencies above a certain limit known as the "cut-off" frequency. This behaviour can best be illustrated by taking extreme examples. Any

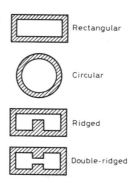

Fig 5.34. Common types of waveguide

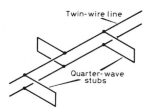

Fig 5.35. Twin-wire line with shunt quarter-wave stubs

attempt to connect the two leads of a dc supply to the metal waveguide will result in a dead short across the supply, so it is obviously incapable of propagating very low frequencies. Conversely, since the waveguide is a hollow pipe which you can look down, very high frequencies such as light must be able to propagate down it.

The lowest frequency which such a guide will propagate depends on its shape, but is roughly when the diameter is equal to half a wavelength. The reason waveguides are restricted to microwaves is now obvious: that of size. For example, at 50MHz the necessary size for a rectangular guide could be used as a garage for a small car!

The parameters of voltage and current have no practical significance in waveguides as there is no unique value for either term. Instead, energy is carried by sinusoidally varying electric and magnetic fields that have instantaneous values, these being functions of both position and time. The quantities measured in practice are always power and impedance.

To explain the operation of waveguide, consider it to be made up of a twin-wire transmission line, with the wires running along the centre of each of the broad faces. This would naturally give an E-field in the correct sense, ie between top and bottom, between the wires. Propagation along the twin line would not be affected if shorted quarter-wave stubs were connected across it from each side (Fig 5.35). An infinite number of these would join up to form a closed pipe.

The reactance of these quarter-wave lines will change with frequency. The net result is that the shunt impedance across the twin line varies from a short at dc, an inductance up to the cut-off frequency and a capacitance above it (see Fig 5.36). At dc the shunt inductors short out the signal, so it cannot propagate low frequencies. Above the frequency where the shunt C and L are parallel-resonant, the shunt reactance

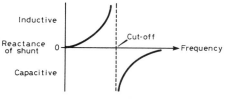

Fig 5.36. Equivalent shunt impedance across a twin-wire line for waveguide

returns to the normal capacitive values and the line will propagate again.

Enclosing an electromagnetic field within conducting boundaries alters the wavelength of propagation from that of free space; it is made longer, and is a function of the guide dimensions. The general expression for any shape of guide is:

$$\lambda_g = \frac{\lambda}{\sqrt{(\varepsilon_r - (\lambda/\lambda_c)^2)}}$$

where λ_c is the cut-off wavelength of the waveguide, λ is the free-space wavelength and ε_r is the dielectric constant of the medium filling the guide (usually air, for which ε_r is approximately one).

So far we have just considered using the waveguide near the bottom limit of its frequency range. The normal operating range is from about 1.25 to 1.9 times the cut-off frequency. Higher-order modes exist whose cut-off is just above this range and, when more than one mode can propagate, it is difficult to control in which way the energy is distributed between them. The most serious problem of using a guide which allows many modes to propagate is that they can all have different

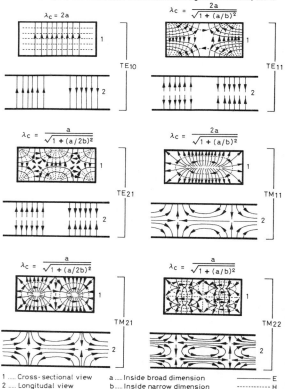

Fig 5.37. Mode patterns in rectangular waveguide

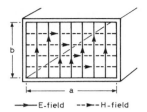

→ E-field   --►-- H-field

Fig 5.38. Dominant mode in rectangular waveguide

velocities and so, if energy were launched into several modes at the same time, it would not all arrive at the far end at the same time. This can result in interference effects between the various modes which will produce peaks and nulls in the line attenuation at certain frequencies, as well as causing dispersion.

The field patterns for these modes are usually different and some mode patterns are shown in Fig 5.37 for rectangular waveguide. There is a standard notation for describing the different modes, shown with each one. They are named firstly according to whether the electric or magnetic field is zero along the direction of propagation, and there are three possibilities: TE, TM and TEM for the electric, the magnetic and both being zero. In waveguide only TE and TM modes exist. Suffixes are then added to describe the number of peaks and troughs in the pattern. They represent the number of times the field goes from zero through a maximum and back to zero again along an axis of the guide. For rectangular waveguide these directions are parallel to the broad face and parallel to the narrow face respectively. In circular waveguide, the directions are around the circumference, and radially.

Thus the dominant mode in rectangular waveguide is known as "TE-10" because there is one variation along the broad face and none along the narrow face.

Components which are designed to work with one mode will be unlikely to work with another. Overmoding also results in unpredictable performance because a probe which couples into one mode may not couple into another as a result of the different field patterns in the guide. If a long run of guide is used, then unless its mechanical dimensions are perfectly accurate it is likely that the mode pattern may change as energy moves from one mode to another. This is known as "mode conversion".

Waveguide losses are comparatively low, usually one or two orders of magnitude lower than coaxial cables when used at the same frequency. Also, at higher frequencies the physical size is such that many components can be built inside it or immediately around it, and a complete transceiver may consist of a number of waveguide components bolted together.

5.6.1 Rectangular waveguide

The most common form of waveguide consists of a hollow rectangular tube. The dominant mode is the TE-10 mode; the electric field is transverse to the guide, extending between the two broad walls (see Fig 5.38). The intensity of the electric field is a maximum at the centre of the guide, and drops off sinusoidally to zero intensity at the edges. The magnetic field is in the form of loops which lie in planes parallel to the broad faces of the guide. The plane of polarisation is parallel to the electric field: for horizontal polarisation the broad faces of the waveguide should be vertical.

For an air-filled guide (ε_r approximately 1), the waveguide wavelength is given by:

$$\lambda_g = \frac{\lambda}{\sqrt{(1 - (\lambda/(2a)^2))}}$$

where λ is the free-space wavelength and a is the larger inside dimension.

Rectangular waveguides are available in a range of standard sizes to cover all microwave frequencies in bands, with some overlap between each band. Waveguides commonly used to cover the amateur bands are listed in Table 5.3 with their dimensions and cut-off frequencies. For a more complete listing see the "Data" chapter in Volume 2.

5.6.2 Circular waveguide

Circular waveguide can also be used to transmit energy. However, it possesses no characteristic that positively prevents the plane of polarisation rotating about the axis of the guide as the wave travels along it. A signal with one plane of polarisation injected into a circular waveguide may not necessarily have the same polarisation at the other end. For short lengths of guide this is not a severe problem, and circular guide is often used for dish feeds.

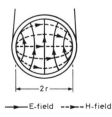

→ E-field   --►-- H-field

Fig 5.39. Dominant mode in circular waveguide

Table 5.3. Waveguide specifications

Band (GHz)	WG no	External dimensions (mm)		Cut-off frequency (GHz)
1.3	WG6	169.16	86.61	0.908
2.3	WG8	113.28	58.67	1.372
3.4	WG10	90.42	47.24	2.078
5.7	WG14	38.10	19.05	4.301
10	WG16	25.40	12.70	6.557
24	WG20	12.70	6.350	14.05
47	WG24	6.807	4.420	31.39

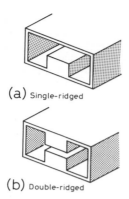

(a) Single-ridged

(b) Double-ridged

Fig 5.40. Ridged waveguide

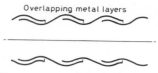

Overlapping metal layers

Fig 5.42. Flexible-twistable waveguide

Like rectangular waveguide, a given size of circular waveguide has a cut-off frequency below which signals will not propagate, and a frequency above which higher modes may also propagate. The dominant mode for circular waveguide is the TE-11 mode, shown in Fig 5.39. The cut-off wavelength for this is given by:

$$\lambda_c = 3.412a$$

where a is the internal radius of the waveguide. Signals with a larger wavelength than this will not propagate.

The wavelength in the guide, λ_g, is given by:

$$\lambda_g = \frac{\lambda}{\sqrt{(1-(\lambda/\lambda_c)^2)}}$$

$$ie \quad \lambda_g = \frac{\lambda}{\sqrt{(1-(\lambda/(3.412a))^2)}}$$

The next higher mode is the TM-01 mode for which λ_c = 2.613a. This represents a frequency which is only about 30 per cent higher than that of the dominant mode. Thus circular waveguide can be used only over a much narrower frequency range than rectangular waveguide if the risk of overmoding is to be avoided. Any cylindrical tubing with a reasonably uniform bore can be used as circular waveguide, eg copper pipe or empty tin cans.

5.6.3 Ridged waveguide

In wideband systems, it may be difficult to use ordinary rectangular waveguide, which has a typical bandwidth of 0.4. Coaxial cables and components may be used but an alternative is ridged waveguide where the bandwidth is increased by adding a centred ridge to one or both of the broad walls (see Fig 5.40).

The double-ridged type has the widest bandwidth, and will typically cover two ordinary waveguide bands, eg 8 to 18GHz. Standard sizes are available and components such as bends, switches etc are available in these sizes.

5.6.4 Flexible waveguide

Short lengths of flexible waveguide are often needed in a system, eg when it is difficult to get exact mechanical alignment between two components or when movement

Fig 5.41. Flexible waveguide

Fig 5.43. Flexible elliptical waveguide (courtesy Andrew Antennas)

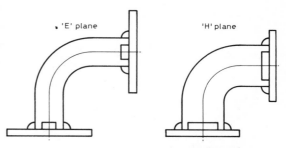

Fig 5.44. E- and H-plane bends in rectangular waveguide

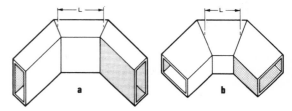

Fig 5.45. Short bends

is required. There are two types of flexible rectangular guide that can be used – flexible and flexi-twistable.

Flexible guide can be bent in both E- and H-planes, but not twisted. It is made in a concertina-like manner from corrugated tube (see Fig 5.41). It is almost always silver-plated and encased in rubber for strength.

Flexi-twistable waveguide is made by winding silver-plated tape with interlocking rings round a rectangular former (see Fig 5.42). It is encased in rubber to hold it together.

Both types are more lossy than plain waveguide, the twistable type being the most lossy. Also, they are particularly susceptible to water – once damp they are difficult to dry out and can be very lossy.

In addition, there is a type of waveguide available called "elliptical waveguide", designed for long feeder runs, eg to dishes mounted on a tower. It is made from a corrugated copper tube, and covered with a plastic protective jacket – see Fig 5.43. It is rather like a very stiff flexiguide. Standard sizes are available, together with flanges which mate with rectangular waveguides. Some, available from Andrews, that could be used on 10GHz are listed in Table 5.4.

5.6.5 Waveguide bends and twists

Bends are sometimes required in the assembly of equipment or connection to an antenna. The simplest form is one in which a piece of waveguide is simply bent with a radius of curvature of several wavelengths. The change in impedance of the guide in the bent section (compared to a straight section) tends to be quite small, and the

wideband nature of the guide is scarcely affected. This approach is an example of the general rule which is applicable to waveguide – you can get away with many things provided you do it gradually over a distance of a number of wavelengths.

Commercially, bends are made by filling a straight piece of guide with sand or a soft, low-melting point alloy to prevent the sides buckling, and bending around a former. Alternatively, they may be made by electro-depositing metal onto a shaped mandrel (electroforming). For the amateur, gentle bends can be produced by clamping one end of a length of guide, applying a light load to the other end, and heating with a brush flame until the correct local deformation has occurred, before moving to the next section. E- and H-plane bends are shown in Fig 5.44; the plane refers to the plane in which the angle of the bend is measured.

The bends made in this way are necessarily large. Bends having a small radius of curvature can be made

Table 5.4. Elliptical waveguide sizes

Type	Frequency range (GHz)	Outer dimensions (mm)
EW85	7.7-10.0	33.5 by 22.9
EW90	8.3-11.7	33.5 by 20.3
EW122	10.0-13.25	27.2 by 18.3

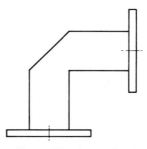

Fig 5.46. Mitred corner bend

Fig 5.47. Waveguide twist

by fitting straight lengths of guide into specially shaped corner pieces which are available commercially. They may also be constructed as shown in Fig 5.45. The mid-point length L should be an odd number of quarter guide-wavelengths so that reflections at the two discontinuities tend to cancel. Mitred corner bends are also possible as shown in Fig 5.46. "Twists" are pieces of waveguide which, as their name implies, are twisted through an angle so that equipment using one plane of polarisation may be connected directly to another of differing polarisation. Commonly, the angle of rotation is made 90° (see Fig 5.47). Twists may be made using the same techniques as for large bends, and their length should again be several wavelengths.

5.6.6 Waveguide flanges

Flanges are used to connect lengths of waveguide and waveguide components together. For each size of waveguide these are standardised, but often there are two or three types. For example, there are two common types used to join WG16 – the square type with four holes for bolts, and the round type which are joined together with a pair of coupling/locating rings (see Figs 5.48 and 5.49).

Within each type there also a number of variations. Often provision is made for an O-ring for sealing, with a circular groove cut in the face of one flange. This type should be used for outdoor joints with a suitable O-ring. Also, the flange may be of the "choke" type, whereby it is arranged that the waveguides do not quite meet at the join but are held slightly apart – see Fig 5.50. One flange of this type is used together with a plain flange (do not use two choke flanges together) and it is intended to provide rf electrical continuity without physical continuity. This is to prevent arcing in high-power equipment across what could otherwise be an intermittent joint, and it also reduces leakage; the powers used in amateur equipment are too low for this to be a problem and plain flanges are satisfactory.

Plain flanges may be fitted to waveguide so that a small amount of the guide protrudes, and then soldered

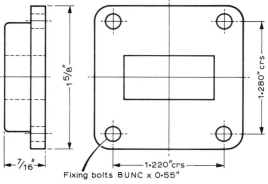

Fig 5.48. Square flange for waveguide 16

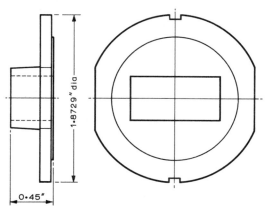

Fig 5.49. Round flange for waveguide 16

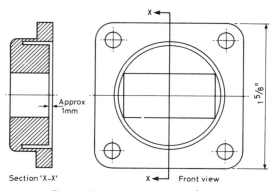

Fig 5.50. Choke flange for waveguide 16

Fig 5.51. Atmospheric ducts

or brazed in place. The excess waveguide may be trimmed off by turning in a lathe or alternatively by filing them and rubbing the end on carbide paper. Choke flanges must either be fitted exactly in the first place or the end trimmed using a lathe.

5.6.7 Dielectric waveguide

Most people are familiar with the idea of using metallic conductors to confine and route electric currents and fields. However, insulating dielectrics can also be used to guide waves. Familiar examples of this are atmospheric ducting at vhf and microwaves, and optical waveguides using glass fibres.

The guiding action can be explained in a number of ways, but in general terms waves can be trapped inside areas of higher dielectric constant. In the same way that waves can be reflected by sudden changes in conductivity, eg at the surface of a metal plate, they can also be reflected by changes in the dielectric constant. At optical frequencies an example is the reflection seen in a plate glass window, which is particularly strong when the light just glances off the surface at a small angle.

However, these reflections are not as strong as those when the light passes from a more dense medium, eg glass, into a less dense medium, eg air. Under the right conditions 100 per cent reflection can be obtained, in which case it is known as "total internal" reflection. The same effect can still occur if the boundary between the different dielectric constants is not sudden, but a gradual change.

In summary, waves travelling in a medium whose dielectric constant varies will tend to be bent towards the more dense medium. The paths of waves in the atmosphere under ducting conditions demonstrate this, as shown in Fig 5.51.

Just as with metal waveguides, there is a limit to how small the dielectric waveguide can be and still guide the waves effectively. In waveguides which are only a few wavelengths across, there are only a limited number of ways (modes) in which the field can propagate down it. When it is sufficiently small, only one mode can propagate down it, and the waveguide becomes known as "single mode". The dimensions of a typical single-mode optical fibre are given in Fig 5.52.

Unlike metal waveguides, the fields are less well confined, and a considerable amount of energy travels in the cladding as well as in the centre. It is possible to use a single piece of dielectric surrounded by air as a waveguide, but there will be a large amount of energy travelling in the air just outside the dielectric. Provided that no other structure is put within a few wavelengths of the guide to disrupt the field, it will work satisfactorily.

An antenna can be made by introducing irregularities in this dielectric, eg corrugations or a taper. This will cause the wave to leave the guide, and radiate into space. An example of such an antenna is shown in Fig 5.53.

5.7 MEASUREMENTS AND MATCHING

5.7.1 VSWR

One of the main reasons for wanting unity vswr is for interchangeability of components. A matched component can be placed in a matched system without disturbing the operation of either. A few general points are:

(a) Few amateur measurements of vswr below about 1.3 are accurate above vhf.

(b) Power reflected from a load which presents a low vswr (eg <2) is neither lost nor dissipated in the transmitter. Any transmitter that is reasonably efficient will appear as a bad match to the line, and so will return reflected power to the load again. The line becomes part of the matching network between the pa and the load, so the transmitter just sees a slightly different load impedance. By retuning the transmitter output and receiver input circuitry, the original performance into a 50Ω load can be restored. This is easier with valve pas than semiconductor types.

(c) A vswr on a feeder does not make it radiate. Radiation results from connecting a balanced antenna to an unbalanced feeder (eg connecting a dipole to coaxial cable, so that currents flow on the outer of the cable). A line can have any vswr on it and still not radiate, or have unity vswr and still radiate. The fields inside and outside the line are completely separate.

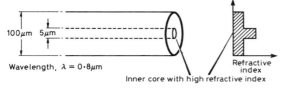

Fig 5.52. Optical-fibre waveguide

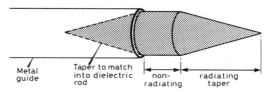

Fig 5.53. Dielectric-waveguide antenna

(d) Using a length of line that is the wrong characteristic impedance, but a multiple of $\lambda/2$, does not prevent a vswr from existing on that piece of line. It means that its input impedance is the same as the load at its far end, so the whole line appears to be matched at that frequency.

(e) The vswr in a system of several components, each introducing their own small vswr, will increase rapidly with the number of components, as the overall worst-case vswr is the product of all the individual vswrs.

(f) The value of a vswr does not tell you what impedance the mismatched line will present. It specifies the degree of uncertainty in the mismatch – there are a large number of combinations of R, L and C that will give a particular vswr. You will go through them all as you increase or decrease the length of line by $\lambda/2$. A poor vswr can mean an impedance greater or less than 50Ω.

5.7.2 Situations where vswr is important

When many antennas are used in a stacked array, the splitting of power between the antennas has to be done accurately, and poor vswr (eg each antenna presenting a mismatch, or a badly matched phasing harness) causes uncertainty in the impedances. This can upset the power distribution between the antennas and prevent the full stacking gain from being realised, or produce an undesirable radiation pattern.

On lines carrying high power (near the maximum rating of the cable), a large vswr (eg greater than 3) will cause peaks of I and V every half-wavelength which can cause breakdown (sparking) in the dielectric, or heating of the inner conductor which may melt the dielectric.

In systems with a large bandwidth and long feeder runs, eg in amateur television, a vswr will cause the impedance at the input of the feeder to vary greatly across the bandwidth. The line length represents a large number of wavelengths, and wavelength changes with frequency, so that even over a small frequency band, the effective line length can vary by more than $\lambda/2$, presenting the corresponding range of impedances. In very long feeder runs, the multiple trips up and down the line can cause ghosting on the picture if the vswr is poor.

Any filters, attenuators or power meters etc will be designed to work in a matched line, and different results may be obtained if there is a vswr on the line because the load and source impedances may be different to the design values. Bear in mind, too, that an antenna usually terminates the line properly only at its design frequency – it may present any impedance at harmonics or spurious frequencies. The same is true of filters which usually work by presenting a mismatch outside their passband.

In very-high-performance systems the slight increase in loss due to vswr may be important. But if it is a high-performance system, the losses or load vswr should not be high enough to increase the line loss in the first place!

Very-low-noise preamplifiers are designed to work from a specific source impedance for best noise figure, and are usually adjusted for a 50Ω source. The

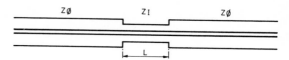

Fig 5.54. Effect of a short length of mismatched line

preamplifier may need to mismatch the feeder and this will create a vswr, but this is intentional and will not degrade the performance in any way, provided that both the antenna and feeder are 50Ω. A vswr due to the feeder or connectors not being 50Ω will degrade the noise figure, unless the preamp matching is re-optimised on that system with that particular piece of feeder.

5.7.3 VSWR due to incorrect line characteristic impedance

If the characteristic impedance and length of each piece of line in a system are known, the vswr can be calculated fairly easily.

First, consider a short mismatch as shown in Fig 5.54. For a piece of line with a vswr of S relative to the rest of the line, if its length L is less than $0.1\times$(wavelength in the cable), the vswr that it introduces to the system will be:

$$\text{VSWR} = 1 + 2\pi \times (S - \frac{1}{S}) \times \frac{L}{\lambda_c}$$

where $S = Z_1/Z_o$. This can be used to estimate the effect of using connectors where parts of them have a different impedance. The impedance Z_1 can be calculated from the dimensions of the conductors and the dielectrics used. The results show that at frequencies up to perhaps 100MHz the effect is not serious, and therefore the mechanical properties of the connector are more important. Above this, however, a constant impedance is desirable.

Second, if the length of mismatched cable is much longer, the vswr can vary between unity and S^2, being unity when the electrical length is an even number of quarter-wavelengths, and S^2 when it is an odd number of quarter-wavelengths. If the actual length of the mismatched section is not known, the worst-case values should be assumed.

When there are several components introducing mismatches, the actual vswr can be calculated if the lengths of line are accurately known. There is, however, a simple expression for the worst-case vswr:

$$\text{VSWR-total} = S1 \times S2 \times S3 \times \ldots$$

where S1, S2, S3 etc are the worst case vswrs of each component. It is evident that a large vswr can build up quite rapidly. If there are four components, each with $S = 1.3$, the total worst case vswr would be 3. Depending on the relative spacing of the mismatches, the overall vswr can vary from unity to the worst-case value, and this effect will be frequency dependent.

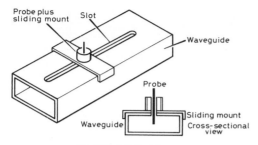

Fig 5.55. A slotted line

If there are just two mismatches in a piece of cable, the worst-case vswr will be S1×S2 and the best case will be S1/S2, where S1 is the larger and S2 the smaller vswr.

5.7.4 Measurement of vswr and impedance

In most cases it is not the existence of an vswr on a line that is important, but the effect that the vswr has on the impedance looking into the input of the line. VSWR can either be measured directly by observing the fields along the line, or be inferred by measuring the input impedance of the line if the load impedance is known. Techniques are:

(a) Use a slotted line to measure the peaks and troughs of the field along the line.

(b) Sample V and I on the line with a coupler.

(c) Measure the input impedance of the line with an impedance bridge.

Slotted lines

This is probably the most direct and basic method of measuring the vswr on a line. At microwave frequencies the wavelength is only a few tens of centimetres, so it is quite practical to observe the actual variations of voltage along the line with a probe.

A slotted line consists of a section of rigid transmission line, either waveguide or coaxial cable, with a thin slot cut along its length so that a probe can be inserted to sample the field (Fig 5.55). It is important that the geometry of the probe in the line should remain constant as it moves along the line, so that any variations seen are due to a vswr and not to mechanical defects of the line.

The relation between maximum and minimum values of the field and the vswr is given below, and plotted in Fig 5.56.

$$\text{SWR} = \frac{1 + r}{1 - r}$$

$$= \frac{V_{max}}{V_{min}}$$

where r is the scalar reflection coefficient, the fraction of the voltage wave reflected from the load.

The term "return loss" is another way of quoting a reflection coefficient. It is the loss in decibels between the incident and reflected waves:

$$\text{return loss (dB)} = 20\log(r)$$

This method is capable of great accuracy provided that the section of line used for sampling is made to a high precision so that its Z_o is accurately known. The accuracy comes mainly from precise mechanical construction, which can be verified with fairly simple instruments such as vernier calipers or a micrometer.

Impedance bridges

There are two types of impedance bridge. The full vector bridge measures both the resistive and reactive parts of the load. The scalar bridge effectively measures the magnitude of the reflection coefficient of the load, which is closely related to the impedance expressed as a vswr.

Often, all that is required is to adjust the impedance of a piece of equipment, eg an antenna, to 50Ω. In this case the scalar bridge is perfectly adequate, and in fact far easier to use.

At hf/vhf it is quite easy to build an accurate scalar bridge which does not require calibration. By using chip resistors and careful construction, a return loss of about 25–30dB can be measured up to uhf. One example of this type of bridge is the noise bridge, which is often used to measure antenna impedance.

The principles of operation are as follows. The bridge is driven with a fixed amplitude signal of a few milliwatts at the frequency at which the impedance is to be measured. A detector must measure the signal level across the bridge without disturbing the balance.

While ferrite baluns are often used to couple out the signal to be detected, it is difficult to make them with the high degree of balance required. It is much easier to use a simple diode detector across the bridge, and bring out the dc voltage through chokes or high-value resistors which will not upset the balance. A design for such a bridge is shown in Fig 5.57. A low source impedance for the rf is needed so that the excitation voltage across the bridge does not change with load.

In practice the bridge is set up in the following way. The drive power is increased to give fsd on the detector with an open- or short-circuit on the test point, and a known load on the other. Then the unknown load is applied and the new detected voltage noted. The return

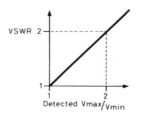

Fig 5.56. VSWR for a slotted line

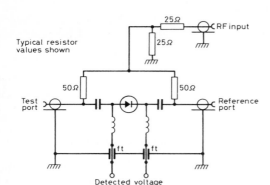

Fig 5.57. Circuit of a resistive bridge

Typical resistor values shown

loss of the load is the ratio of the two detected powers. At low levels the detected voltage is proportional to power, and so the ratio of voltages is often used. It is always a good idea to cross-check measurements on any test gear that is available. It is not unknown for even the most expensive equipment to go wrong sometimes. The relation between vswr and detected power is shown in Fig 5.58.

Couplers

Even though standing waves are produced by interference effects between a forward and a reflected wave, at any instant there is only one value of V and I (or E and H) at any point on the line. Knowing the line Z_o, the swr can be calculated from this one simple measurement.

All conventional swr meters operate by sampling the line current and voltage. At hf it is easy to use lumped components, eg a current transformer in the centre conductor, and a potential divider to get the voltage (Fig 5.59(a)). At vhf/uhf a current transformer would disturb the main line too much, and a short coupled line is used (Fig 5.59(b)). This also samples V and I – the inductive coupling with the inner induces a voltage proportional to the line current. The capacitance between the line and the loop, and the loop and the outer, then provides the potential divider to sample this voltage. Forward and reflected power are then obtained by adding or subtracting the rf

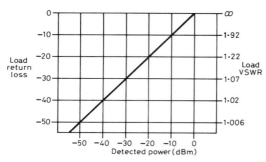

Fig 5.58. Return loss and vswr for detected power

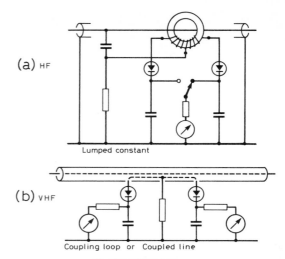

(a) HF

Lumped constant

(b) VHF

Coupling loop or Coupled line

Fig 5.59. VSWR bridges

voltages derived from the V and I samples, as shown in Fig 5.60, and detecting the result. If you consider all possible combinations of phase and amplitude of the two signals, you will see that there is only one combination where the two signals are equal in amplitude and 180° out of phase, so they cancel to give zero output. This is arranged to correspond to zero reflected power by choice of the component values as below.

The voltages induced in the coupling loop are given by:

$$V_i = j \times w \times M \times I$$
$$V_e = j \times w \times C \times R \times E$$

This assumes that the reactance of C is much greater than that of R. The condition for the two voltages to cancel each other is that:

$$M \times I = C \times R \times E$$

The ratio E/I is the characteristic impedance of the line Z_o, giving as the condition for balance:

$$R = \frac{M}{Z_o \times C}$$

The same exercise for the case where a separate coupled line is used shows that a null is obtained when the resistive load on the coupled line is made equal to

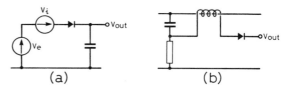

(a)   (b)

Fig 5.60. Equivalent circuits of vswr bridge

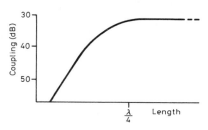

Fig 5.61. Coupling versus line length for a coupler

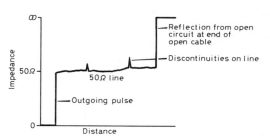

Fig 5.63. Typical display on a tdr

the Z_0 of the coupled line, so that it is matched. This also applies to designs which use coupled lines which are short compared with a wavelength, and these are the main type used at microwaves.

The coupling is relatively independent of frequency when the coupled part of the lines is a quarter-wavelength. When the coupled lines are much shorter than a quarter-wavelength, the coupling increases with frequency. Once they are longer than a quarter-wavelength, the coupling becomes more narrowband again. A graph of coupling coefficient against length of the coupled section is shown in Fig 5.61.

Thus any accurate directional coupler or swr bridge either needs to be built to a high degree of precision, or needs setting up with a known load on the main line. These instruments are easier to build and calibrate if the coupling between any probes or lines and the main line is fairly weak, eg less than 20dB.

The instruments used professionally to measure rf impedances and vswr are the time-domain reflectometer (tdr) and the network analyser. Both essentially make the same measurement on the device to be tested, but do so in different ways. They both send energy out of their test port at all frequencies in the band of interest, and measure and display what is reflected back. Although these instruments are very expensive, it is often possible to make use of these techniques at home albeit with lower accuracies or reduced frequency coverages.

The time-domain reflectometer

A tdr is basically a pulse generator with a 50Ω source impedance and a high-input-impedance oscilloscope (see Fig 5.62). The pulse generator produces a series of rectangular pulses at a low repetition rate, say, hundreds of kilohertz, with very fast rise times – from 1 to 0.01ns. The scope has a rise time similar to that of the

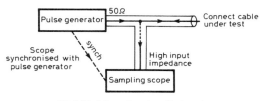

Fig 5.62. A time-domain reflectometer

pulses, and would in this case be a sampling scope. The pulse generator has a source impedance of 50Ω and sends pulses down the line to be examined. Any discontinuity in this line reflects some of the pulse's energy, and both the outgoing pulses and reflected signals are seen on the scope. The pulse generator matches the line, so that signals returned to it are not sent down the line again, which would confuse the display.

The scope sweep is synchronised to the pulse repetition frequency, so a display such as Fig 5.63 would be seen. Thus the pulse is seen on the scope as it is generated, the voltage corresponding to a 50Ω "surge impedance" of the cable. The signal reflected from the end of the cable will return after the time taken to travel twice the length of the cable. An open-circuit reflects the voltage in phase with the incident signal, a short-circuit in anti-phase.

The main application of this instrument is in examining connectors and short lengths of cable to check their characteristic impedance, as the scope display is essentially a plot of Z_0 against distance along the cable. It will show up incorrectly assembled plugs, eg where an air gap has been left if the dielectric has been cut too short, resulting in a higher Z_0. An example is shown at "a" in Fig 5.64. An air line with a slug of dielectric in it would reduce the Z_0 at the slug. This would be seen at "b" in Fig 5.65. The magnitude of the reflection coefficient can be measured by:

$$\frac{\text{height of reflected wave}}{V_{out}}$$

To get the resolution needed to examine the small distances involved in connectors, very fast rise times are

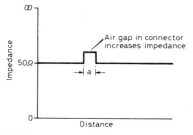

Fig 5.64. TDR display of an incorrectly assembled rf connector

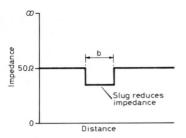

Fig 5.65. TDR display of an air line, showing slug of dielectric in the line

necessary, of the order of 10 to 20ps, which implies frequencies up to 10 or 20GHz are present. This can only be used with short lengths of low-loss line, typically up to a few feet long, otherwise the high-frequency components will be attenuated by the line and lost, which effectively increases the rise time of the reflected pulse and impairs the resolution.

It is also used with much slower rise time pulses to look at much longer lines, and locate faults in cables. The resolution obtained along the length is approximately one-tenth of the wavelength of the frequency corresponding to the rise time, eg:

20ps	10GHz	0.1in	(approx 2.6mm)
100ns	200MHz	5in	(approx 127mm)
10ns	20MHz	4ft	(approx 1,219mm)

A simple tdr for use at lower frequencies could be built using ttl or ecl gates to generate pulses, and an ordinary scope for display. In many ways, a tdr is like a radar system, looking down a cable instead of out into space.

The pulses which the tdr sends down the line contain energy at almost all frequencies up to a limit defined by the pulse rise time, so it is probing the line at all frequencies simultaneously, and displays the result as a plot of impedance against line length. The only slight disadvantage with it is that it only works on lines which have a response down to dc, so it will not work in waveguides (which are dispersive anyway).

The network analyser

The other instrument, the network analyser, has an oscillator which it sweeps over the band of interest, and a directional coupler which samples the reflected signals, so their phase and amplitude relative to the forward signal can be measured (see Fig 5.66).

This information is displayed on a screen as the frequency is swept and is usually presented in one of two display modes: return loss or polar (Smith chart) display (see next section). Return loss plots the magnitude of the reflected signal vertically on a logarithmic display, and frequency horizontally. From this, the reflection coefficient and hence the vswr can be calculated. The

phase information is discarded as in an ordinary vswr bridge.

For the polar display, the phase information is utilised, and a Smith chart overlay of coordinates is often provided. The magnitude of the reflected signal deflects the spot radially, and the phase deflects it around the circle so that it plots the impedance at its test port directly on the Smith chart. This is the basic instrument used to measure S-parameters of devices.

So far only its application to a single-port network has been mentioned, but it can also be used to measure the gain or attenuation (ie transmission characteristics) of two-port devices. If a signal from the output of the network under test, rather than the signal reflected from its input, is compared with the forward (reference) signal, the amplitude and phase response from the input to the output of the network can be measured. Thus the amplitude and phase response of amplifiers, filters and attenuators can easily be plotted against frequency.

This can also be used with either type of display, depending on whether the phase information is required. So the instrument can be used either to measure impedances of single-port or two-port networks (eg loads or the input and output impedances of an amplifier), or the gain and phase characteristics of any active or passive two-port networks (eg amplifiers, attenuators etc).

The network analyser can be used over any band of frequencies, and does not require the line or device to respond down to dc, as is the case with the tdr. This instrument also probes the device to be tested at all frequencies, but does so sequentially rather than simultaneously, and presents the information in a completely different way to the tdr – the display is a plot of impedance against frequency.

In principle it would be possible to convert the information from either a tdr or network analyser display to the other. The same information is there in both displays, but the process is quite complicated and would require the services of the infamous microprocessor.

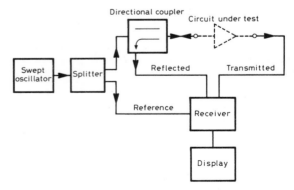

Fig 5.66. Block diagram of a network analyser

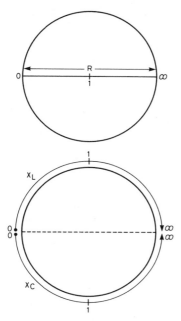

Fig 5.67. Basic axes of a Smith chart

5.7.5 Smith charts

These are often thought of as being rather esoteric and theoretical, and they can certainly be used in that way. However, they can also serve as a useful aide-memoire for the whole subject of transmission lines, matching and vswr, as well as being useful for calculations and as a means of displaying impedances. They will be explained quite simply from this viewpoint, starting from a few basic principles about vswrs.

By using a seemingly rather strange set of non-linear scales, the Smith chart manages to represent all of the infinite number of possible combinations of reactance and resistance (ie vswrs) within a single circle. Those interested in a mathematical treatment should consult the standard reference text [10].

The main axes of the chart are shown in Fig 5.67. Any purely reactive impedance can be represented by a point somewhere on the outer circle. Capacitive reactances ranging from zero to infinity are on the bottom semicircle, inductive reactances from zero to infinity are on the top semicircle. A pure resistance between zero and infinity will be a point along the horizontal diameter line. These are the basic axes of the chart. All combinations of resistance and reactance will be points somewhere within this circle. All the other lines correspond to specific values of resistance or reactance, and circles, or parts of circles, which all pass through a point on the right-hand edge of the chart. The values are given in units normalised to the line impedance used. Usually this is 50Ω, so an impedance of 100 + j50 would be

given by the coordinates 2 + j1. The chart is therefore useful as a means of presenting a complex impedance as a function of frequency – many transistors now have their parameters presented as a line on a Smith chart in the data sheets. The line has markings to indicate frequencies at which the impedances were measured.

The next step is to apply the chart to transmission lines. Since the centre of the chart represents the line's characteristic impedance, the input impedance of a length of line when correctly terminated will be at the centre of the chart. If the line has a mismatched load, say, a 200Ω resistor, this corresponds to a load of 4 + j0, and a vswr of 4:1. However, as the length of cable between the load and the impedance meter increases, the impedance will vary through all the range of impedances which correspond to a vswr of 4:1, one particular value being 12.5 + j0 at a quarter-wave from the load. In fact, the range of impedances seen as the line length varies is a circle on the Smith chart centred on the centre of the chart (Fig 5.68). The radius becomes larger the larger the vswr. A vswr of 1:1 corresponds to a radius of zero, ie a dot in the centre, always 50Ω; an infinite vswr is a radius of the outside of the chart, ie purely reactive impedances. The vswr can be easily seen by the value of resistance where the circle crosses the resistive diameter – a resistance of 12.5 or 200Ω.

The radius of the vswr circle is another "axis" of the chart, and can be used to specify a particular range of impedances.

It is well known that voltage and current values repeat themselves every half-wavelength on a mismatched line. For this to occur, one trip round the circle

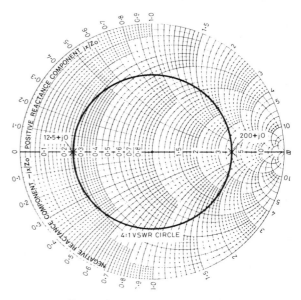

Fig 5.68. Smith chart showing a 4:1 swr

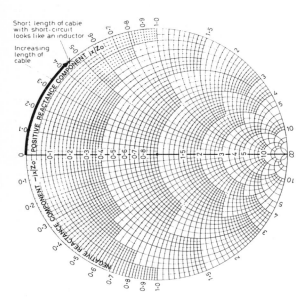

Fig 5.69. Smith chart plot of a shorted stub

must correspond to travelling one half-wavelength along a cable. A quarter-wavelength then corresponds to 180° around the chart. This illustrates the quarter-wave transformer effect, where a short-circuited quarter-wave line looks like on open-circuit, and vice versa.

Take a short length of cable with a short-circuit across it. You would expect it to look like a small inductance – the reactance is given by rotating the corresponding amount clockwise from the short-circuit

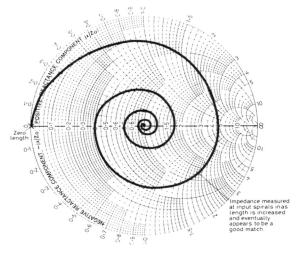

Fig 5.70. Smith chart of a long length of lossy line

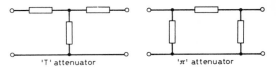

Fig 5.71. T and π attenuators

point on the chart (Fig 5.69). Likewise, a short length of cable with an open-circuit looks like a capacitance – rotate a small amount clockwise from an open-circuit, and you see a small capacitive reactance.

So putting a length of cable between the load and the test port is equivalent to travelling around a circle of constant vswr (the load). In real life cables are lossy, and this loss improves the apparent vswr of the load. In fact a very long length of lossy cable looks like a perfect match (Fig 5.70). Losses in the cable improve the apparent vswr as the cable length increases and thus correspond to spiralling in to the centre from the outside (a perfect mismatch).

This has hopefully provided an introduction to the Smith chart, and made it possible for readers to at least get a feel for the impedances presented on it. If you want to use the chart for some of the more theoretical calculations then you should refer to other textbooks where these applications are explained.

5.8 SIMPLE PASSIVE COMPONENTS

5.8.1 Coaxial loads and attenuators

There are two types of coaxial attenuators. The first, and most common, uses discrete resistors in series and shunt with the inner conductor. This type works down to dc, but is limited at high frequencies by inductances in the resistor leads. At microwave frequencies, it is not possible to use normal-leaded components, and chip or coaxial resistors are used. To avoid an impedance mismatch, the resistors are arranged in either a "T" or "π" form within the coaxial line (see Fig 5.71), so that the correct characteristic impedance is seen from either end.

The second type of attenuator consists of either a lossy inner conductor or dielectric (Fig 5.72). Provided the losses are low, in terms of decibels per wavelength, the match will be very good; however, this type does not

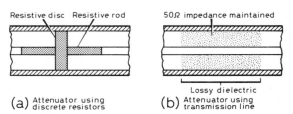

Fig 5.72. Transmission-line attenuators

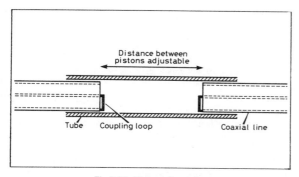

Fig 5.73. Piston attenuator

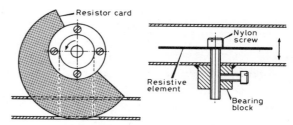

Fig 5.75. Variable waveguide attenuators

work down to dc and the attenuation varies with frequency.

Loads may similarly be built from either discrete resistors or long lengths of lossy line. This second type is particularly convenient for dissipating high powers, and a long length of coaxial cable (with 10 or 20dB of attenuation) is often used as a dummy load for a transmitter (see the "Data" chapter in Volume 2 for cable losses). For a high-power load, the main problem is getting heat away from the lossy element. This conflicts with the requirement that the load should be small to minimise stray reactances. Often special cooling techniques are used, eg oil or beryllia.

Variable attenuators are often made by switching fixed attenuators, eg in steps of 1dB or 10dB. At microwave frequencies this becomes difficult to do without the switch degrading the vswr and a more practical approach is the piston attenuator, as shown in Fig 5.73. This relies upon using a length of metal tube as a waveguide below cut-off, in which signals decay exponentially with distance. The signals are coupled in and out of the tube using small loops. These are capable of providing smoothly adjustable attenuation over a range of 100dB, with fairly linear calibration.

5.8.2 Waveguide attenuators and loads

The function of an attenuator is to absorb power from a transmission line without reflecting it – ie by converting it to heat. The most common form in waveguide is a sheet of lossy material (eg carbon-coated card) mounted parallel to the E-field, as shown in Fig 5.74.

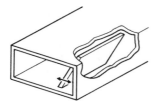

Fig 5.74. Waveguide attenuator

For maximum attenuation, the material should be mounted in the region of maximum E-field, between the middle of the two broad faces. The attenuation can be increased by moving the lossy card into the centre of the guide from either one side or the top, or by rotating the card from being perpendicular to being parallel to the E-field. Some methods of construction are shown in Fig 5.75.

A piece of lossy material in the guide represents a discontinuity which would reflect energy. This is avoided by tapering each end over a wavelength or so. This provides a gradual, matched transition between normal waveguide and the lossy section of line. Suitable materials are wedges of wood or conductive (cmos) foam, or card with graphite powder bonded to it. Be warned that the resistivity of cmos foam can vary considerably between types and can be very high. Lower-resistivity types are usually needed for attenuators and loads. Homemade resistive card can be prepared with a soft pencil on stiff card, and then sprayed with lacquer. The supports for the absorbing material should, of course, be insulators.

A matched load is an attenuator where all (or virtually all) the power is absorbed in the lossy material before it reaches the end, where there is generally a short-circuit. The most common form is a length of tapered wood or lossy ferrite-loaded material mounted in the guide with a shorting plate at the far end, as shown in Fig 5.76. The material usually tapers in thickness across both the broad and narrow faces of the guide until it occupies the whole cross-section of the guide. This taper is normally done over a distance of several wavelengths – the longer the taper, the better the match. The loss should be

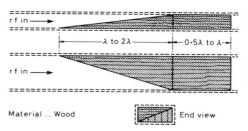

Fig 5.76. Matched waveguide load

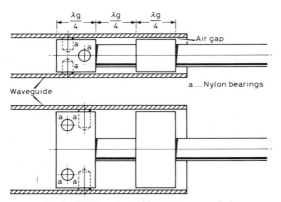

Fig 5.77. Sliding short with quarter-wave chokes

greater than half the return loss required of the load, ie the loss should be 15 to 20dB.

5.8.3 Sliding shorts

Sliding shorts can be used to form an adjustable cavity and can be a useful item of test equipment. If a micrometer is fitted to the moving short, it can be used as a simple wavemeter.

The simplest form of short consists of a block which is clamped in place after adjustment. If the block is a good fit in the guide then its length is uncritical. However, it should be about $\lambda_g/4$ in length if not. Fingering, or braiding fitted in a groove in the block, can be used to ensure good contact with the waveguide.

A better form of short includes a choke as shown in Fig 5.77. Here two blocks are used, each $\lambda_g/4$ and spaced $\lambda_g/4$ apart, which are insulated from the waveguide, forming quarter-wave chokes. Using this arrangement there will be no intermittent contact between the short and guide, thus making it more reliable.

5.8.4 Baluns

These are used to convert signals between lines which are balanced and unbalanced with respect to earth. Their most common use is to match between a balanced antenna, eg a dipole, and an unbalanced feeder, eg coaxial cable. They are also used in some components,

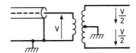

Fig 5.79. Schematic diagram of a 1:1 balun

eg a balanced mixer, and may provide an impedance step-up or step-down.

Examples of unbalanced components are coaxial cable, microstrip, stripline, quarter-wave whips on a ground plane, and any transmission line with only one conductor which works against a ground plane. Balanced components include twin-wire transmission line and dipoles.

Fig 5.78 shows a balanced and an unbalanced line which have to be connected together. Each has the same Z_0 so, for the same power to exist on each, the voltages have to match as shown. A 1:1 balun therefore has to convert a single voltage V into two voltages each V/2, and 180° out of phase with each other. These are represented as phasors in the figure. A 1:1 balun is therefore a transformer with a centre-tapped output, as shown in Fig 5.79. At hf and vhf quite broadband baluns are possible using transmission-line type transformers on ferrite cores, and bandwidths of over a decade are common for small-signal devices. At uhf and microwave frequencies the stray reactances make it difficult to use transformers, and resonant baluns are used.

The quarter-wave balun consists of a twin-wire line with one end short-circuited. This end is connected to earth, as shown in Fig 5.80. Due to the symmetry, any voltage which appears across the two ends must be symmetrical about earth. It can be likened to a parallel-tuned circuit with an earthed centre tap. The unbalanced input signal is connected between earth and one of the ends of the twin line, and the balanced output is taken from the two ends of the twin line. This balun produces a voltage step up of two, and so an impedance ratio of 4:1.

The Z_0 of the twin line is not critical, but should be of the same order of magnitude as the input line. The ratio between the two affects the bandwidth of the balun.

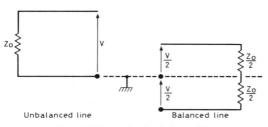

Fig 5.78. Balanced and unbalanced lines

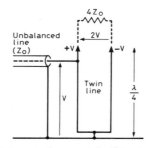

Fig 5.80. Schematic diagram of a quarter-wave 4:1 balun

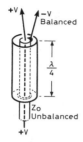

Fig 5.81. 4:1 quarter-wave sleeve balun

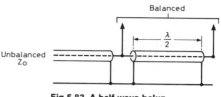

Fig 5.83. A half-wave balun

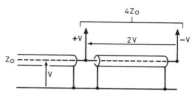

Fig 5.84. Operation of a half-wave balun

Practical examples of this type are the sleeve balun, and one made from semi-rigid cable.

The sleeve balun is shown in Fig 5.81. In this case the quarter-wave stub is made from a coaxial line, not a twin line. The outer metal sleeve is connected to the coaxial cable outer conductor at a quarter-wavelength from the end of the cable. This quarter-wavelength has to be in the dielectric between the outer metal sleeve and the cable's outer conductor. It may be air or the plastic jacket of the cable, but is not related to the velocity factor of the coaxial cable itself.

The other type makes the twin line by cutting slots in the cable outer for the last quarter-wavelength, as shown in Fig 5.82. In this case the velocity factor will be somewhere between that of the cable and that of air.

The half-wave balun is also very similar. This uses a half-wavelength of line to provide the 180° phase shift to generate the other balanced output, as shown in Fig 5.83. This is also a 4:1 impedance ratio. The relevant voltages are shown in Fig 5.84. The load on the far end of the half-wave line is half the balanced output load, so the line must have this Z_0, which will be twice that of the input, ie 100Ω in a 50Ω system.

5.8.5 Waveguide transitions

Very often it is necessary to change between waveguide and coaxial line. This can be done quite simply using a transition, which basically consists of a probe from a coaxial socket protruding into a shorted length of waveguide. A simple design is shown in Fig 5.85.

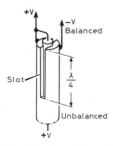

Fig 5.82. Another form of sleeve balun

The position of the probe relative to the short, the length of the probe and its diameter determine the operating frequency and the impedance seen looking into the coaxial socket. For a given impedance, which will normally be 50Ω, only certain combinations of these three parameters are possible. Some commercial transitions also have a dielectric surrounding the probe. Some designs for individual bands are given in the appropriate chapters in Volume 3. The bandwidths can be increased by the dielectric sleeve, or using a larger-diameter probe.

The simple probe type of transition is usually narrowband but broader band transitions may be made by tapering the guide as shown in Fig 5.86. This reduces the impedance of the guide from its normal value of a few hundreds of ohms to a similar value to that of the coaxial line. A third type uses a T-bar across the guide,

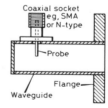

Fig 5.85. A simple waveguide transition

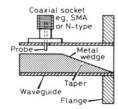

Fig 5.86. Tapered waveguide transition

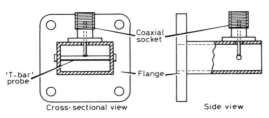

Fig 5.87. T-bar type transition

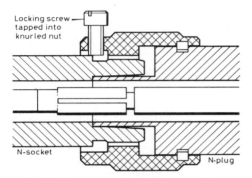

Fig 5.88. Contacting rotary joint for coaxial lines

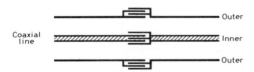

Fig 5.89. Non-contacting rotary joint for coaxial lines

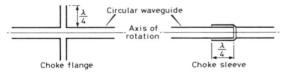

Fig 5.90. Rotary joint for circularly polarised waveguide

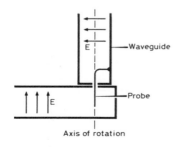

Fig 5.91. Rotary joints for linearly polarised waveguide

as shown in Fig 5.87. These also operate over a wider band than the simple probe.

5.8.6 Rotary joints

These are useful at microwave frequencies because the cables and waveguides used are much less flexible than at hf or vhf. Their main application is to connect fixed equipment to a rotatable antenna.

Coaxial joints may have fingering to maintain a connection at dc, but a moving metallic contact is undesirable as it is likely to generate noise and become unreliable. The best coupling relies on capacitance between the two conductors.

The contact type is illustrated in Fig 5.88. This can be made using an N-type plug and socket, and not tightening the outer knurled nut fully; the nut can be locked against the socket body with a grub screw. Although not waterproof, and of limited life, such a joint has carried several hundred watts at uhf while slowly rotating.

At uhf and microwave frequencies it is relatively easy to make a capacitance whose reactance is small compared with 50Ω, either by a simple pin and sleeve, or a more complex set of concentric cylinders with a thin dielectric, rather like a beehive trimmer (see Fig 5.89). If the overlap is a quarter-wave long, then the open-circuit at the inside end will appear as a low impedance between the lines at the outside end. An alternative for the outer would be two large-diameter discs. These quarter-wave chokes can provide a very effective connection with low rf leakage.

In circularly polarised waveguide the relative angular position of the two guides does not matter provided the rotational speed is small compared with the frequency (this is not usually a problem!). It is then only necessary to provide enough capacitance between the ends of the guides to reduce the leakage. This can be done with a choke flange, which could be implemented as a sleeve overlap, as shown in Fig 5.90.

In linearly polarised waveguide the fields have to be transferred between the two guides by a means which is independent of angle; one such method commonly used in rectangular waveguide is shown in Fig 5.91. It uses a loop to couple the signal into a coaxial line which then passes through the rotating joint and couples into the new guide as an E-field probe, its coupling being independent of angular position. Another method is to make a transition to circular guide, passing through the rotary joint in circular guide, and returning to linear on the other side. A waveguide rotary joint of the latter type is shown in Fig 5.92.

5.8.7 Coaxial relays

Coaxial relays are required primarily for changing over from transmit to receive. On the lower bands this probably means switching the antenna from the power amplifier output to the preamp input, and possibly switching over a transceiver or transverter.

Coaxial relays vary from simple types capable of handling a few watts with acceptable losses up to perhaps 500MHz or 1GHz, to precision high-power types that can be used up to 10GHz. The performance is determined by the internal construction and, in addition to the loss and vswr, it is also important what happens during switching.

The simple types do not maintain a true 50Ω characteristic impedance through the relay. Often the relay will work by having a line between the common port and the two other ports, sprung so that it rests against one or the other port when unenergised, and a solenoid is used to move it to the other port when activated. A relay of this type is shown in Fig 5.93. The principal disadvantage of this type is that, when switching, the moveable contact will momentarily lie between the two ports and there will be very poor isolation between them. If one port has a high-power amplifier connected to it and the other a low-noise preamp, there could be a serious problem!

A particularly good type is shown in Fig 5.94. This type uses two moveable line sections, such that the common port is connected to one or other port with one of these line sections in place. When the relay is energised this line section is moved away and the other section to the other port moved into position. Using this method it is possible to keep the characteristic impedance inside the relay close to 50Ω, and to provide a much higher isolation between ports compared to the simple type. These relays, when properly constructed, are capable of carrying hundreds of watts at microwave frequencies, and have isolations of around 50dB.

Another useful type of relay is the miniature TO5 can type, for use at i.f (see Fig 5.95). These can be used up to about 500MHz and several watts, for example to switch a vhf transceiver on the input to a transverter. Unfortunately they are rather expensive in amateur terms, and their use is mainly restricted to professional equipment.

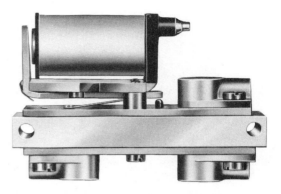

Fig 5.93. Conventional coaxial changeover switch

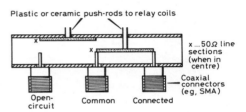

Fig 5.94. Coaxial relay with improved isolation and match

5.8.8 Waveguide switches

Waveguide switches are also useful for transmit/receive changeover. Commercial switches are usually four-port devices as shown in Fig 5.96. The switch consists of an outer block, usually square, with one port in each face. Inside this is a round inner block with two bends cast so that two pairs of adjacent ports are joined together. This inner block is free to rotate so that the ports connected together can be swopped over. Stops are provided to limit the rotation to exactly 90° and ensure exact alignment of the bends with the ports.

With this simple arrangement it is possible for a small amount of power to leak round the gap between the rotating block and outer block. To overcome this,

Fig 5.92. Waveguide rotary joint

Fig 5.95. Miniature TO-5 relay

Fig 5.96. Professional waveguide switch

high-performance switches have grooves machined in the circumference of the rotating block. These are a quarter-wave deep and act as chokes, and may be filled with a lossy material to improve the isolation. Usually there will be two of these, spaced a quarter-wave apart for maximum attenuation, which can be around 70dB.

If waveguide relays are required, the basic switch is fitted with a solenoid operated stepper motor (known as a "Ledex"). When operating, these relays take large pulses of current and provide sufficient torque to turn the switch round quickly. They can produce high-voltage, high-energy transients which can damage power supplies or other equipment, and should be suppressed with diodes or voltage-dependent resistors (vdrs).

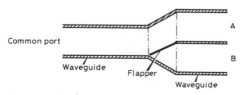

Fig 5.97. Simpler amateur version of changeover switch

This type of switch is not easy for the amateur to build, and an alternative is shown in Fig 5.97. Here a flapper is used to switch one common waveguide port between two other ports. This type will not have a very good isolation, but this is not important for many applications.

5.8.9 Phase shifters

These are used to add a variable phase shift to a signal. They operate by introducing dielectric into the guide, which reduces the velocity and makes the waveguide appear longer. The delay is usually variable over the range 0 to 360°.

The construction is similar to that of waveguide attenuators, as shown in Fig 5.98. A thin strip of dielectric is mounted on rods so that it can be moved from the edge into the centre of the guide. Its effect is negligible when against the conductive wall, and maximum when in the middle of the guide in the maximum part of the E-field. The ends are usually tapered to minimise reflections from the discontinuity.

5.9 SPLITTERS AND COMBINERS

These devices are used to divide power from one source amongst a number of other loads. A two-way splitter will be used for the purposes of illustration, but it could apply to any number of ports.

A number of types of splitter are used, differing in the insertion loss and isolation they provide between each of the ports.

An ideal, lossless, two-way splitter would split the signal into two parts, with a loss of 3dB into each port. No power would be lost, as it would all end up at one port or the other. Such a splitter could be built from a transformer, as shown in Fig 5.99. However, there would be little isolation between the ports and, if one of the loads had a poor vwsr, it would alter the amount of power reaching the other load. Hybrid splitters have been developed to give a minimum loss and good isolation between the ports.

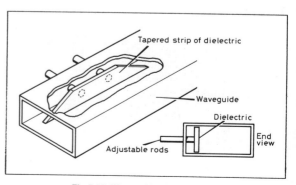

Fig 5.98. Waveguide phase shifter

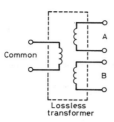

Fig 5.99. 3dB splitter using a transformer

Table 5.5. Losses of matched resistive and hybrid splitters

No of ways	Loss resistive (dB)	Loss hybrid (dB)	Excess loss for resistive combiner (dB)
2	6.02	3.01	3.01
3	9.54	4.77	4.77
4	12.04	6.02	6.02
6	15.56	7.78	7.78
8	18.06	9.03	9.03

The losses of matched resistive and hybrid splitters are compared in Table 5.5.

5.9.1 Resistive splitters

Several types of resistive splitters are used, shown in Fig 5.100. Resistor values for the two-resistor splitter are given by:

$$R = (N-1) \times Z_o$$

$$\text{Loss (dB)} = 20\log(N)$$

where N is the number of output ports.

While the input presents a good match with both loads connected, the impedance looking into each output port is not a good match. This type is only meant for use as an output to a detector in a levelling loop, where the loop will affect the output impedances anyway by varying the generator output level.

Resistor values for the three-resistor combiner can be calculated from the expression:

$$R = Z_o \times \frac{(N-1)}{(N+1)}$$

Insertion loss is given by:

$$\text{Loss (dB)} = 20\log(N)$$

This type gives a good vswr at all ports when the other ports are matched. It can also be built as a delta instead of a star network. This type of splitter must be used if a number of pieces of equipment are to be connected together, so that they all "see" each other equally.

5.9.2 Hybrid splitters

If you want to ensure that each port always presents a matched load when the load on the other port varies,

you must use a hybrid splitter. This has a 3dB insertion loss and theoretically infinite isolation between the output ports. If one load is mismatched, this does not alter either the impedance seen by the source, or the power reaching the other load. In practice, the isolation is around 30dB.

The basic device is shown in Fig 5.101. It has two inputs and two outputs. The outputs are the sum and difference of the two input ports. In normal operation the difference port is connected to a 50Ω load.

As a splitter, it divides the input power equally between the two output ports, with no other losses. If one port is mismatched, this does not affect the power appearing at the other port. The imbalance is concealed by the fact that some power is now being dissipated in the internal termination. When the device is used as a combiner, the signal from each input is split equally between the internal load and the output. Thus there is a loss of 3dB from each input to the output.

Hybrid splitters can be built in either coaxial or waveguide circuitry. In coaxial circuitry the splitter is made using transformers to generate the in-phase and out-of-phase signals.

In waveguide the hybrid splitter is known as a "magic tee" or "hybrid tee", which probably gives some idea that its operation was not well understood. It has four ports (Fig 5.102), all of which are accessible. In normal operation a load is placed on the sum or difference port, depending whether an in-phase or 180° splitter is required. The operation is shown in Fig 5.103, where the splitting of power is represented by E-field vectors.

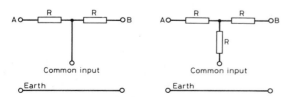

Fig 5.100. Circuits of resistive splitters

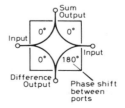

Fig 5.101. Circuit of a hybrid splitter

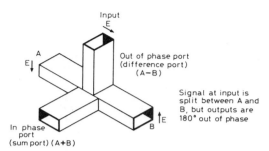

Fig 5.102. The magic tee

5.10 DIRECTIONAL COUPLERS

A directional coupler consists of two transmission lines which can interact electrically so that a proportion of the power flowing in one line is fed to the second in one direction only – see Fig 5.104. If power is supplied to port A, then a fraction appears at port D and the remainder at port B. In practice some power will also appear at port C. The coupling factor, which is the loss between the power in the main line and that in the coupled line, is defined as:

$$\text{Coupling factor (dB)} = 10 \times \log(\frac{P_a}{P_d})$$

Typical values range from 3 to 60dB. With a 3dB coupling factor there will also be a 3dB loss from port A to port B. As the coupling is reduced, this loss will also decrease. A graph of insertion loss versus coupling is shown in Fig 5.105.

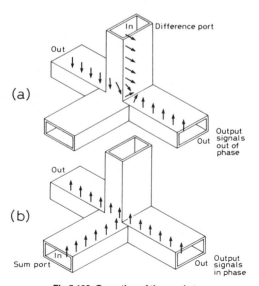

Fig 5.103. Operation of the magic tee

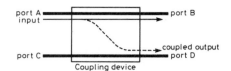

Fig 5.104. Power flow in a directional coupler

The directivity is defined as the ratio of the powers at each end of the coupled line, when the main line is correctly terminated:

$$\text{Directivity (dB)} = 10 \times \log(\frac{P_d}{P_c})$$

In a well-designed coupler the directivity will be typically 30dB. A more-detailed explanation of its operation can be found in the section on vswr and impedance bridges.

Directional couplers can be constructed from a variety of transmission lines and some common types are described below.

5.10.1 Coaxial couplers

Coaxial couplers can be made by placing two coaxial lines side by side with a part of the outer of each removed. An example is shown in Fig 5.106, built from two semi-rigid lines soldered together.

The slots, which are less than a quarter-wave long, allow the field to leak out into the coupled line and reproduce the forward and reflected waves in the coupled line. A high directivity can be obtained, provided the coupling is not too great, and lines of equal characteristic impedance are used. This means in practice a maximum coupling of around 30dB, otherwise the slots become too wide and begin to alter the impedance of the lines.

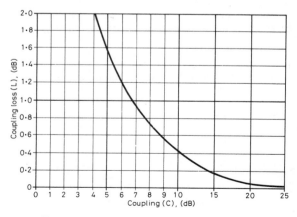

Fig 5.105. Insertion loss versus coupling coefficient

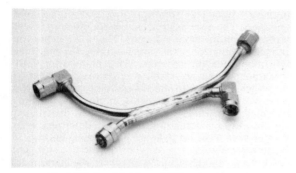

Fig 5.106. Semi-rigid coaxial directional coupler

5.10.2 Stripline and microstrip couplers

Stripline and microstrip couplers may be made in a similar manner to the simple coaxial-line coupler described above. An example is shown in Fig 5.107(a), where it is arranged for two sections of microstrip to run close to each other to allow coupling to take place. Coupling factors up to 10dB can be readily obtained. With stripline couplers, higher coupling factors of up to 3dB can be readily achieved.

An alternative method of coupler construction is shown in Fig 5.107(b). Here two quarter-wave lengths of line join the main transmission lines together. The operation is as follows.

Consider a signal entering port A. A portion of it will pass to port D via the first interconnecting branch, and a similar portion via the second branch. The two signals will thus arrive at port D in phase and reinforce each other. Next consider the signals arriving at port C. A portion from port A will pass to port C via the first branch. A similar portion will arrive via the second branch, but it will have travelled an extra half-wavelength and be of opposite phase to the first portion. The signals tend to cancel, hardly any signal leaves port C, and thus the coupler is directional.

The directivity is limited by the fact that the amplitudes of the signals travelling by the two different routes will not be quite equal. This problem is more serious for closer values of coupling. To overcome this, more complicated structures are used, with more interconnecting branches, and errors in construction then become more important.

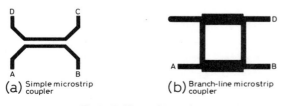

(a) Simple microstrip coupler

(b) Branch-line microstrip coupler

Fig 5.107. Microstrip couplers

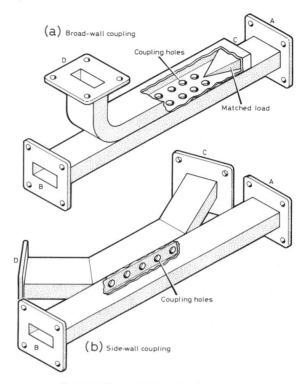

(a) Broad-wall coupling

Coupling holes

Matched load

(b) Side-wall coupling

Coupling holes

Fig 5.108. Waveguide directional couplers

5.10.3 Waveguide couplers

The transfer of energy between two waveguides may take place at openings made into the common wall of the two guides. These may be run parallel to each other for a sufficient distance, either on top of each other (broad-wall coupling) or side by side (side-wall coupling), as shown in Fig 5.108. Alternatively they may simply cross, in which case the coupler is known as a "cross" coupler, as shown in Fig 5.109. For low coupling coefficients, round holes may be used. However, for closer coupling (10dB or closer), the round holes would have to be so big that they would merge into each other and so cross-shaped holes are used.

To understand how these couplers operate, consider the coupler shown on Fig 5.110. Two holes are spaced $\lambda_g/4$ apart connecting the two guides. The size of these two holes determines the coupling. Waves moving from port A pass through both holes and arrive at port D in phase, regardless of the distance between the two holes, since they both travel the same distance. The two sets of waves thus reinforce each other. However, the two sets of waves arriving at port C travel distances which differ by twice the distance between the coupling holes. If the

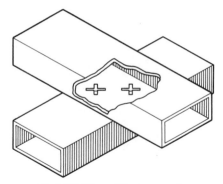

Fig 5.109. Waveguide cross coupler

spacing is made $\lambda_g/4$, then the path difference will be $\lambda_g/2$ and consequently the waves will cancel.

Since this distance depends directly on λ_g, the cancellation in a given design (ie the directivity) will change somewhat if the coupler is used at another frequency. In most applications this is not an important factor – port C will often be terminated in a matched load. The degree of coupling will also change, which may be a problem when using a coupler over a wide frequency range.

The coupling is determined by the size and positioning of the common openings and may be anything from –3dB (ie half power) down to –60dB. A very large directivity (up to 50 or 60dB) may be obtained by using a large number of holes, although the structure then becomes very long and very accurate manufacture is needed.

5.11 TUNERS

Several types of tuner are used to provide adjustable matching between components. They are particularly useful as items of test gear as they allow minor adjustment to matching between pieces of equipment to optimise its performance, without disturbing adjustments within the equipment. Two examples of this use are in

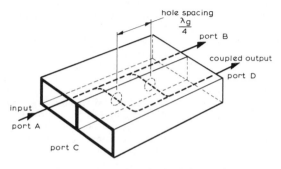

Fig 5.110. Operation of a two-hole coupler

aligning low-noise preamplifiers and high-power amplifiers. The noise figure of low-noise preamps is very dependent on the input matching. The tuner allows you to alter this matching without disturbing the matching networks inside the preamp. Many high-power valve power amplifiers have a limited range of adjustment on the pa loading, due to the difficulty of making adjustable, very-low-loss components in circuitry handling very high voltages. A tuner allows you to experiment with the output loading so that you can determine what changes need to be made to the pa matching network.

There are three types of tuner: the screw, stub and slug tuners. The screw and stub tuners use shunt reactances across the transmission line; the screw tuner is used in waveguide and the stub in coaxial line. The slug tuner uses lumps of dielectric to form moveable quarter-wave transformers.

In theory it should be possible to match between any two impedances by using two shunt reactances spaced $\lambda/4$ apart on a transmission line. This can be likened to the π-network matching circuit. An example of such matching is shown in Fig 5.111. In practice the components producing the reactances are not lossless, and so have a resistive component as well as a reactive one. It may also be difficult to obtain the complete range of reactances. To ease the stringent requirements on their performance, three reactances are usually used instead of two, the extra one being put midway between the outer two, the net result being three, each spaced by $\lambda/8$.

A slightly different approach is to insert two sections of line with a different characteristic impedance in series with the main line. These operate as quarter-wave transformers. This technique is normally used in coaxial lines, but could also be applied to waveguide.

5.11.1 Screw tuners

These are used in waveguide, since a convenient way of producing a variable reactance is to use a metal rod protruding from one of the broad walls of the guide part of the way across to the other (Fig 5.112). This is easily achieved by drilling and tapping a hole in the broad face of the waveguide wall and inserting a screw into the guide. During experimental work, the screws may be spring loaded to eliminate play, but after final adjustment the screws should be fixed using a lock nut.

The reactance as a function of penetration into the guide and the screw diameter is shown in Fig 5.113. For small penetrations the reactance is capacitive, since it is effectively bringing the two walls closer together. At a

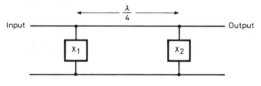

Fig 5.111. Two-stub tuner

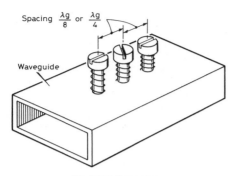

Fig 5.112. Screw tuner

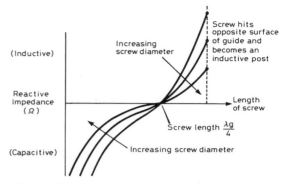

Fig 5.113. Reactance of a screw versus penetration into guide

certain length, depending on the screw diameter, the screw becomes a series-tuned circuit across the guide, ie a reactance of zero ohms. The screw can then be thought of as a quarter-wave whip or stub. As it protrudes further, it becomes inductive.

In the case of the three-screw tuner, usually only one or two screws will have a significant effect. The screws should be inserted the minimum amount necessary to achieve a good match. If screws have to be inserted well into the waveguide, then the component is probably a bad match; if all three screws have little effect, then the component is probably well matched.

The screw tuner in waveguide is an excellent example of why waveguide construction appeals to the amateur constructor. By using cheap, simple components, eg brass screws and nuts, you can build a cheap, versatile, low-loss matching network which is very easy to adjust. While microstrip is easier to mass produce, it is less easy to adjust. Adjustments can be made, however, by sliding small metal tabs or discs along the line to provide extra capacitance, and then soldering or silver-epoxying them in place.

5.11.2 Stub tuners

In coaxial lines, the most convenient form of variable reactance is the sliding short. The variable reactance consists of a piece of rigid transmission line (stub) with a sliding short-circuit which can be moved along the line so that its length can be varied from zero to a quarter-wave. The impedance at the open end of this line varies from zero to infinity ohms of inductive reactance. If the line can be made longer than a quarter-wave, then the reactance becomes capacitive (Fig 5.114).

5.11.3 Slug tuners

The operation of the slug tuner can best be described in terms of the familiar quarter-wave transformer which uses a quarter-wavelength section of line to match between two resistive impedances. A load impedance Z_l can be matched to a line whose impedance is Z_o by using a quarter-wavelength of line whose impedance is $\sqrt{(Z_o \times Z_l)}$, ie the geometric mean of the two. This is illustrated in Fig 5.115(a). The impedance that would be seen looking towards the load at any point along the cable is shown in Fig 5.115(b). The dotted lines show the characteristic impedance of the quarter-wave line segments. A logarithmic resistance scale is used as it illustrates the symmetry of the impedance transformations about the line characteristic impedance – a given vertical distance represents a fixed ratio of resistances.

The impedance of a line is determined by the geometry of its conductors and the dielectric constant of the material between them. In a 50Ω air line, a section (slug) with a ptfe dielectric constant of approx 2 will have a characteristic impedance of $50/\sqrt{2}$, ie 37.5Ω. Referring to Fig 5.116(a), a slug that is quarter-wave long will transform a 25Ω resistive load up to a 50Ω resistive impedance. This is shown in Fig 5.116(b) for a 50Ω line. If a quarter-wave length of the original 50Ω air line is inserted between the load and the slug, this will transform between 25 and 100Ω, as shown in Fig 5.116(c). The slug can thus generate the two extremes of a 2:1 vswr, namely 25 and 100Ω. By varying the length of air line between the load and the slug from zero to one quarter-wavelength, a 2:1 load vswr of any phase can be transformed to 50Ω resistive.

The snag with the single slug tuner is that the magnitude of the vswr cannot be varied – a single ptfe slug can only match loads whose vswr is located actually on

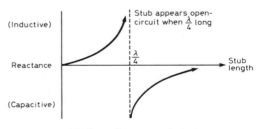

Fig 5.114. Reactance of a stub

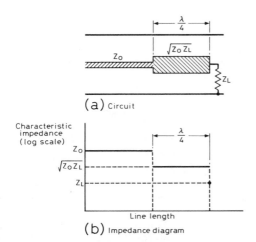

(a) Circuit

(b) Impedance diagram

Fig 5.115. Quarter-wave transformer

the 2:1 circle on a Smith chart. This can be overcome by using two slugs.

Consider the various configurations that can be used. If two quarter-wave slugs are placed adjacent to each other in the line, there is no net impedance transformation (Figs 5.117(a) and 5.117(b)). This is equivalent to inserting a half-wavelength of line of different impedance in a system, which has no effect.

Next consider what happens when the slugs are moved so that they are one quarter-wavelength apart. There are now three sections of line, each one terminated in a

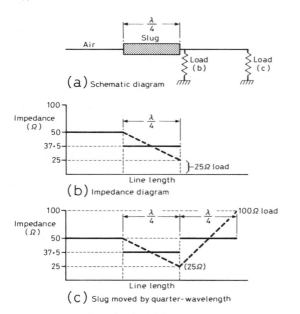

(a) Schematic diagram

(b) Impedance diagram

(c) Slug moved by quarter-wavelength

Fig 5.116. Quarter-wave slug

mismatch (Fig 5.117(c)). This represents the greatest possible transformation, of 50Ω to 12.5Ω. This is twice that which can be obtained from one slug, ie 4:1. Again, if a further quarter-wave of air line is inserted between the load and the slug, the 12.5 is transformed to 200Ω (Fig 5.117(d)). Thus the two-slug tuner can transform from 50Ω to any impedance whose vswr is between 1:1 and 4:1, at any phase. This should be more than adequate for "mopping up" small residual mismatches, eg between pieces of equipment or between the transmitter and the antenna feeder.

The range of dielectric materials available limits the matching range that can be covered by a single tuner. However, it is possible to make slugs with a larger effective dielectric constant by building them from concentric cylinders of metal and dielectric.

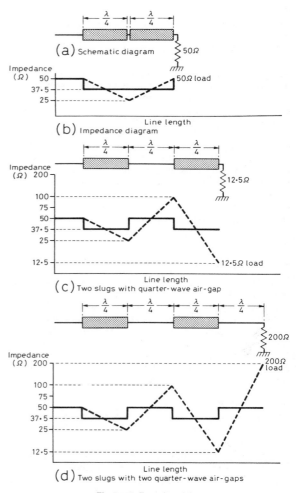

(a) Schematic diagram

(b) Impedance diagram

(c) Two slugs with quarter-wave air-gap

(d) Two slugs with two quarter-wave air-gaps

Fig 5.117. Two-slug tuner

The slug tuner can be used to provide independent adjustment of phase and magnitude of an swr as shown in Fig 5.118. By terminating one end of the tuner with a load equal to the characteristic impedance of the coaxial line used to make the tuner, and looking in the other, the magnitude of the swr can be varied from 1:1 to 4:1 by moving the two slugs apart symmetrically about their midpoint. By moving both of them equally in the same direction, the phase of the swr can be varied.

One advantage of a dielectric tuner is that there are no sliding metallic contacts which can arc or produce unpredictable results if they are intermittent.

5.12 RESONATORS

Resonators are important microwave components used in filters and in other applications such as narrowband amplifiers. Whereas resonant circuits are usually made from coils and capacitors at hf and vhf, at microwave frequencies these are formed from sections of transmission line or resonant cavities. These types are covered below, but their application in filters is left to the "Filters" chapter in Volume 2.

5.12.1 Transmission-line resonators

The simplest type of transmission line resonator is a quarter-wave line shorted at one end. At the other end, this short will appear as a high impedance at the resonant frequency. More commonly used is a length of line shorter than a quarter-wave, tuned to resonance by an end capacitor (see Fig 5.119).

The impedance of such a line at the open end is given by:

$$Z_{in} = Z_o \times \tanh(\gamma \times l)$$

where Z_o is the characteristic impedance of the line, γ is the propagation constant, and l the line length. For a lossless line, γ is simply:

$$\gamma = \frac{j \times 2\pi}{\lambda}$$

Thus, the impedance simplifies to:

$$Z_{in} = Z_o \times \tanh(j \times 2\pi \times l/\lambda)$$

or $$Z_{in} = j \times Z_o \times \tan(\frac{2\pi \times l}{\lambda})$$

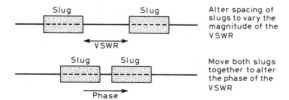

| Slug | Slug | Alter spacing of slugs to vary the magnitude of the VSWR |

VSWR

| Slug | Slug | Move both slugs together to alter the phase of the VSWR |

Phase

Fig 5.118. Operation of the slug tuner

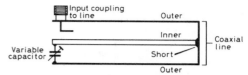

Fig 5.119. Transmission-line resonator

For a short line (less than $\lambda/4$), the input impedance of the line is inductive, signified by the j. When l is exactly a quarter-wave long, the input impedance is very high – the above expression gives a Z_{in} of infinity, but losses in any practical transmission line reduce the impedance to finite value. Above $\lambda/4$, the input impedance appears as a capacitance, signified by a –j. The impedance is plotted in Fig 5.120.

Note that when the line is filled with a material of dielectric constant ε_r, the wavelength will be reduced:

$$\lambda = \frac{\lambda_{fs}}{\sqrt{\varepsilon_r}}$$

An inductive line can be made to resonate at a frequency F by placing a capacitance C in parallel with it:

where $$C = \frac{1}{(2\pi \times F)^2 \times L}$$

or $$C = \frac{1}{2\pi \times F \times Z_{in}}$$

Transmission-line resonators may be constructed from coaxial lines, striplines and microstrip. For example, consider an air-spaced 50Ω coaxial line, 5cm long, at 1.3GHz, which is a little under a quarter-wave long:

$$Z_{in} = j \times 50 \times \tan(\frac{2 \times 3.142 \times 5}{23})$$

$$Z_{in} = j \times 50 \times \tan(1.366)$$

ie $Z_{in} = j \times 240.7$ ohms. To resonate at 1.3GHz, the required C is:

$$C = \frac{1}{2 \times 3.142 \times (1.3 \times 10^{-9}) \times 240.7}$$

$$C = 0.51pF$$

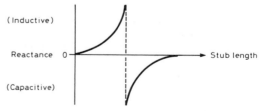

Fig 5.120. Impedance of shorted stub

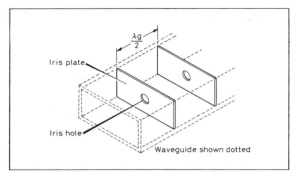

Fig 5.121. Waveguide cavity resonator

If the above line were now filled with ptfe dielectric, where ε_r is 2.1, the input impedance will be:

$$Z_{in} \quad = \quad j \times 50 \times \tan(1.980)$$

ie $\quad Z_{in} \quad = \quad - j \times 115.3 \, ohms$

Thus, the input impedance is now a capacitance, whereas before it was inductive.

With microstrip the velocity will be reduced below that of free space, due to the dielectric, but the amount it is reduced, and hence the wavelength, is not so easily calculated. In this case, the graphs in Fig 5.30 should be used to determine the effective velocity, and hence the effective value of λ.

As already stated, the quarter-wave line shorted at one end is the simplest form of transmission line

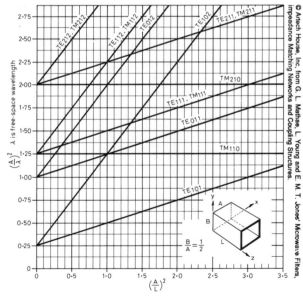

Fig 5.122. Mode chart for rectangular cavities

resonator, and it is normally made slightly shorter and tuned onto frequency with a small capacitance. This type of resonator will have higher resonances, the first being when it is three quarter-wavelengths long, and these may be used by design.

It is also possible to use an open-circuited length of line as a resonator. A short length will look like a capacitance but, as the length is increased beyond a quarter-wavelength, it will also look like an inductor. The input impedance of such a line is given by:

$$Z_{in} \quad = \quad - j \times Z_o \times \cot(\frac{2\pi \times L}{\lambda})$$

Calculation of Zin, and hence the required capacitance for the line to resonate at a particular frequency, is similar to the calculation for the shorted line. There is a simple and very useful relation between the loss of a transmission line and the Q that it will give when used as a resonator, which can be used to estimate the Q that can be obtained from the lines available. Alternatively, the loss of a cable can be predicted by making a resonator out of a short length and measuring the Q.

$$Q \quad = \quad \frac{0.091Fx}{kL}$$

where F is the frequency in megahertz, k the velocity factor of the line, and L the loss in decibels of a cable of length x metres.

As a rule of thumb, the resistance across the open-circuit end of a shorted quarter-wave line is $Q \times Z_o$, and across the open-circuit end of a shorted half-wave line is Z_o/Q.

5.12.2 Cavity resonators

Cavity resonators may be formed from a variety of hollow structures, including rectangular boxes, cylinders and spheres. The most common are rectangular cavities and, in particular, waveguide cavities.

A cavity can be formed in waveguide by partitioning off a portion of the guide with iris plates. One or both of these plates will have a hole (or iris) in it to provide coupling to the cavity (see Fig 5.121). However, it is not necessary to actually partition the waveguide in this manner and alternative methods of defining the cavity may be used, eg posts across the waveguide. See the "Filters" chapter in Volume 2 for more information.

The lowest frequency of resonance of a cavity formed in this manner is when the wavelength (in waveguide) is twice its length. It is usual to make the length slightly small and tune the cavity onto frequency using a capacitive tuning screw protruding into its centre. There will be other resonances on higher frequencies.

For example, a half-wave cavity resonator is required at 10GHz, built in WG16 waveguide. For WG16, λ_c = 45.75mm. At 10GHz, λ = 30mm.

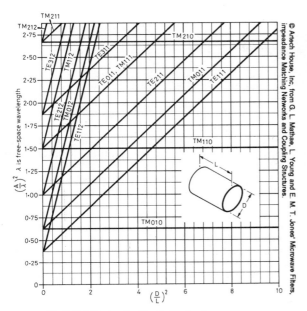

Fig 5.123. Mode chart for right-circular cavities

$$\lambda_g = \frac{30}{\sqrt{(1 - (30/45.75)^2)}}$$

ie λ_g = 39.7mm. Thus a half-wave cavity would be 19.8mm long, and a suggested length to allow for tuning would be 18mm long.

When a filter is constructed from such cavities coupled together the loading of the cavity due to coupling in and out will affect the resonant frequency slightly, and this is compensated for by shortening the length slightly (see the "Filters" chapter in Volume 2).

The cavity type just described uses the dominant mode of rectangular waveguide. Many resonators make use of higher-order modes, usually to get a higher Q. The most common type is either a cylindrical or rectangular box. Figs 5.122 and 5.123 show the frequency ranges of various modes in such cavities. The mode is described in a similar manner to modes in waveguide, except that a third suffix is added to specify the number of field variations along the length of the cavity. For example, the dominant mode in a rectangular waveguide is TE-10, giving a TE-101 mode in a cavity.

Higher-order modes are often used for wavemeter cavities where a high Q is important. The snag with these modes is that undesired modes may have resonances in the frequency range of interest. The mode chart is used to select a suitable mode to cover the frequency range so that this does not occur.

5.12.3 Dielectric resonators

Dielectric resonators consist of a ceramic resonator with a high dielectric constant (eg 30), usually cylindrical in shape, and resonating at the frequency of interest. They are essentially cavity resonators. Coupling into and out of the resonator is achieved by running a microstrip line next to it. At 10GHz, a typical size is 6mm diameter by 2.5mm high.

They are mainly used for stabilising GaAsfet oscillators. The cylinder is simply placed next to the fet oscillator, which is usually built on a ptfe or ceramic-based substrate. Fine tuning of the resonant frequency is possible by moving a tuning screw near to one face of the cylinder (see Fig 5.124).

5.12.4 YIG resonators

The yig resonator is constructed from an yttrium iron garnet (yig) sphere which is tuned by a magnetic field. Again, it is a form of cavity resonator.

The sphere is cut from yig crystals and is typically 0.3 to 1mm in diameter in order to resonate at the frequency of interest. It is placed in an electromagnetic field which is altered to tune the resonant frequency (see Fig 5.125). RF is coupled in and out of the sphere by two coupling loops at right angles. There is normally no coupling between the two loops except when the sphere provides it at resonance. The tuning is very linear, eg it is possible to tune the whole of X-band (from 8 to 12GHz) with a worst error of only 10MHz.

The yig resonator may be used as a filter or more frequently as part of a GaAsfet oscillator. In this latter case the fet is placed near the yig sphere so that power is coupled into it before being coupled into the output circuitry. The yig is used to set the frequency of oscillation and a broadband oscillator can be produced with highly linear tuning. Frequency modulation can be applied to the signal, usually by using a second, smaller tuning coil which permits faster modulation rates than the main tuning coil.

5.13 NON-RECIPROCAL COMPONENTS

Several forms of non-reciprocal devices exist which rely on the special properties of ferrites for their operation. Ferrites are magnetic oxides of iron usually "doped" with other metals such as manganese, nickel and "rare earth" elements. Depending on their exact composition, they can present high permeability and very high resistivity, and may thus be almost "transparent" to microwaves. Conversely, other compositions can be made almost totally absorbent to microwaves.

The magnetic properties of ferrites are related to the existence of unpaired "spinning" electrons in the structure and, if the ferrite is placed in an externally generated magnetic field, the atoms within the structure of the ferrite will align themselves along the induced

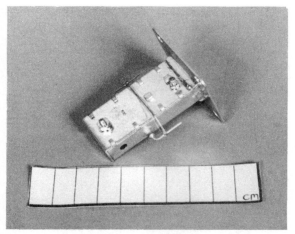

Fig 5.124. Dielectric-resonator oscillator and mixer (Mitsubishi FO-UP11KF). The oscillator bias input is connected via the feedthrough on the middle bottom, the mixer output via the feedthrough on the top. The larger screw to the rear is the dr tuning screw, used for "band-setting" the oscillator, while the smaller screw, towards the flange, is used to largely cancel oscillator radiation from the open end of the waveguide. The flange mates with a standard WG16 flange. Note: the two feedthrough terminals are shown shorted in this photo. This is to prevent static damage to the mixer and oscillator GaAsfet while the unit is unconnected

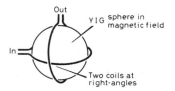

Fig 5.125. YIG resonator

internal field, giving a net (volume effect) magnetisation. Magnetisation of the ferrite increases with the applied field until saturation occurs – when this point is reached, no further increase in induced magnetisation occurs with the increasing external field.

The saturation magnetisation determines the low-frequency limit of the ferrite, and this expressed in megahertz approximates to the saturation magnetisation expressed in gauss. Such a saturated ferrite exhibits different permeabilities in opposite directions of propagation when magnetised in the transverse plane. If the ferrite is mounted within waveguide and suitably magnetically "biased" by means of an external permanent magnet, then the external magnet effectively controls propagation within the waveguide and propagation becomes non-reciprocal. This property is exploited in both the isolator and the circulator.

5.13.1 Isolators

An isolator is a two-port device in which the transmission loss is very low in one direction and high in the reverse direction. As its name implies, it is used to isolate one circuit from another. It is frequently used to protect oscillators, so that power generated by the oscillator can pass unimpeded to the external circuitry, but any power reflected by the circuit is heavily absorbed and therefore does not influence the oscillator's frequency. The operation of an isolator depends on the special magnetic properties of ferrites described above.

Three types of isolator are available and are known respectively as the "Faraday rotation" isolator, the "resonance" isolator and the "field displacement" isolator. Each has its particular advantages and disadvantages from a professional point of view, although it matters little to the amateur which type is used.

The Faraday rotation isolator exhibits low insertion loss but operates over a comparatively narrow bandwidth of 5 to 10 per cent. The resonance isolator has low insertion loss and large bandwidth but requires a very high magnetic-bias field strength. This can make it susceptible to malfunction if the biassing magnet is damaged by loss of strength caused by dropping, or exposure to other strong magnetic fields. The field displacement type offers low insertion loss and good isolation and is very compact. However, it cannot be used at high power levels, although this is unlikely to be a factor in most current amateur equipment. This type is probably the most useful on account of its small size and light weight.

A common form of waveguide isolator consists of a length of waveguide inside which is a ferrite bar (see Fig 5.126). This is biased by the field from a permanent magnet outside the guide. The rf fields corresponding to forward and reverse waves passing through the waveguide are distorted by the ferrite in different ways. A lossy material is placed within the waveguide at a point where the field due to the forward wave is zero, and where that due to the reverse wave is at a maximum. The forward wave therefore passes through with little attenuation, usually with a loss of 0.5 to 1dB, while the reverse wave is heavily attenuated, generally by 20dB or 30dB. Fig 5.127 shows a commercial waveguide isolator.

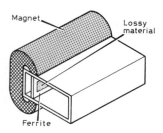

Fig 5.126. Waveguide isolator

Fig 5.127. Waveguide isolator

Coaxial isolators are also available, but these are really circulators with one port terminated with a matched load.

Although isolators can greatly simplify the construction and operation of equipment, there are a number of precautions which should be taken in their use. Clearly they must be connected the right way around. Their performance can be permanently degraded by a change in the magnetic properties of the biasing magnet caused by large mechanical shocks, or by allowing the isolator near steel components or strong magnetic fields. They provide isolation over a restricted range of frequencies, in some cases as low as 5 per cent bandwidth, and harmonics may be only poorly attenuated.

5.13.2 Circulators

A circulator is a non-reciprocal device with three or more ports. It contains a core of ferrite material in which energy introduced into one port is transferred to an adjacent port, the other ports being isolated. This is illustrated in Fig 5.128 for a three-port circulator.

Energy entering into port 1 emerges from port 2 and energy entering into port 2 emerges from port 3 etc. In this direction of circulation the loss is typically 0.5 or

1dB. In the reverse direction, the isolation is 20 or 30dB. Circulators may be constructed in either waveguide or coaxial line.

In the waveguide type, three (for a three-port device) waveguides usually intersect each other at 120°, as shown in Fig 5.129. Exactly in the centre of the intersection is a piece of ferrite, located between two magnets. Posts or tuning screws may also be fitted in the waveguide branches to achieve a good match.

A coaxial circulator is illustrated in Fig 5.130. In this type three copper strips intersect each other at 120° in the centre of the circulator. These are mounted between two earth plates, thus forming striplines. In the centre of the circulator two ferrite discs are mounted, one above and one below the copper strips. These are then sandwiched between two magnets. Tuning screws may be provided for fine adjustment of the centre frequency.

When the signal enters the ferrite disk, it splits into two parts, one propagating in a clockwise and the other in an anticlockwise direction around the disc. The velocities in the two directions are different. The circumference of the disc is chosen so that when the signals meet at one of the other ports on the circumference they either add or subtract, giving either the coupled or isolated ports.

It is the presence of the external biasing magnetic field that produces a difference between the velocities in the two directions. Only certain values of field can be used if the losses in the ferrite are to be kept small, as shown in Fig 5.131. These are just below or above

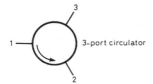

Fig 5.128. Schematic of a circulator

Fig 5.129. Waveguide circulator

© Philips Components Ltd.

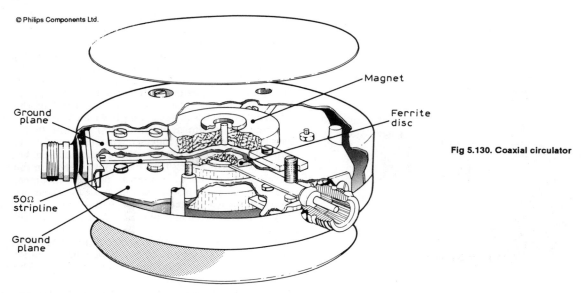

Fig 5.130. Coaxial circulator

resonance. The resonance occurs because the magnetic field causes the electrons in the ferrite to precess. Operation can be above resonance for frequencies from about 50MHz to 2.5GHz, and below resonance from 500MHz to around 24GHz. Above-resonance operation gives a bandwidth of about half an octave, and below-resonance operation about an octave or more.

The main use for a circulator is in "duplexing", ie connecting a transmitter and receiver to the same antenna. Also, if one port is terminated with a matched load, the device may than be used as an isolator. Again, as with isolators, care must be taken to keep circulators away from other magnetic fields. They can be optimised to work over a narrow bandwidth or be made to cover a wider frequency range with a reduced performance.

5.14 CONSTRUCTION TECHNIQUES

5.14.1 Microstrip

Professionally this is produced by photographic methods, as for normal pcbs. However, this technique is

rather expensive for amateur development work, and it is possible to obtain adequate results with rather more "barbaric" techniques, particularly if the circuit will need adjustment anyway.

Lines can be produced by much simpler techniques such as using black tape or ink directly on the board to cover the resist. Alternatively the track pattern can be cut out with a sharp knife, and the unwanted copper removed with a knife and hot soldering iron (Fig 5.132).

Fine tuning can be performed by sticking self-adhesive copper foil on the track to form a stub; it can be bent up to adjust the capacitance to earth. Also small copper discs can be slid along the line to add capacitance at various places and soldered in position.

Do not be put off by the very high precision used in professional artwork. Most amateur circuitry will not require such critical tolerances and will often need optimising for individual devices anyway.

5.14.2 PCB materials

At lower frequencies glass-loaded epoxy pcb is used, which has a dielectric constant of approximately 4. At

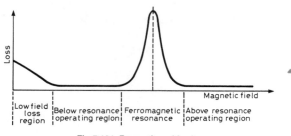

Fig 5.131. Properties of ferrite

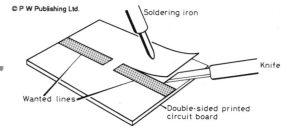

© P W Publishing Ltd.

Fig 5.132. Making prototype microstrip

L (in)	W (in)	T (in)
0·080	0·050	0·050
0·120	0·100	0·065

Common sizes

Fig 5.133. Chip resistors and capacitors

microwave frequencies this material is quite lossy and alternatives such as ptfe and ceramic-loaded types can be used. The ptfe types are available under several trade names such as RT-Duroid and CuClad, and have dielectric constants ranging from about 2.1 to 2.5. The disadvantage of these types is the cost – typically 10 times that of glass-loaded epoxy types.

The various types are available in a range of thicknesses, from a fraction of a millimetre to several millimetres, with copper coatings on one or both sides. Common thicknesses are 0.01in (0.25mm), 1/32in (0.79mm) and 1/16in (1.59mm). The thickness of the copper coating(s) is normally specified in ounces per square foot, and 1 or 2oz/ft^2 is the most common. In addition, some types can be obtained with a uv-sensitive coating applied to the copper, ready for exposure, developing and etching.

5.14.3 Screening

This is particularly important in the case of cavity resonators in high-power amplifiers. Lids to such cavities should be earthed to the box every $\lambda/10$ or so by means of screws, which should be done up tightly. It is very difficult to maintain a good electrical contact along the length of a lid by any other means. Leads running inside such a cavity, eg power supplies to a valve, should be screened and the screens earthed at frequent intervals.

Similar comments apply to the lids of filters and low-noise amplifiers using high-Q resonators. Otherwise, unwanted coupling can occur between resonators, altering the response. Detuning may also occur as an intermittent contact between the lid and box changes.

5.14.4 Stray impedances

At microwave frequencies, the dimensions of many components are comparable with the wavelength and their size becomes significant. The inductance of leads can appear as a high impedance in series with the component and a quite small stray capacitance may appear as a low shunt impedance.

The internal construction of components is also important. For example, wirewound resistors are unsuitable even at vhf. At uhf, carbon-composition or metal-oxide types can be used, provided the lead lengths are kept to a minimum. At even higher frequencies, eg 10GHz, it will be necessary to use unpackaged chip resistors.

Unpackaged chip resistors and chip capacitors are readily available for use at microwaves (see Fig 5.133). These include high-Q types for better performance,

although these are more expensive. Unpackaged semiconductor devices (diodes, transistors and fets) are used commercially but are difficult for the amateur to use and not easily obtained.

5.14.5 Radiation coupling and losses

When using open transmission lines, eg microstrip, or any components on the surface of a pcb, there is a risk of stray coupling due to radiation from the lines. The amount of radiation depends on the line length in wavelengths, and also on the degree to which the field is confined within the dielectric. Low-dielectric constant boards are undesirable at higher microwave frequencies for this reason. However, higher dielectric constant board also means that the track widths will be narrower for a given impedance.

This radiation can cause instability, and also degrade the noise figure if it allows an amplifier to pick up noise. Such circuitry should be kept in a screened box, and screens also used between stages above the board if necessary.

5.15 REFERENCES

[1] *Reference Data for Radio Engineers*, 6th edn, ITT, Howard W Sams, 1979. A general-purpose reference book.

[2] *Microwave Engineer's Handbook*, ed T Saad, Artech House, 1971 (two volumes). A good collection of useful data on practical microwaves.

[3] "The realm of microwaves (2) – Microwave transmission lines", *Wireless World*, March 1973.

[4] *Microwave Transmission Line Impedance Data*, M A R Gunston, Van Nostrand Reinhold, 1972. A lot of data on impedances of lines, especially stripline and microstrip.

[5] "Simple design of $\lambda/4$ stripline circuits", W Lerche, DC3CL, *VHF Communications*, 1/1980, pp25–28.

[6] "Dimensioning of microstripline circuits", W Schumacher, *VHF Communications*, 3/1972, pp130–143.

[7] "Reflectometers and directional power meters", M M Bibby, G3NJY, *Radio Communication*, June 1968, pp362, 363, 372.

[8] "The rotating loop reflectometer", W H Elkin, *Marconi Instrumentation*, Vol 5, No 8, pp221–227.

[9] "Using Smith diagrams", E Stadler, *VHF Communications*, 1/1984, pp23–28.

[10] *"Electronic applications of the Smith chart, in waveguide, circuit and component analysis"*, P H Smith, published by McGraw-Hill, 1969. A comprehensive treatment of Smith charts.

[11] "Understanding coaxial circulators and isolators", B Sekhon et al, *Microwave Systems News*, June 1979, pp84–103.

[12] "Shielding barriers block electromagnctic waves", P Grant, *Microwaves*, June 1982, pp97–102 (Part 1); Microwaves July 1982, pp79–86 (Part 2).

[13] *"Waveguide Handbook"*, ed N Marcuvitz, McGraw Hill, 1951. A comprehensive study of waveguide, though very mathematical.

[14] "Taking the magic out of the 'Magic-Tee'", A J Burwasser, *RF Design*, May/June 1983, pp44–60.

Catalogues

The following manufacturers have catalogues which contain a lot of useful information, including application notes.

1. Suhner, for precision connectors, including SMA, SMB, SMC, APC-7 etc.

2. Sealectro, for a good range of connectors and also semi-rigid cable.

3. Greenpar, for a general range of coaxial connectors.

4. Andrew Corporation, for Heliax cable and its connectors.

5. Anzac, for splitters and combiners (plus mixers and amplifiers, see next chapter).

6. Minicircuits, again for splitters and combiners (also mixers).

7. Hewlett Packard have a wide range of application notes on a wide range of subjects, including rf components, and rf test equipment and its use (eg network analysers).

8. Gabriel, for rigid and flexible waveguide, flanges and waveguide components.

CHAPTER 6

Microwave semiconductors and valves

6.1 INTRODUCTION

Microwaves were first seriously used in radar during the second world war. These used pulse magnetrons and germanium point-contact detectors. Since then, considerable progress has been made, and in the last 20 years the trend has been away from free-running oscillators to crystal-controlled sources. Devices operating to around 100GHz are now available, and the frequencies continue to increase into the realms of optics.

A great variety of special-purpose valve and semiconductor devices have been developed for microwave use because conventional devices are not able to function effectively at these frequencies, mainly because of transit-time effects. Their applications are outlined below.

Detectors: These are used to convert rf to dc, usually to look at the envelope of an rf signal. They are often referred to as "video detectors" because they were originally used in that application, but the term has been used to cover any application where the bandwidth of the detected signal ranges from dc to a few megahertz. A variety of types of diode are used as detectors, including germanium point-contact diodes, silicon Schottky diodes and backward diodes.

Mixers: The same range of diodes that are used as detectors are also used for mixer applications, with the exception of the backward diode. For best noise-figure performance, GaAs Schottky diodes are often used. Diodes used as mixers rather than detectors may be optimised for slightly different parameters, though.

Oscillators: These can be divided into two- and three-terminal devices. At lower microwave frequencies, conventional three-terminal devices such as valves and transistors can be used; GaAsfets operate up to tens of gigahertz. At higher frequencies there are a variety of special two-terminal devices such as tunnel diodes, Gunn diodes, impatt and trappatt diodes. However, these solidstate devices are generally limited to mean powers of a few watts. Any amplifying device can also be used as an oscillator, so at the lower frequencies microwave valves such as the 2C39 can be used to produce a few tens of watts. A number of special valves use magnetic fields to either focus or control the path of

the electron beam, examples being the magnetron, gyratron and backward-wave oscillator. Some of these are capable of very high mean or peak powers. The bwo is essentially a broadband, travelling-wave tube type of amplifier with internal feedback to produce oscillation.

Multipliers: Multipliers are used to generate power at microwave frequencies when fundamental oscillators are not suitable. They operate by converting the fundamental energy into harmonics. For a low order of multiplication, eg two, three or four times, varactor diodes are commonly used to give output powers of tens of watts. For a high order of multiplication, snap or step-recovery varactors should be used instead.

Amplifiers: Amplifiers at lower frequencies can be built using transistors, fets and valves. At higher frequencies GaAsfets can still be used, and there are a number of devices peculiar to microwaves such as travelling-wave tubes and klystrons. Other types of amplifiers include low-noise parametric amplifiers and reflection amplifiers.

Attenuators: Variable attenuators and switches can be made with pin diodes. These are effectively rf resistors whose resistance is determined by the dc current flowing through them. Limiters are a special type of attenuator which is controlled by the rf level and limits the power passing through it to a specific level. They are used to protect receivers, and were originally developed to protect radar receivers against the transmitted pulses. This chapter introduces the more common devices and their applications.

6.2 DIODES

The first microwave diodes were germanium point-contact detectors. These are still used, particularly at frequencies above 100GHz, where other types are difficult to manufacture. There are now a variety of other detector and mixer diodes, silicon Schottky-barrier types being the most popular. Gallium arsenide is used for ultimate low-noise and high-frequency performance.

There are now a number of oscillator diodes available based on negative-resistance effects; these include

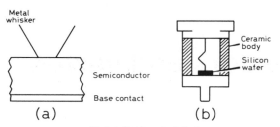

Fig 6.1. Point-contact diode

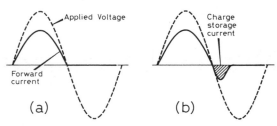

Fig 6.3. (a) Ideal junction with zero recombination time. (b) Typical junction showing effects of finite recombination time

impatt and trapatt devices. The most popular is the Gunn diode, which is fully described in a separate section.

6.2.1 Point-contact diodes

The point-contact diode is formed by bringing a pointed metal wire into contact with a piece of semiconductor (Fig 6.1(a)). A pulse of current is sometimes passed through the junction to fuse the wire to the semiconductor to make it more robust. Since there is a metal-to-semiconductor junction it is in effect a type of Schottky-barrier junction.

The junction capacitance is determined by the area of contact, and so diodes for use at microwave frequencies are quite delicate devices, both electrically and mechanically. They tend to be of lower capacitance than the diffused-junction types. A typical construction for an 10GHz diode is shown in Fig 6.1(b).

The equivalent circuit of a junction diode is shown in Fig 6.2. R_s is the series resistance of the bulk semiconductor material. R_j and C_j are the junction resistance and capacitance.

The junction diameter is usually small compared with the thickness of the semiconductor. For microwave diodes, the junction radius should be as small as possible. The highest cut-off frequency will be obtained with gallium arsenide, followed by germanium and then silicon, since this is related to the carrier mobility in the material.

When the junction is forward biased, majority carriers cross the depletion region and become minority carriers on the opposite side. They diffuse away from the junction where they recombine in under 10^{-8} seconds.

If the bias reverses before all the carriers have recombined, then the uncombined ones will flow back across the junction and form a pulse of current in addition to the normal reverse leakage current. This is shown in Fig 6.3. This delay in recombination has the effect of added capacitance, and is called "diffusion" or "storage" capacitance.

6.2.2 Schottky-barrier diodes

Schottky-barrier diodes (also known as "hot-carrier diodes") are more efficient rectifiers at high frequencies. This is because they use only majority carriers which do not suffer from the recombination times of minority carriers.

Modern diodes are made using a planar process, where a thin layer of insulating silicon dioxide is grown over the semiconductor, and the junction is formed by etching a small hole in the insulator and depositing a metal film onto the semiconductor through the window formed. This disc of metal might be 5μm diameter (10 times the wavelength of green light). A wire is then bonded to this film to take the connection out to the package. The construction is illustrated in Fig 6.4.

This type of construction has the following advantages over the point-contact diode.

(a) A lower series resistance.

(b) Better burn-out rating and lower low-frequency noise due to the larger junction area and increased junction capacitance.

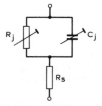

Fig 6.2. Equivalent circuit of junction diode

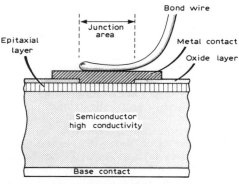

Fig 6.4. Schottky-barrier diode

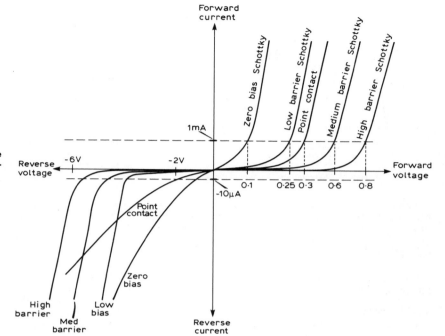

Fig 6.5. V-I characteristics of the Schottky-barrier diode and point-contact diode

(c) More rugged and reproducible since the mechanical construction is more robust.

The net result of the lower series resistance and higher capacitance is an upper frequency limit similar to that of point-contact diodes, since the limit is determined by the product $R_s \times C_j$. The junction radius has no effect on the cut-off frequency in practice. The theoretical expression for the V-I characteristic is:

$$I = I_s \times (\exp\left(\frac{eV}{nkT}\right) - 1)$$

where: I_s is the saturation current

e the electronic charge, 1.6×10^{-19} coulombs

T is the absolute temperature, in Kelvin

k is Boltzmann's constant, 1.38×10^{-23} joule/K

V is the voltage across the diode junction, in volts

n is a factor allowing for the diode being non-ideal; n = 1 for an ideal diode.

$\dfrac{e}{kT}$ for a perfect diode is therefore 1/25mV

Fig 6.5 illustrates the V-I characteristic for the Schottky-barrier diode, together with the characteristic for point-contact diodes for comparison. Table 6.1 lists typical values for reverse-leakage currents and forward-voltage drops.

6.2.3 Tunnel diodes

This diode is of similar construction to the conventional pn junction diode, but has a much higher doping level (level of wanted impurities) and a very abrupt junction with a narrow depletion layer. This heavy doping reduces the width of the depletion layer to around 10–100 atom diameters. Electrons can therefore pass from one side to the other without going through the usual diffusion and recombination process, which gives it a very fast response, but the junction area must be kept much smaller than usual because the narrower junction increases the capacitance per unit area.

Table 6.1. Reverse-leakage currents and forward voltage drops for Schottky-barrier diodes

Diode type	Typical reverse leakage current	Typical forward voltage drop	Typical video impedance
Zero-bias Schottky	100μA at 1V	0.12V at 1mA	1kΩ
Low-barrier Schottky	1nA at 1V	0.25V at 1mA	10kΩ
Point contact	10nA at 1V	0.3V at 1mA	100kΩ
Medium-barrier Schottky	1nA at 1V	0.45V at 1mA	above 1MΩ
High-barrier Schottky	100pA at 1V	0.65V at 1mA	above 1MΩ

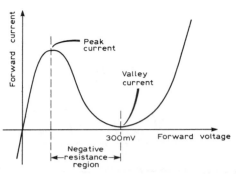

Fig 6.6. V-I characteristic of a tunnel diode

"Tunnelling" is a term that describes how the electrons can pass from one side of a potential barrier to the other, when they would not normally have sufficient energy to get over the barrier. The doping levels are such that the increase in tunnelling current is followed by a decrease as the voltage is increased. The net result is a region of negative resistance in the diode characteristic. Fig 6.6 shows the V-I characteristic.

6.2.4 Backward diodes

A backward diode is similar to a tunnel diode, except that the tunnelling current is reduced to a very low value so that the negative-resistance region does not exist. The V-I characteristic is shown in Fig 6.7. It is mainly used as a low-level, broadband detector or mixer. It has a very low value of slope resistance at zero bias. The name "backward diode" arises because the detected voltage is of the opposite polarity to normal.

Unlike the Schottky diode, it has very low flicker noise, so it can be used for receivers with i.fs in the audio frequency range – doppler receivers. However, it does only have a very limited dynamic range.

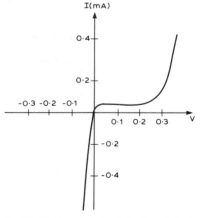

Fig 6.7. V-I characteristic of a backward diode

Fig 6.8. PIN Diode

6.2.5 PIN diodes

PIN diodes are used as current-controlled resistors at rf. They have an incremental resistance that is controlled by the dc current flowing through them, in a similar manner to the ordinary junction diode. However, their resistance is much more linear and does not produce the distortion that a normal exponential diode characteristic would. They are therefore useful in rf switching and current-controlled attenuators.

The pin diode consists of p-type and n-type regions that are separated by an intrinsic (i) region, ie a region in which there are negligible impurities or charge carriers (Fig 6.8). Charge carriers from the doped p and n regions have to cross this intrinsic region, and at low frequencies the diode acts as a rectifier. At high frequencies the storage time in the intrinsic region is so great (ie the transit time is so long compared to the period of the signals) that the diode ceases to act as a rectifier, and instead acts as a linear resistance and conducts in both directions. Its effective resistance is inversely proportional to the amount of charge in the intrinsic region, and this can be controlled by the dc bias current. In this way the conductivity can be varied by several orders of magnitude.

The complete equivalent circuit of a packaged diode is shown in Fig 6.9, and at microwave frequencies the package reactances are very significant. At microwave frequencies the junction capacitance C_j is constant and purely a function of the junction geometry. At zero or reverse bias the intrinsic region is depleted of charge and has a relatively high resistance of several thousand ohms. Under forward bias electron and hole-charge carriers are injected into the intrinsic layer and the resistance of the layer drops to below an ohm. The variation of resistance with current is shown in Fig 6.10, and the minimum value is limited by R_s.

These properties only apply at high frequencies, where the period of the rf is smaller than the recombination time (t) of the carriers – this is typically 10–300ns. At frequencies below $f = 1/(2\pi \times t)$ the injection and

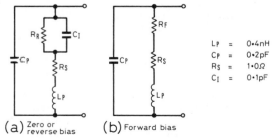

(a) Zero or reverse bias   (b) Forward bias

$L_P = 0.4nH$
$C_P = 0.2pF$
$R_S = 1.0\Omega$
$C_I = 0.1pF$

Fig 6.9. Equivalent circuit of package pin diode of (a) zero or reverse bias and (b) forward bias

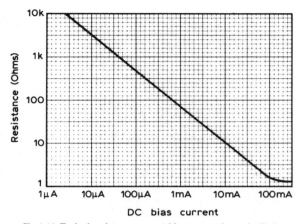

Fig 6.10. Typical resistance versus bias current for a pin diode

removal of charge can follow the rf waveform, producing inefficient rectification of the signal. Above it, the charge level is determined mainly by the dc bias current, and is only modulated very slightly by the rf signal. Conversely, the rf may be modulated by applying a low-frequency signal superimposed on the dc bias.

A short carrier lifetime allows very fast switching of the diode, but limits use of the diode to higher frequencies. A compromise must be chosen between switching speed and lowest rf operating frequency. Compared with other types of diode the pin type has a low junction capacitance and high reverse-breakdown voltage, and so can handle quite high powers at high frequencies.

6.2.6 Tuning diodes

Tuning varactor diodes are optimised to use the variation of junction capacitance with reverse voltage, instead of the variation of junction resistance with forward voltage. They are basically similar to pin diodes, but do not have the intrinsic region between the p and n layers.

The capacitance change is not a result of stored charge as in the pin diode, and so can be made to change much more rapidly. However, the diode reactance is now a function of the rf signal voltage, and so much more intermodulation will occur. They are lower-power devices because the junction is much thinner. The continuously variable capacitance can be used to produce continuously variable phase shifts.

As tuning diodes, they can tune oscillators or tuned circuits over several octaves in low-power applications at lower frequencies. The junction capacitance is related to the applied voltage:

$$C_j \quad = \quad (V + V_o)^{-n}$$

where V_o is the built-in junction voltage and n a function of the junction doping. For an abrupt junction, n = 0.45 to 0.48; for a hyperabrupt junction n is greater than 0.5. Examples of doping profiles and voltage-capacitance characteristics are shown in Fig 6.11. The tuning range is given by:

$$C_{max}/C_{min} \quad = \quad \frac{(V_{max} + V_o)^n}{(V_{min} + V_o)^n}$$

Typical values of V_{max} and V_{min} are 20V and 2V.

ABRUPT

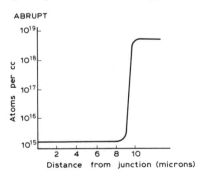

HYPERABRUPT

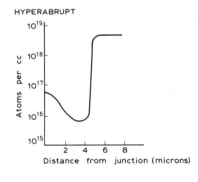

Fig 6.11. Doping profiles and voltage-capacitance characteristics for varactors

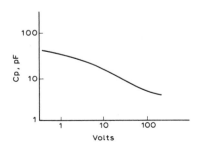

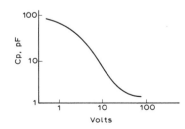

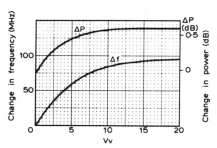

Fig 6.12. Variation of power and frequency with tuning voltage in a half-wavelength WG18 cavity oscillator at 13GHz

A lower doping level will give a higher breakdown voltage and a larger tuning range, but at the expense of a lower Q. Heavier doping will give a higher Q but a smaller tuning range.

The tuning range that a varactor will give in a real circuit depends on the proportion of the total energy in the tuned circuit which is stored in the varactor. In a lumped-component circuit, this is simply a matter of the fraction of the total capacitance across the coil which is provided by the varactor. In a cavity resonator this is

more difficult to identify, but the varactor should be very tightly coupled to the cavity for maximum tuning range. A typical tuning curve for a varactor in a waveguide cavity is shown in Fig 6.12. Note that the losses increase rapidly at the higher capacitances.

6.2.7 Multiplier varactor diodes

Another application of the variable-capacitance diode is as a frequency multiplier (or mixer). This uses the variation of junction capacitance with applied voltage to provide the desired modulation, as illustrated in Fig 6.13. This process is more efficient as the variable impedance is almost lossless.

As multipliers, they can handle powers of tens of watts at around 1GHz, and hundreds of milliwatts at 10GHz. The main difference between these and tuning varactors is that the multipliers are built to dissipate much higher powers.

6.2.8 Step-recovery diodes

Step-recovery varactors (snap diodes) are a variant of the normal multiplier varactor diode. The diode has a low impedance while forward biased which, when the voltage reverses, remains low until the carriers are

Fig 6.13. Operation of a varactor multiplier

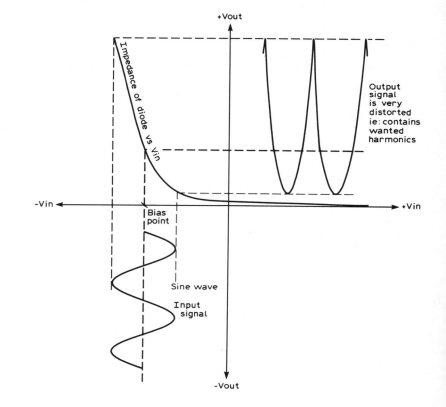

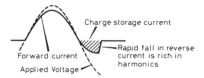

Fig 6.14. Characteristics of an srd

swept out of the depletion region. At this point it rapidly changes to a high impedance (in typically 50ps), shunted by the reverse capacitance of the diode. This rapid switch-off is used to generate high-order harmonics. The characteristic of the srd is shown in Fig 6.14.

Consider the circuit in Fig 6.15. With suitable choice of the circuit values, it can be arranged that there is maximum current from the low-frequency drive source in the inductor at the instant the diode changes to a high impedance. In practice, the bias voltage is usually supplied by the diode rectifying the rf across a resistor. The voltage pulse across the diode travels down the line and, if the line is tuned to a harmonic of the input frequency, these pulses will reinforce.

6.2.9 IMPATT diodes

The V-I characteristic of a semiconductor diode has the general form shown in Fig 6.16. Under sufficient reverse bias, avalanche breakdown occurs, and this effect is utilised in the familiar zener voltage-reference diode. In the impatt diode, the combination of the build-up time of the avalanche current and the time taken for the carriers to drift across the depletion region causes a phase delay between the current and voltage, which can result in a negative resistance, and hence the possibility of oscillation. This term "impatt" stands for "impact avalanche transit time".

The efficiency of the impatt is about 10 per cent for silicon diodes, and about 15 per cent for GaAs devices. This compares with about two per cent for Gunn diodes. At frequencies above 70GHz, the impatt is the only solidstate microwave source available, and is useful as a pump source in parametric amplifiers. The principal disadvantages of the impatt compared with the Gunn diode are its noise performance and the need for a high bias voltage. The impatt (and trapatt) are fundamentally noisier than the Gunn diode, the noise originating in the avalanche multiplication process. A typical X-band impatt (single drift) will produce a cw output power of 1.5W at an efficiency of 10 per cent.

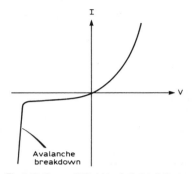

Fig 6.16. General V-I characteristic of diode

This corresponds to a dc bias supply of 80V at about 200mA, and a dissipation of about 15W. Thus the diode must be constructed in such a way that the heat generated can be efficiently removed, and it is usually built with an integral heatsink (see Fig 6.17 for a typical impatt package).

6.2.10 TRAPATT diodes

In 1967 a second mode of avalanche oscillation was discovered. This new mode remained unexplained for some time, and was initially referred to as the "anomalous mode".

If the voltage is applied sufficiently rapidly, a different type of breakdown occurs because it is possible to over-drive the field and create a dense hole-electron plasma. This state, in which the diode is filled with plasma and the voltage has dropped to a low value, is referred to as a "trapped plasma state". The diode then recovers gradually as the holes and electrons drift slowly out of the active region, thereby restoring the field and voltage to their initial level. This has been called the "trapatt" ("trapped plasma avalanche triggered transit") mode.

The efficiency of the trapatt is much higher than that of the impatt, being up to 60 per cent at low frequencies (around 1GHz) and dropping to about 25 per cent at 10GHz. The trapatt is best suited to high-power pulsed applications.

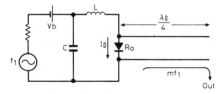

Fig 6.15. SRD in multiplying circuit

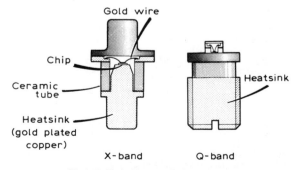

Fig 6.17. Typical impatt diode package

Table 6.2. S-parameters for low-noise transistor

Frequency (MHz)	200	500	1,000	1,500
S11	0.72	0.51	0.47	0.51
Angle (deg)	−65	−125	155	135
S22	0.83	0.62	0.51	0.49
Angle (deg)	−25	−35	−40	−50
S21	5.25	3.06	1.70	1.20
Angle (deg)	130	95	65	50
S12	0.08	0.11	0.14	0.17
Angle (deg)	55	45	55	65

Device: BFR91 (V_{ce} = 5.0V, I_c = 2mA, nf = 2.5dB typical at 1GHz)

6.2.11 Burn-out rating

This is determined by the amount of energy that a diode can absorb without damage. High-frequency diodes will obviously be more delicate since their junctions occupy a smaller area, so the energy will be more concentrated. They are also more susceptible to damage from static charges since their junction capacitance is lower, and thus a higher voltage will exist across the capacitance for a given amount of applied charge. In general terms, point-contact diodes have better resistance to short transients, and Schottky diodes have a better cw rating. Silicon diodes are more robust than germanium, while the germanium backward diode is the most delicate.

The circuit in which the diode is used can also be a major factor in burn-out, since it can determine how much of the incident power is absorbed by the diode. As the power in the diode increases, its impedance decreases. The diode will protect itself to some extent if it is already matched to the line impedance at low signal levels, since it will reflect most of the incident power as its impedance decreases. The diode circuitry should thus be arranged so that the match between the diode and the power source always degrades as the power

Table 6.3. S-parameters for high-power transistor

Frequency (GHz)	1	2	3	4
S11	0.74	0.64	0.32	0.32
Angle (deg)	−178	153	129	−145
S22	0.37	0.51	0.73	0.80
Angle (deg)	−92	−119	−148	−177
S21	3.91	2.32	1.86	1.38
Angle (deg)	59	10	−49	−113
S12	0.06	0.07	0.09	0.08
Angle (deg)	7	−8	−42	−98

Device: HP HXTR-5102 (V_{ce} = 1.8V, I_c = 110mA, power o/p = 0.8W at 2GHz (11dB gain), 0.5W at 4GHz (7dB gain))

level increases. In practice these effects are probably more important than the type of diode chosen.

In the case of very-high-power devices such as varactors, heatsinking is very important, and it is necessary to maintain a very low thermal resistance path between the package and the outside world, as well as keeping stray reactances down to a minimum.

6.3 TRANSISTORS AND FETS

6.3.1 Transistors

Bipolar transistors are useful up to the low microwave frequencies. Fairly low noise figures can be obtained, but the gains are not as high as can be achieved with GaAsfets. Virtually all the types that are of use at microwaves will be in packages designed for mounting on microstrip. Popular type numbers for low-noise devices are BFR90, BFR91, BFR96 and NE021.

Power devices exist, but are somewhat expensive. Cellular construction can be used to combine many low-power chips to give a high-power device. At 1GHz, up to about 10W can be achieved fairly cheaply. These packages again are usually designed for mounting on microstrip, and often have heatsink studs. Many power devices at this frequency on the surplus market are designed for common-base circuits and are difficult to use in a linear fashion, though useful for Class C operation.

The characteristics of microwave transistors (and fets) are usually specified by S-parameters. A typical set of values for a low-noise transistor and for a high-power one are shown in Tables 6.2 and 6.3. The input impedance of the low-noise device is close to 50Ω. High-power devices normally have an input impedance of under 10Ω, though the example given has some matching built into the transistor which makes it easier to use. External matching is essential if internal matching is not present. Similar comments apply to the output.

6.3.2 GaAsfets

Gallium arsenide fets (GaAsfets) have become so popular because they not only have quite high gains up to 10 or 20GHz, but they also have extremely low noise figures. They have provided a great step forward in the performance of solidstate microwave devices. One of the reasons for their improved performance is that gallium arsenide has a much higher carrier mobility than silicon; this reduces the transit times in the material and hence gives better performance at high frequencies.

The construction of a dual-gate GaAsfet is shown in Fig 6.18. A layer of gallium arsenide is deposited on a substrate by "vapour-phase deposition" – passing GaAs over the substrate as a hot gas, which condenses and grows as a crystalline layer on the cooler substrate. The gate is isolated by a Schottky diode which is reverse

Table 6.4. Absolute maximum ratings for the MGF1402 (T_a = 25C)

Symbol	Parameter	Limits
V_{GDO}	Gate-to-drain voltage	–6V
V_{GSO}	Gate-to-source voltage	–6V
V_{DSX}	Drain-to-source voltage	8V
I_D	Drain current	100mA
PT	Total power dissipation	300mW
T_{ch}	Channel temperature	150C
T_{stg}	Storage temperature	–55 to +150C

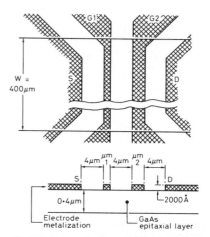

Fig 6.18. Schematic view of 3SK97 GaAsfet

biased when the gate is negative with respect to the channel. The dopants and metallising are then diffused in the usual way.

In order to achieve a good microwave performance, the structure must be extremely small. This accounts for its delicate nature. The channel length is about 1 micron, and the gate metallising 0.5 micron wide and of similar thickness. The cross-sectional area of the gate conductor is thus 0.25^{-6} sq mm. A current of 1mA in this gate metallising corresponds to a current density of 4,000A/sq mm! Similarly, a voltage of 5V between the gate and drain, a distance of 0.5 micron, is a voltage gradient of 100kV/cm, which is well above the breakdown field for air. The dielectric strength of gallium arsenide is many times that of air, however, but it is evident that even when running these devices at 5V and currents of milliamps, they are operating as close to catastrophic breakdown as some high-power devices, so the manufacturer's limits must be taken seriously. In particular, the gate must not be taken positive because the diode becomes forward biased and then currents of many milliamps can flow. The results of exceeding the ratings can be a catastrophic failure – the resulting crater looks like there has been a small explosion; in a way, there has. Similar damage can occur due to discharge of static into the device.

Being fets, the input and output impedances of the devices are very high at hf/vhf/uhf. They reduce with frequency, and are in the region of 50Ω at 10GHz, but are generally higher than bipolar transistors at the same frequency. Fig 6.19 and Table 6.4 give some data for a typical GaAsfet, the Mitsubishi MGF1402. Fig 6.20 and Table 6.5 give S-parameter data for the same device.

The packaged fet is intended for use in microstrip applications, but it can be mounted in waveguide with a little ingenuity. Professionally, naked chips are often mounted directly on alumina and connections from the chip to the lines made direct by bondwires.

6.4 DETECTORS

A wide variety of types of diode are used as detectors, but they can be grouped into two types – those with an exponential V-I characteristic and those with other

Table 6.5. S-parameters for the MGF1402 (T_a = 25C, V_{DS} = 3V)

I_D (mA)	f (GHz)	S11 Magn	S11 Angle	S12 Magn	S12 Angle	S21 Magn	S21 Angle	S22 Magn	S22 Angle
10	2	0.935	–47.4	0.040	54.1	2.848	133.4	0.758	–33.1
10	4	0.835	–88.4	0.065	21.3	2.469	92.3	0.710	–62.6
10	6	0.800	–119.1	0.054	13.6	2.333	65.8	0.713	–75.8
10	8	0.709	–164.5	0.048	–9.5	2.286	27.7	0.643	–97.6
10	10	0.658	155.7	0.052	–59.3	1.805	–13.9	0.599	–138.7
10	12	0.713	130.0	0.044	–37.4	1.488	–37.1	0.480	177.3
30	2	0.916	–53.1	0.032	55.2	3.864	130.8	0.676	–32.5
30	4	0.787	–198.0	0.048	25.1	3.203	88.3	0.632	–60.9
30	6	0.742	–129.7	0.034	39.4	2.928	61.8	0.657	–71.3
30	8	0.661	–176.7	0.035	27.4	2.751	23.3	0.604	–91.9
30	10	0.640	144.1	0.037	–29.3	2.160	–15.7	0.580	–134.0
30	12	0.720	121.2	0.046	9.7	1.770	–37.6	0.433	–178.0

All angles are in degrees.

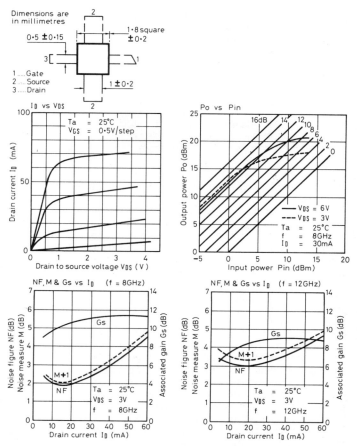

Fig 6.19. Mitsubishi semiconductor (GaAsfet) MGF-1402 (2SK274)

special characteristics. The first group includes conventional junction diodes, point-contact diodes and zero-, low-, medium- and high-bias Schottky diodes. The second includes backward diodes.

Germanium point-contact diodes were the first type made and are still used. They have a low barrier height. Silicon Schottky diodes are more commonly used nowadays, and are available in zero-bias, low-, medium- and high-barrier versions. For best performance at low signal levels backward diodes are used.

6.4.1 Operation of the diode detector

Junction diodes are used to detect low-level rf signals by operating as a normal half-wave rectifier. They are essentially very simple broadband power detectors, and are often mounted in coaxial line or waveguide to monitor the power in a transmission line, or across a simple antenna to indicate radiated power. The basic circuit is shown in Fig 6.21.

As can be seen from the dc V-I characteristic (eg Fig 6.5), the diode has a low resistance when forward biased and a high resistance when reverse biased. This circuit

will detect rf power over a wide range of levels, but its characteristics vary over the range. At rf levels below about a few hundred millivolts, the detected voltage or current is directly proportional to the rf power, while above this the output voltage is proportional to the rf input voltage, ie V_{out} is proportional to the square root of the power.

The operation at high power levels is fairly easily understood, in that the diode operates as a switch and the output follows the maximum positive value of the rf waveform. This is therefore a peak voltage detector. However, at lower levels the operation has to be studied more closely. The characteristic of a Schottky diode will be used to illustrate the operation. Its exponential V-I characteristic is shown in Fig 6.22 together with the incremental resistance of the diode (ie the slope of the V-I curve).

Consider how current flows through the diode during one complete cycle of sinusoidal rf input.

As the input voltage goes through its positive half-cycle, current flows forwards through the diode, increasing from zero to maximum and back to zero. The total

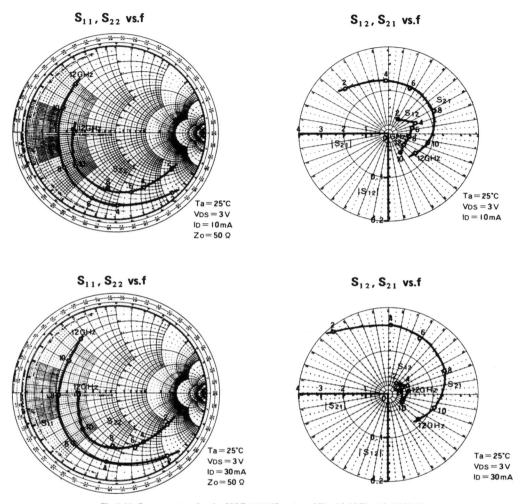

Fig 6.20. S-parameters for the MGF-1402 (Courtesy Mitsubishi Electric UK Ltd)

amount of charge is the current multiplied by the time, ie the area shown under the V-I curve. This charge would be stored in the capacitor. However, in the negative half-cycle the same process occurs, but this time the current is in the opposite direction and a net charge is taken out of the capacitor. After this single cycle, the capacitor holds the difference between the amount of charge supplied and removed. This net amount of charge passed through the diode represents the rectified current, and the voltage on the capacitor the detected voltage.

This operation is very obvious when large input voltages are used, because the ratio of the forward and reverse resistances is very high, and in practice charge only travels in the forward direction – almost none is removed in the negative half-cycle. However, at low levels the changes in resistance between forward and reverse bias are very small, and consequently almost all the charge given to the capacitor is taken back in the second half cycle. The net difference between the two is a very small fraction of the total charge moved. The diode is therefore behaving as a non-linear resistor, its mean value being the slope of the diode curve at zero applied voltage.

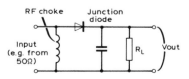

Fig 6.21. Junction diode as a detector

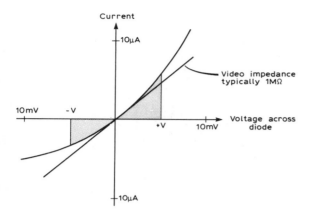

Fig 6.22. V-I characteristic of Schottky diode

The reason why the diode produces an output proportional to power at low levels is that, although the diode characteristic is an exponential, the difference between the currents for an equal positive and negative voltage is proportional to the square of the voltage. It follows that the difference between the forward and reverse currents averaged over a cycle is a square law, ie the mean current is proportional to the square of the input voltage.

This can be verified by putting a value for V into the expression for the diode characteristic and calculating the current for +V and −V. The difference between

these two will be found to be proportional to V^2 provided V is small, ie under 100mV, but the exact values will differ between types of diodes.

6.4.2 Video impedance and tangential signal sensitivity

The difference between various types of detector diode should now be clear. Almost all diodes have basically the same exponential characteristic; the main difference between the various zero-bias, low-, medium- and high-bias diodes is the position of this curve relative to the origin. This manifests itself in two ways. The reverse leakage current I_s is higher in the lower-bias diodes, and the slope resistance at zero bias voltage, which is known as the "video impedance", is lower in the low-bias diodes. Diodes are often biased with a small dc current to lower the video impedance by shifting the operating point into the forward bias region.

Diodes used in this way are much less sensitive than a narrowband receiver. The limit is about −50 to −60dBm and is known as the "tangential signal sensitivity", tss.

The sensitivity of a variety of detector diodes is compared below. Fig 6.23 compares the sensitivity of diodes with an infinitely large load resistance with and without dc bias; Fig 6.24 shows the effects of lower load resistances. In general, a low load resistance is needed if a wide bandwidth is required, eg many megahertz, but the sensitivity then suffers. The low-barrier diodes are best suited to operating into low-resistance loads. The load resistance relative to the type of barrier height also has a marked effect on the linearity of the detector.

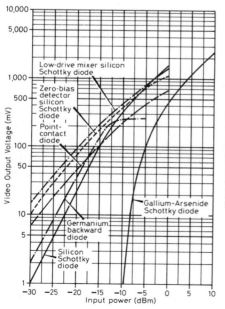

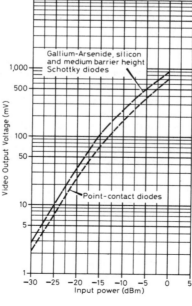

Fig 6.23. Output voltage versus input power for detector diodes

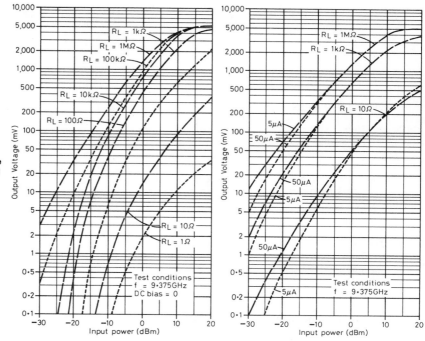

Fig 6.24. Effects of load resistance on output power of a typical X-band detector diode

6.4.3 Figure of merit

The quality of a detector diode can be compared in terms of the short-circuit current sensitivity and video impedance, by using an arbitrary figure of merit M:

$$M = B \times \sqrt{Z}$$

where B is the short-circuit current sensitivity and Z is the video impedance. The video impedance is usually given on a manufacturer's data sheet.

This only refers to the diode's operation at zero bias, and does not take into account its noise performance.

6.4.4 Selecting a diode

For high efficiency, the diode capacitance must be minimised. This is particularly important as the sensitivity depends on the square of the capacitance.

For maximum detector sensitivity the curvature of the characteristic at the origin should be as large as possible, and thus low- or zero-bias diodes are best. The back diode has one of the highest slopes at the origin, and is thus a very sensitive detector. However, there is a price to be paid for these high sensitivities. The greater the slope, the greater effect temperature has on the sensitivity.

The values of the components in the detector circuit have to be related to the diode impedance to obtain best sensitivity, particularly the rf source impedance and the dc load resistance. Low-barrier devices operate with rf and dc resistances of a few hundred ohms, while high-barrier devices need tens of kilohms or megohms.

For optimum efficiency and linearity from a low-level detector, the rf source resistance should be equal to or lower than the diode video impedance. The load resistance should be much greater than the video impedance for a voltage detector, and equal to or less than it for a current detector.

6.5 MIXERS

Mixers are mostly used to translate signals up or down in frequency without changing them in any other way. However, the same basic function also appears in modulators, phase detectors, multipliers, gain-controlled stages and switches – anywhere where the circuit requires that one signal controls the amplitude of another. In all these cases, the amplitude of one signal is being multiplied by another.

Most practical mixers at rf use the properties of semiconductor diodes to perform this function, and consequently have many shortcomings. Transistors, valves or fets are also used as mixers, but they still operate on the same basic principles that will be described for the diode mixer, in that they all have a non-linear transfer function. It is perhaps surprising that such good results can be obtained from devices based on the humble diode, despite its non-linear nature.

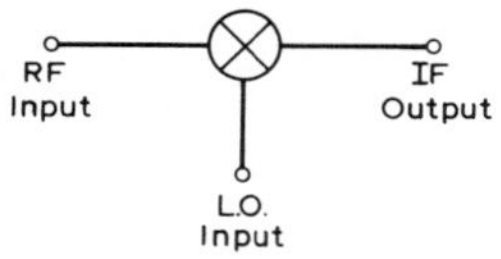

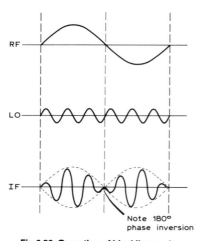

RF Input — IF Output — L.O. Input

Fig 6.25. Basic mixer

The main shortcomings of real mixers are that they generate outputs at other than the wanted sum and difference frequencies, and they produce non-linear distortion on the signals passing through them. Better performance can be obtained by combining a number of diodes to form single- or double-balanced mixers.

The basic types of mixer in common use are listed below in increasing order of complexity and quality of performance:

    Single-diode
    Balanced
    Double-balanced
    Product-return
    Termination-insensitive
    Parametric
    Transistor/fet

However, in many applications no one type of mixer is obviously the best; there are often many parameters which need to be traded off against each other, eg conversion loss, noise figure, 1dB compression point, degree of balance, local oscillator power and noise sidebands, and bandwidth, to name a few! Their characteristics will be described in more detail after explaining the basic operation of a mixer.

6.5.1 Theory of an ideal mixer

Shortcomings in mixer performance are often blamed on "non-linearity". This may seem to be rather contradictory since it is also said that a mixer must have

RF

LO

IF

Note 180° phase inversion

Fig 6.26. Operation of ideal linear mixer

non-linear properties to produce the mixing effect. First we will explain what properties an ideal mixer should have.

Fig 6.25 shows the representation of a mixer with two inputs, rf and local oscillator (lo), and one output, i.f.

An ideal mixer has the property that there is a perfectly linear path from each input to the output, but the fraction transmitted through one path is controlled linearly by the voltage at the other input. Mixers can operate in either a switching or linear mode. In a linear mixer the attenuation of the rf to i.f path is smoothly varied from zero to infinity by a sine-wave lo signal. In a switching mixer, the rf to i.f path is either turned fully "on" or fully "off" by a square-wave lo. The mixer is therefore rather like a voltage-controlled attenuator, but with the important difference that if the controlling input goes negative the polarity of the output signal is inverted. This is illustrated in Fig 6.26.

This ideal mixer produces outputs only at the sum and difference frequencies of its two inputs. Two input signals W_a and W_b would produce outputs at $W_a + W_b$ and $W_a - W_b$ (eg as in Fig 6.27). The amplitude of the outputs would be proportional to the amplitude of the inputs.

This operation can be described mathematically by using two sine-wave input signals at frequencies W_a and W_b, and amplitudes A and B. The voltage of each of these signals varies with time t in the following way:

$$A \times \cos(W_a t)$$

and $$B \times \cos(W_b t)$$

The mixing process consists of multiplying these two input voltages, giving:

$$A \times B \times (\cos(W_a t) \times \cos(W_b t))$$

This product of the two cosine functions can also be written as:

$$(A \times B/2) \times (\cos((W_a + W_b)t) + \cos((W_a - W_b)t))$$

This represents two products on frequencies which are the sum and difference of the two input frequencies, and corresponds to the output from a double-balanced mixer. The output waveform is similar to that of a double-sideband suppressed-carrier signal in an ssb transmitter.

In most rf applications mixers are used in the switching mode, and the lo input is usually a square wave so that the diodes are either fully "on" or "off". The lo signal effectively switches alternate pairs of diodes into conduction, reversing the polarity of the rf input signal at the lo frequency. The operation is then simply that of a reversing switch, as shown in Fig 6.28. The switching mode usually gives better linearity of the rf to i.f path, and a lower conversion loss. Linear mixers are more common at audio frequencies than at rf.

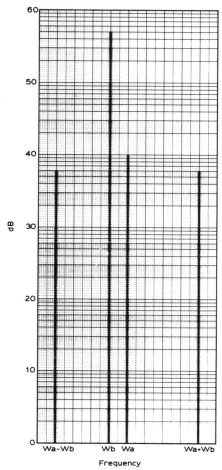

Fig 6.27. Output spectrum from ideal mixer

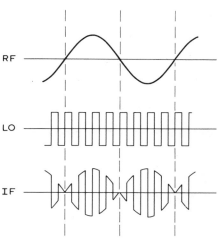

Fig 6.28. Operation of ideal switching mixer

6.5.2 The single-diode mixer

The simple single-diode mixer is still in common use, as well as being the basic building block of the more advanced types. Its operation is very easy to explain, and this will illustrate some of the problems, and reasons for developing the more complex circuits.

The operation of a simple diode mixer can be described from the V-I characteristic of a ideal diode. The relationship is fairly accurately exponential for I_d between a few nanoamps and a few milliamps. The diode current is given by:

$$I_d = I_o \times (\exp(eV/kT) - 1)$$

where e is the charge on an electron, 1.6×10^{-19}; k is Boltzmann's constant, 1.23×10^{-23}; V is the voltage across the diode; T is the absolute temperature; I_o is the reverse leakage current. At room temperature (T =

290K), e/kT is about 40 per millivolt. For an ideal diode, I_o is constant, and a function of barrier height; in practice, of course, it increases due to breakdown at high reverse voltages.

The resistance of the diode is given by the ratio V/I at any point on the curve, and thus varies with diode current. The incremental (small-signal) resistance is the tangent to the curve, and is given by $25/I_d$ ohms for a silicon diode, where the current is in milliamps. So, by varying the diode current, the small-signal resistance can be varied from a very high to a very low value. By using the diode as part of a potential divider circuit, it can act as a variable attenuator (Fig 6.29). The "on" resistance will be limited by the series resistance of the diode, which is typically 10Ω.

This circuit will function as a mixer provided that the local oscillator power is sufficient to change the diode current and hence impedance significantly, and that the signal is much weaker than the local oscillator. This deviates from our ideal mixer mentioned earlier in a number of ways.

1. The signal path is not very linear – it has the same characteristic that we are using with the local oscillator to produce the variable attenuator effect! So

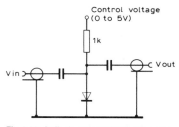

Fig 6.29. A diode as a variable attenuator

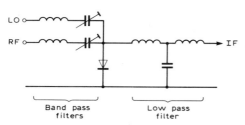

Band pass filters   Low pass filter

Fig 6.30. Typical arrangement of single-diode mixer

intermodulation products and harmonics will also be generated by the input signals.

2. The three ports will all be very poorly isolated from each other. High levels of lo signal will be present at the rf and i.f ports. The input signal will appear at the i.f port. RF bandpass filtering will be necessary to prevent the energy from each of the input signals from being wasted in the sources connected to the other ports. Fig 6.30 shows a typical arrangement.

3. The input impedance to the large local oscillator signal will vary with I_d, and hence will vary during the lo cycle. Thus the lo sine wave will become very distorted as harmonics of it are generated within the mixer diode.

The single-diode mixer, while not optimal in many respects, is still popular in waveguide circuitry because of its simplicity. A diode is either mounted directly across the waveguide, or in a coaxial mount adjacent to it.

A variety of types of diode with different barrier height is available. These are chosen according to the dynamic range required and the local oscillator power available. A low barrier height will give poor strong-signal handling.

6.5.3 Conversion loss of a diode mixer

The overall noise figure of a mixer/i.f combination is given by:

$$F = L_c \times (F_{if} + N_r - 1) \qquad \text{(as a ratio)}$$

where L_c is the conversion loss, F_{if} is the noise figure of the i.f amplifier and N_r is the noise temperature ratio of the diode. All values are as ratios, not in decibels.

In this simple circuit the diode will be switched off for approximately half a cycle and, depending on the drive level, the conduction angle may vary from 120 to 170°. The effect that those other diode parameters not present in an ideal model have on the conversion loss is summarised in below. The conversion loss (in decibels) is given by:

$$L_c = 3.9 + 17 \times F/F_{co} + 9 \times R_b/Z_o$$

F_{co} is the cut-off frequency which is derived from the time constant of the junction series resistance and

capacitance. R_b is the forward resistance of the diode when the lo current is at a maximum (typically a few ohms). Z_o is the impedance of the line in which the diode is mounted, and also the impedance of the signal and lo sources as seen by the mixer (typically 50–100Ω). Note that the ratios are not converted to decibels. If the package reactances are significant, they may transform Z_o to a different value at the mixer chip. The factor of 3.9dB depends slightly on what is done with the other mixing products, as mentioned earlier.

The minimum possible conversion loss depends on the slope of the log-log plot of the diode V-I characteristic. At a frequency w (w = $2\pi \times F$), the loss is given by:

$$L_c = \frac{R_s + \dfrac{R_b}{1 + (w \times C_b \times R_b)^2}}{\dfrac{R_b}{1 + (w \times C_b \times R_b)^2}} \times L_o$$

where L_o is the If conversion loss determined from the V-I curve; R_b is the barrier resistance; C_b is the barrier capacitance; and R_s is the series resistance.

Thus, at any frequency where the barrier capacitance is significant, the product $C_b \times R_s$ must be minimised for lowest loss.

Noise included in the noise temperature ratio includes thermal noise in the series resistance, shot noise in the barrier (due to the charge being quantised), and flicker noise. Shot noise dominates at rf, but flicker noise becomes more important at audio frequencies.

6.5.4 Switching mixers

The simple diode mixer can be improved by a number of measures. The simplest one is to use a high lo drive level. Taken to the limit, this is equivalent to driving it with a square-wave lo. This means that the diode spends most of its time either reverse biased and open-circuit, or heavily forward biased, the "on" resistance being limited to a few ohms by the series resistance. Thus the diode always appears as a fairly linear resistor, and the non-linearity in the signal path is reduced. This also minimises the conversion loss for a single-diode mixer, as the input signal is then being 100 per cent modulated.

Further increases in the lo power will only increase the noise figure, either due to the oscillator sideband noise, or broadband shot noise associated with the rectified current flowing in the diode ($2e \times I \times B$). While this may increase the maximum signal power that the mixer can handle, it will reduce the dynamic range.

At very low frequencies the ideal element for a mixer is a mechanical relay. This is lossless and extremely linear. However, in practice some solidstate device or valve has to be used, and these are far from linear. In fact all the devices used for mixers are inherently nonlinear, and have either a square-law or exponential

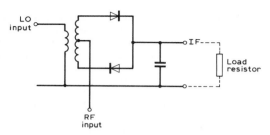

Fig 6.31. Single-balanced mixer

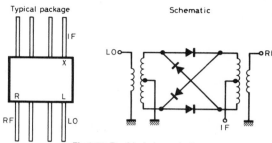

Fig 6.32. Double-balanced mixer

characteristic, so they have to rely on the rf signal only making small changes to the device operating point.

6.5.5 Balanced mixers

The first improvement over the simple diode mixer is to balance it to one port, as shown in Fig 6.31. This improves the linearity and suppresses one of the inputs at the i.f output, eg the lo and its a.m noise sidebands. This technique is often used in ssb transmitters to generate dsb suppressed carrier, the balance suppressing the carrier.

The lo is fed 180° out of phase to two mixing elements (in this case diodes). Such a mixer has a slightly more linear signal path as there are two diodes in series or parallel in the signal path, with the rf current flowing in opposite directions in them. However, it needs more lo power than a single diode. Any changes in diode current due to the signal are of opposite sense in each diode, so, as the resistance of one increases, the other decreases. Over a small range these cancel each other out, reducing the even-order distortion products. The diodes have to be matched for junction capacitance, series resistance and forward voltage drop at the particular current. Ideally they would be on the same chip.

6.5.6 Double-balanced mixers

In this type (see Fig 6.32) both the lo and signal inputs are cancelled at the i.f port. The diodes act as a single-pole changeover switch which reverses the connections at the lo frequency. This is a very close approximation to an ideal mixer, and characteristics of a typical device are shown in Fig 6.33. It is a good design, since all the ports are well isolated from each other over a broad frequency range.

The double-balanced mixer is particularly popular at vhf and uhf, and usually purchased in an eight-pin rectangular metal can. They are available from a number of manufacturers, eg Minicircuits, Anzac and Avantek. Alternatively, you can make your own by mounting diodes in a microstrip circuit; this method is more common at microwave frequencies.

6.5.7 Product-return mixer

This is also known as the "image-rejection mixer". Any product at the i.f port which is derived from the rf input

signal must have taken energy from the signal input to generate it. This energy detracts from that available for the wanted output. Thus all unwanted outputs represent wasted power and increased conversion loss. An ideal mixer would be able to convert all the signal power to the i.f. In practice, the losses vary from 4 to 10dB.

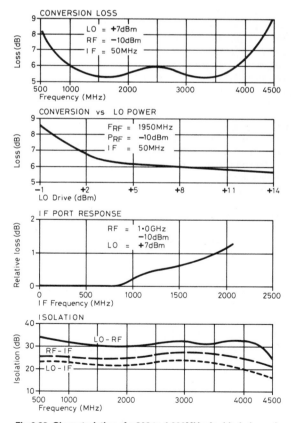

Fig 6.33. Characteristics of a 800 to 4,000MHz double-balanced mixer

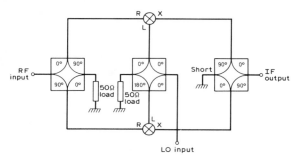

Fig 6.34. Product-return mixer

The product-return mixer reduces the conversion loss between the rf input and the i.f output by returning any unwanted mixer products to the mixer, so the energy in them is reflected back for another attempt at conversion to the wanted output frequency. The equivalent circuit is shown in Fig 6.34.

If F_{lo} and F_{rf} are mixed, most of the energy goes into $F_{lo} + F_{rf}$ and $F_{lo} - F_{rf}$. However, because of the high level of the lo, its second and third harmonics are also present in the mixer at quite a high level. These will also mix with the input signal to give outputs at $2 \times F_{lo} + F_{rf}$, $2 \times F_{lo} - F_{rf}$, $3 \times F_{lo} + F_{rf}$ and $3 \times F_{lo} - F_{rf}$, as in Fig 6.35. The correct impedance must be presented to all the unwanted products to minimise the conversion loss. Since many of them are well above the normal operating frequencies of the mixer, it is evident that for high efficiency the mixer circuitry must be designed to function well at many times the normal working frequencies. One of these is the frequency which would correspond to the image response if the mixer were used in a receiver; hence the name "image-rejection mixer" is also used.

When correctly set up, this type of mixer will only produce either a sum or a difference output frequency – the unwanted one will be suppressed by about 20dB. It is therefore somewhat similar to an ssb generator.

There are several ways of recovering the energy from these unwanted products. They can all be thought of either as reflecting them back into the mixer in the appropriate phase, or terminating the mixer ports in the appropriate impedance at all the unwanted product frequencies. Some of the techniques used are:

(a) Separating the unwanted products from the wanted output using filters, and returning them to the i.f port by reflecting them in the appropriate phase with a mismatched load.

(b) Designing the circuitry in the immediate vicinity of the diode so that the unwanted products are terminated in open- or short-circuits.

(c) Using broadband phase shifter and combiner techniques to return the products.

The familiar G3JVL transverter used on 10GHz applies these methods to achieve a very low conversion loss from a single-diode mixer. The diode is mounted across the waveguide between two narrowband filters – one for the local oscillator and one for the signal frequency. The image frequency is reflected by both of these filters back to the diode, and hence the mixer is often called an "image-recovery mixer".

6.5.8 Termination-insensitive mixers

This class of mixers is similar to the product-return mixer, in that the impedance presented to unwanted mixer products at the i.f output does not affect the intermodulation performance of the mixer. One way of achieving this is to prevent the unwanted products from emerging at the i.f port.

Fig 6.36 shows such a mixer. Isolation between each hybrid's opposite ports allows the lo to control independently the switching action of alternately conducting diode sets.

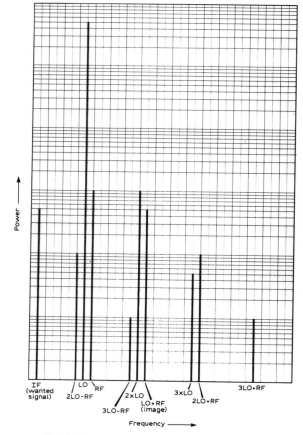

Fig 6.35. Frequencies present in product-return mixer

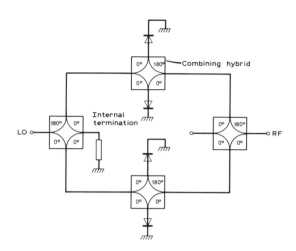

Fig 6.36. Schematic of a termination-insensitive mixer

Owing to its complexity, this type is generally only used at vhf and uhf in high-performance equipment.

6.5.9 Parametric mixers

All the mixers described so far have been passive, in that the mixer has always been a lossy, variable-resistance device. If a reactive device such as a varactor diode were used, then losses could be further reduced as no power could be dissipated in the diode. (In fact, under the right conditions the lo can act as a pump and some gain obtained, as in a parametric amplifier). These are particularly popular for high-level mixers in the microwave area, as multiplication and mixing can be performed in the same diode. Otherwise they are similar to a single-diode mixer.

6.5.10 Transistor and fet mixers

Transistors and fets are most often used as mixers in the same way as the simple diode mixer (see Fig 6.37). The main difference is the slightly lower lo power requirements and conversion gain provided.

Transistor mixers have much in common with the simple diode mixer, as the mixing action occurs in the base-emitter diode of the transistor. They are essentially the same as a diode mixer followed by an amplifier. FET mixers are somewhat different, as their gate-source characteristic is closer to a square law, in contrast to the exponential diode characteristic.

A real benefit comes from using a dual-gate fet, and applying the signal to one gate and the lo to the other. This gives a considerable amount of isolation between the two ports.

Transistors are often used as transmit mixers when high-level mixing is required. Such a mixer can give an output of several watts from an input of several hundred milliwatts.

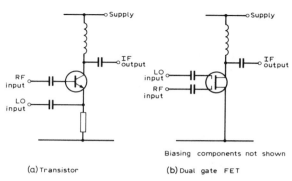

(a) Transistor   (b) Dual gate FET

Fig 6.37. Using transistors and fets as mixers

Another configuration is to use the fet as a voltage-controlled switch, as in Fig 6.38. The drain and source are treated as a switch and connected in the same circuit, as for example a balanced-diode ring mixer. The lo is then applied to the gates and used to control the resistances of each of the channels. This technique can give good lo isolation and very wide dynamic range mixers, provided a suitable type of fet is used, generally a medium-power device. Such circuits have been described by Ulrich Rohde in [2].

Dual-gate GaAsfets are available quite cheaply for use at around 1GHz, mainly intended for tv tuners, and they can be used at the lower microwave frequencies. At higher microwave frequencies single-gate GaAsfets are becoming popular as mixers, mainly because of the low lo power required and the low-noise gain they provide.

6.6 MULTIPLIERS

Multipliers are used to convert power at low frequencies, where it can be easily generated, to higher

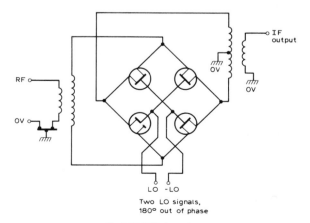

Fig 6.38. FET ring mixer

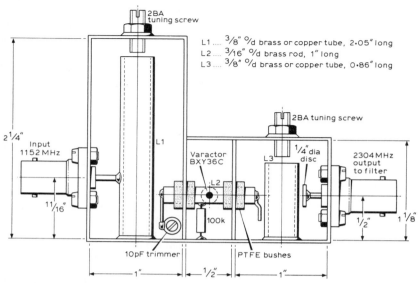

L1 ..... 3/8" %d brass or copper tube, 2·05" long
L2 ..... 3/16" %d brass rod, 1" long
L3 ..... 3/8" %d brass or copper tube, 0·86" long

Fig 6.39. UHF multiplier

frequencies where it cannot! Conventional varactors are used as doublers or triplers, while for higher harmonics step-recovery varactors are used. Typical applications are to produce several watts at a few gigahertz or tens of milliwatts at 10–20GHz, starting from uhf (typically around 400MHz).

Transistor amplifiers are often used as multiplier stages. One reason for their high efficiency is that the collector-base junction is acting as a varactor diode, and the harmonics are generated more by this effect than by signal clipping in the amplifier stage.

A bandpass filter is always needed on the output of a multiplier to select the required harmonic of the input signal. A filter is also needed on the input to stop the energy in the harmonics from getting back into the source. In a low-order varactor multiplier, other tuned circuits (idlers) are sometimes used to put a specific

impedance across the diode at the intermediate harmonics to improve the efficiency. The multiplier is thus built combined with a set of resonant circuits. A simple doubler is illustrated in Fig 6.39. For high-order multiplication the input will normally be in coaxial line and the output in waveguide. A typical design is shown in Fig 6.40.

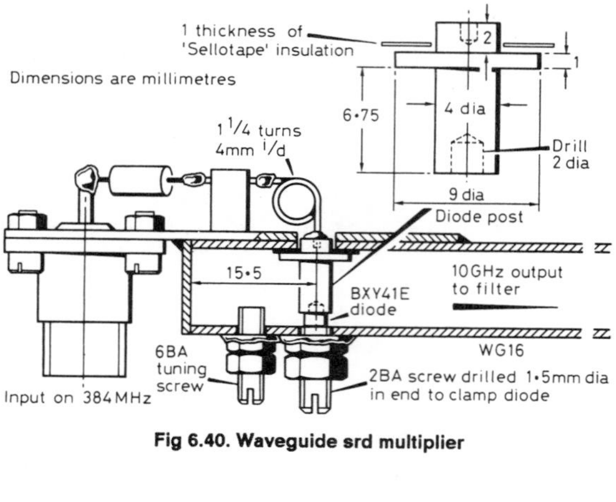

6.6.1 Selecting a step-recovery diode

In selecting a diode for an application there are five important parameters to consider. These are the diode capacitance C_t, the snap time T_s, the lifetime T_l, the breakdown voltage V_b, and thermal resistance θ_j.

The capacitance at the normal dc operating bias should have a reactance of between 30 and 60Ω: see Fig 6.41. For example, at a 10GHz output frequency, a good value for C_t is 0.5pF.

The "snap time" is the time taken for the diode to switch from a conducting to a non-conducting state. It should be less than the reciprocal of the output frequency (see Fig 6.42).

The "lifetime" is a measure of the time required for the stored charge to be recovered, and must be long enough for the rf current to reach a negative peak before it snaps. The lifetime should be at least 10, and preferably 20 to 30, times the period of the input frequency. See Fig 6.43.

The breakdown voltage, along with thermal resistance, determines the power handling. Note that a low thermal resistance increases the diode capacitance and thus lowers its maximum frequency.

6.6.2 Bias resistors

All diodes require a bias resistor to provide a path for the dc current resulting from the diode rectifying the rf.

Fig 6.40. Waveguide srd multiplier

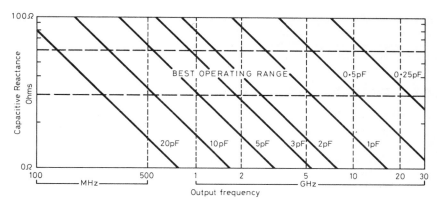

Fig 6.41. Multiplier varactor capacitive reactance versus frequency

This current flowing in the resistor must produce the correct bias voltage across the diode. This value can be estimated for srds using the following expression:

$$R_{bias} = \frac{5 \times T_l}{N^2 \times C_t}$$

where T_l is the lifetime, N is the order of multiplication and C_t the diode capacitance. The resistor should be non-inductive.

6.6.3 Efficiency

Efficiencies of around 30–50 per cent can be obtained for doublers and triplers. To obtain these efficiencies the impedances around the diode need to be defined at all the frequencies being generated – for a tripler a circuit is particularly necessary at the second harmonic, known as the "idler". For higher-order harmonics the efficiency is lower, eg at the 20th harmonic the efficiency is around one per cent using a single diode. A higher efficiency can be obtained by using several low-order stages in cascade. This is at the expense of complexity and possibly stability.

6.6.4 Reliability

In order to guarantee reliable operation of a multiplier, a number of tuned circuits are needed to ensure that energy at the various frequencies is confined to the correct places. In general the input requires a bandpass filter on the input frequency, the output a bandpass filter on the output frequency. This prevents changes in load impedance at other frequencies from altering the circuit operation.

For good reliability the multiplier must be isolated from changes in the impedance seen at the input and output. Isolators (or circulators) can provide this with minimal loss, but may not be easily obtainable by the amateur. Note that filtering is still required, as isolators or circulators will not work at harmonics of their nominal frequency. Alternatively, a resistive attenuator on the input can be used, if sufficient drive power is available, to isolate the input. At least a 3dB attenuator is desirable; a 6dB one is preferred. Such isolation is particularly important when several multipliers are cascaded, otherwise they interact, become very difficult to set up and may become unstable as thermal and other changes occur with prolonged use.

Heatsinking is important for medium- and high-power diodes. Note also that a bad mismatch on the output when running at high efficiency might double the dissipation in the device, causing failure if it is operating near its maximum ratings.

There is not much difference between a parametric amplifier and a varactor multiplier in theory, and the varactor multiplier can thus have regions of negative resistance which may produce outputs on a variety of spurious frequencies. This effect is known as the output "breaking up", and usually results in the device producing a very broad output spectrum. The total output power can be similar to that produced in normal

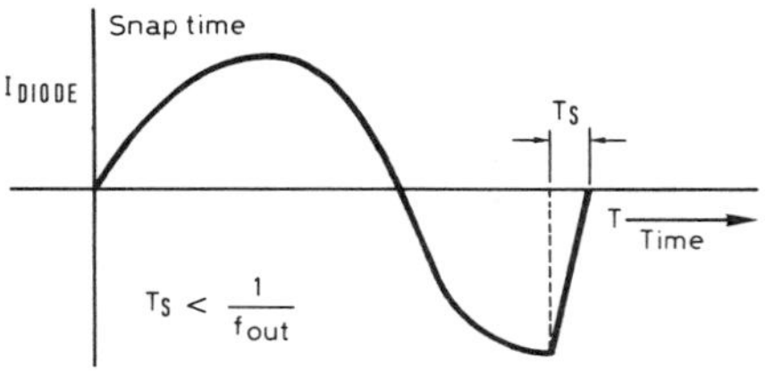

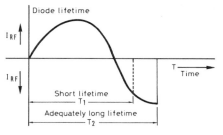

Fig 6.42. Snap time

Fig 6.43. Diode lifetime

operation, and so adequate test equipment is needed to check operation of the multiplier before it is connected to an antenna. It should be noted that an improperly matched load could lead to such instability.

6.7 GUNN DIODES AND OSCILLATORS

6.7.1 The Gunn effect

The Gunn effect was discovered in 1960 by the British physicist J B Gunn:

> "When I pushed the electric field up to the neighbourhood of 1,000 to 2,000V/cm something entirely unexpected happened. Instead of simple variation of current with voltage, all hell broke loose – the current started to jump up and down in a completely irregular way that very much resembled electrical noise mechanisms I knew. The current variations were the order of amperes rather than the nano-amperes you normally see..."

The Gunn effect proved to be the first of several solidstate microwave oscillator effects, which have since become well established in many radar and communications applications.

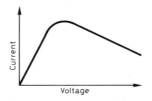

Fig 6.44. Voltage/current characteristics of a Gunn diode

Gunn diodes are made from gallium arsenide (GaAs). The electrons in GaAs can be in one of two conduction bands. In one band, the electrons happen to have a much higher mobility than the other. The electrons are initially in the higher-mobility band but, as the electric field is increased, more and more are scattered to the lower-mobility band. The average electron velocity lies somewhere between the individual band velocities. As more electrons are scattered to the lower band, the average velocity drops. The electric field at which the velocity begins to drop is called the "threshold field", and in GaAs is 320V/mm. Since current is proportional to electron velocity, and voltage is proportional to electric field, the device characteristic will have a region of negative resistance. This is illustrated in Fig 6.44.

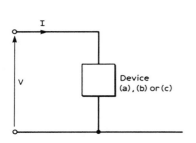

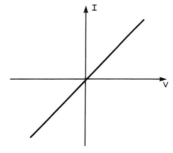

(a) Resistor

Fig 6.45. Explanation of negative resistance

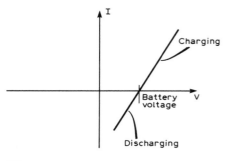

(b) Battery

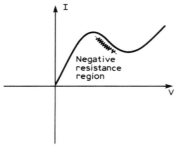

(c) Active device

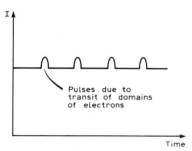

Fig 6.46. Current in Gunn diode

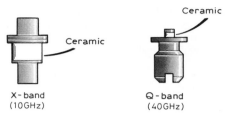

Fig 6.48. Typical Gunn diode packages

Negative resistance is a somewhat strange concept, so a brief explanation will be given. Resistance is defined as the slope of the line from the origin to the point on the V-I characteristic, $R = V/I$. For a resistor this slope is constant and positive, as in Fig 6.45(a), so the resistor always absorbs power. A device which generates power, eg a battery, has negative resistance and this is shown in Fig 6.45(b). Active devices normally only exhibit negative resistance over a small part of the V-I characteristic (ie negative "differential" resistance), and so considered over their whole characteristic do actually absorb power. This is shown in Fig 6.45(c).

The current through the device takes the form of a steady dc current upon which are superimposed pulses of current (Fig 6.46). These pulses are due to the transit of so-called "domains" of electrons across the device, and propagate at the electron velocity (10^5m/s). The repetition frequency of the pulses is governed mainly by the thickness of the layer of GaAs, so the diode must be made such that its thickness is close to a "transit-time length" at the frequency of interest. This ranges from 20μm for a C-band (4GHz) device to 1.5μm for a Q-band (40GHz) device (the upper practical limit). A transit-time length is defined as the distance an electron travels during one rf cycle. It is expressed as:

$$L = v \times T$$

$$\text{or } L = v/f$$

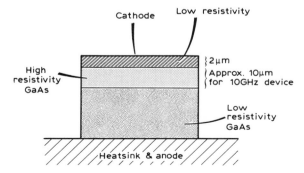

Fig 6.47. Construction of Gunn diode

where v is the electron drift velocity and f is the frequency. This shows that the frequency of oscillation of a device may be varied by changing v with the bias voltage.

The active part of the device consists of a thin layer of n-type GaAs grown epitaxially on a substrate of low-resistivity GaAs about 60μm in diameter. This substrate acts as a connection to one side of the epitaxial layer (anode), and in turn is bonded to the metallic base which forms a heatsink. A lead bonded to a metallic film evaporated onto the other face of the epitaxial layer, or to a second layer of low-resistivity material (which produces more reliable devices), forms the second connection (cathode). In high-power devices, the heatsink is formed by depositing a thick (50μm) layer of metal with high thermal conductivity, such as gold, silver or copper, directly on the surface of the semiconductor slice. This is known as the "integral heatsink process". Fig 6.47 shows the active part of the device, and Fig 6.48 shows typical packaging for X-band (10GHz) and Q-band (40GHz) diodes.

It should be appreciated that the device is not a diode in the conventional sense, since it does not consist of a pn junction, but rather a GaAs resistor biased into the region of negative resistance.

6.7.2 Gunn oscillators

A Gunn oscillator is made by mating a diode with a microwave circuit which provides a positive resistance equal to the negative resistance of the diode. The frequency of operation is determined by the resonance of this circuit. A simplified rf equivalent circuit of such an oscillator, excluding the dc paths, is shown in Fig 6.49. It consists of a lossless resonant circuit (L and C) in parallel with three resistors.

R_1 represents the losses in the tuned circuit.

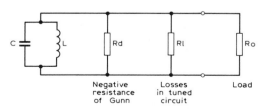

Fig 6.49. Simplified equivalent circuit of Gunn oscillator

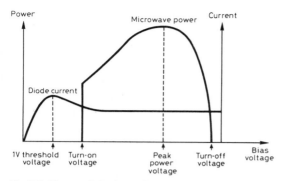

Fig 6.50. Characteristic shape of a Gunn oscillator's bias power curve

R_0 represents the load to which the oscillator is coupled. The power dissipated in this resistor is the output power.

R_d represents the negative differential resistance of the Gunn diode. It will usually be negative.

The L-C circuit would oscillate continuously if it were lossless (all resistors of infinite value). In reality losses will be present, so oscillations, once started, would die away. The circuit is made to appear lossless by placing a negative resistance (the Gunn diode) in parallel with it, so that the negative resistance cancels out the positive ones corresponding to the circuit losses and load. The condition for stable oscillation is then that $R_1//R_0 = -R_d$ (// denotes "in parallel with"). When no power is taken out, R_0 is infinity, so $R_1//R_d = 0$, ie $R_1 = -R_d$. This is the condition for oscillations to just start, and corresponds to the turn-on voltage in Fig 6.50. It depends on the Q of the tuned circuit, ie the lower the Q, the greater the difference between $V_{threshold}$ and $V_{turn-on}$. This is all just another way of saying that the Gunn diode replaces power dissipated in the circuit losses and the load.

The value of R_d varies with the bias on the diode. If R_d can be made smaller than R_1, then R_0 can be decreased to the point where $R_0//R_1 = -R_d$ again. So the smaller the negative resistance, the more power can be taken from the circuit.

A particularly important characteristic of a Gunn oscillator is its power-bias swept response. Fig 6.50 shows a typical response. Power turn-on occurs at some voltage above the V-I threshold voltage, depending on the Q. For voltages above turn-on the power increases until the power peak voltage is reached, when the negative resistance is at a maximum. Going still higher in voltage causes the power to drop, and eventually oscillations cease at the turn-off voltage. Obviously it is better to operate close to peak power, except that this may make it difficult to apply frequency modulation superimposed on the dc bias.

6.7.3 Gunn oscillator cavities

There are three main types of Gunn oscillator cavity, based on different ways in which the waveguide cavity is formed: (a) the post-coupled cavity; (b) the iris-coupled cavity; and (c) the reduced-height waveguide cavity. These are illustrated in Fig 6.51.

Of these, probably the most widely used and most successful is the iris-coupled waveguide cavity. It offers many advantages, such as high stability, low fm noise, wide mechanical tunability and low susceptibility to load variations pulling the frequency (load pulling). It is a relatively simple circuit to scale in frequency and power level, and also simple to build with basic metalworking facilities.

The fundamental mode of the cavity is excited when the distance from the iris to the effective rear wall of the cavity is half a guide wavelength. Lower-power diodes (less than 25mW) work best when mounted

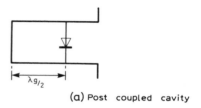

(a) Post coupled cavity

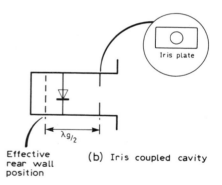

(b) Iris coupled cavity

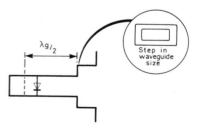

(c) Reduced height cavity

Fig 6.51. Types of Gunn oscillator cavity

centrally, while higher-power ones (greater than 200mW) work best when offset from the centre of the guide. However, the post position is not usually a critical parameter.

Output coupling is proportional to the iris size. Although circular irises are very popular, elliptic and square ones work equally well. Over-enlargement of the iris will over-couple the cavity, causing the power to drop, and eventually oscillations cease. Enlarging the iris also lowers the cavity frequency, and this change in frequency can be 5 to 10 per cent between very loose coupling and critical coupling (where the power output is a maximum). A good rule of thumb is to design the cavity to operate initially 10 per cent above the highest frequency required; it can then be tuned down to frequency using the methods described below.

6.7.4 Oscillator tuning

There are three accepted methods of tuning Gunn oscillators: (a) metallic tuning screw; (b) dielectric tuning screw; and (c) varactor tuning.

(a) Metallic tuning screw

In this method of tuning, a metallic screw is introduced through the top wall parallel to the E-field plane, which has the effect of lengthening the cavity and hence reducing its resonant frequency. The screw may be introduced into the side wall of the cavity, in which case it has the effect of shortening the cavity and hence raising its resonant frequency. Unfortunately, in this second case the electric field in the region of the side wall is relatively small so that the tuning range is also small, and hence broad-wall tuning is usually used.

The tuning rate of a metal screw depends on the degree of penetration, and ranges from a few megahertz per turn as it just enters the guide to tens of megahertz per turn when several millimetres are inserted. Consequently it is desirable that the tuning screw should be operated with the minimum penetration for the most reliable operation. This implies that the highest frequency required should be set by other means (eg by a separate bandset screw).

The chief problem with metallic screws is obtaining a reliable, precise point of contact between the screw and the cavity wall, as any mechanical shortcomings can cause erratic tuning and poor stability.

(b) Dielectric rod tuning

In this method the cavity may be loaded with a low-loss dielectric material, the behaviour of which may be considered to be similar to a dielectric capacitor acting in parallel with the cavity capacitance. Dielectric tuning screws have the great advantage over metal screws in that they require no contact with the waveguide and cause less of a disturbance to the field in the cavity, so that they afford a very smooth tuning characteristic.

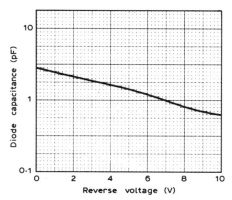

Fig 6.52. Typical plot of diode capacitance versus reverse voltage for microwave tuning varactor

A dielectric rod inserted midway between the iris and the post serves as a smooth, convenient method of tuning. The widest tuning range (up to 30 per cent) is obtained with materials of high dielectric constant (eg ceramic), though ptfe (dielectric constant 2.1) allows up to 10 per cent range which is usually satisfactory for amateur use. Nylon can also be used. Tuning range may be increased by using a larger-diameter tuning rod, but excessively large rods can cause loss of power by acting as circular waveguides, radiating the signal to the outside world and degrading the stability. At X-band the rod diameter should not exceed about 5mm. The tuning rate of the dielectric screw is linear (decreasing frequency with increasing depth of penetration) except at the extremities of the cavity, ie the screw first entering the cavity or approaching the opposite wall.

(c) Varactor tuning

The third method of tuning is by varactor. Varactor diodes have a capacitance characteristic which is continuously variable with bias voltage, from a small value at large reverse bias to a large value at forward bias (Fig 6.52). The Q of the diode is maximum at high reverse bias, decreasing steadily towards zero as the bias is reduced and reversed. A varactor may be coupled to the cavity either by a post or by a loop, though posts are most common as they make use of the same feedthrough hardware as the Gunn diode post.

The amount of tuning that a varactor can provide is controlled in two ways: (a) the capacitance of the varactor; (b) the coupling between the varactor and cavity.

Raising the capacitance reduces the amount of tuning. This is because the varactor chip, which acts as a variable capacitor, is in series with the package ribbon inductance. If the chip capacitance is very large, its reactance is quite small compared to the reactance of the ribbon. This means the series combination looks almost like the ribbon inductance alone. Since tuning is accomplished by changing the reactance of the series combination, a large chip capacitance provides very little tuning. Only when the reactance of these elements is nearly equal can considerable tuning range be achieved. When they are equal, a resonance occurs which results in the varactor being very "lossy". This is thought to be due to the high rf voltage, which occurs at resonance across each element, shifting the varactor into forward conduction where, as has already been noted, its Q is low. This effect is observed as a "suck-out" of the rf power at some point in the oscillator's tuning curve. The cure is to use a higher-capacitance varactor in order to lower the resonant frequency below the operating frequency. At 10GHz, varactors should have zero-bias capacitances exceeding 1pF. At 6GHz, this capacitance should exceed 2pF.

A post-coupled varactor will provide maximum tuning when the post is near the cavity centre. As the post is moved towards the side wall, coupling into the varactor can cause considerable power variation across its tuning range. This can only be cured by decoupling the varactor, or by using a lower-loss varactor.

On balance, the dielectric rod tuning is probably the most attractive tuning method for the amateur, being simple and easy to build.

6.7.5 Starting problems

Turn-on problems can plague a cavity oscillator and are caused by oscillations occurring at spurious cavity resonances. The problem is to identify the causes of these resonances, which are most likely to be due to: (a) higher-order cavity modes; (b) coaxial modes associated with the diode's mounting post; and (c) radial modes which are set up in the bias feedthrough structure.

Higher-order cavity modes are controlled by moving the mode cut-off frequency as high as possible, and a simple way to accomplish this is to use a reduced-height waveguide. The guide height has no effect on the fundamental-mode cut-off frequency, but higher-order modes are cut off at progressively higher frequencies by reducing the height. However, a price is paid in terms of a lower cavity Q. A good rule of thumb is to use the standard waveguide height for the next waveguide band above the desired operating frequency.

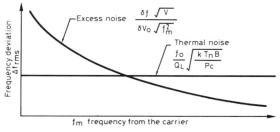

Fig 6.53. Excess and thermal components of a Gunn oscillator's fm noise spectrum

Coaxial modes have a TEM field pattern in the immediate vicinity of the diode and its post. The resonant frequency of this mode is determined by equating the combined post and diode height to half a wavelength. Coaxial modes may be interrupted by placing the diode in the middle of the post as this will double the resonant frequency, but the price to be paid is lower output power.

Another source of starting problems is the bias feedthrough structure. Ideally the feedthrough should appear as a short-circuit at all frequencies above dc. Unfortunately many choke structures can support resonant radial modes inside their sections. There is no easy solution to this problem; each situation must be treated individually. Another type of feedthrough which has been used successfully is the simple rf capacitor, either the disc or tubular type. The trick seems to be to get the capacitor as close as possible to the microwave circuit, which with a waveguide cavity oscillator means getting the capacitor very close inside the guide cavity.

6.7.6 Gunn oscillator noise

A limitation of Gunn oscillators is their high level of fm noise. Measurements have shown that this originates from two sources. The first is a thermal source which contributes a "white" deviation spectrum, and the second is a low-frequency flicker source. Gunn oscillators are bias-tunable and so bias fluctuations will randomly push the oscillator's frequency.

Analysis of thermal fm noise leads to an rms deviation which is inversely proportional to the cavity's loaded Q multiplied by the square root of the carrier power. Also, measurements have shown that the fm noise close to the carrier is directly proportional to the oscillator's voltage pushing. Thus, to minimise the noise here, the bias voltage should be adjusted to a region where the bias-frequency curve is most nearly flat. This region often occurs near the maximum safe bias voltage. A typical plot of noise against distance from the carrier for an X-band oscillator is shown in Fig 6.53.

6.7.7 Temperature effects

A sad story of erratic starting goes something like this. Someone builds an X-band oscillator which works well at room temperature. However, when taken out to a cold, windy hilltop, all oscillations in X-band suddenly cease. A check with a spectrum analyser would show that the the only output was a little power up in Ku-band.

Let us consider what happens to the swept bias response as the temperature is varied. Fig 6.54 gives the results of sweeping a diode through its bias range at -30, $+20$ and $+70°C$. No circuit changes have been made. Notice that both the turn-on voltage and peak power voltage creep up as the temperature is lowered. The creep rate is about 2V/100°C for X-band diodes. For reliable operation, you must ensure that you are operating sufficiently high above room temperature turn-on to guarantee turning on at the lowest operating temperature. Generally, a 20 per cent margin at room temperature is sufficient to assure starting down to minus 40°C. A related point is that the operating voltage should not exceed the high-temperature power-peak voltage. This is because the power will drop very quickly above its peak, and in many cases the a.m noise will also then become excessive.

A Gunn oscillator will also drift with temperature. There are two causes of this drift: (a) metal expansion and (b) diode capacitance change.

Metal expansion causes drift because the cavity grows physically longer as it is heated and this lowers the resonant frequency. The ratio of frequency change to centre frequency is the same as the ratio of length increase to original length. Copper expands at a rate of 15ppm/°C which means a frequency drift of 150kHz/°C. This is very close to that observed in an uncompensated cavity, but the agreement is only close if the cavity Q is high.

A Gunn diode's capacitance changes at a rate of approximately 10^{-4} pF/°C. This will tune the cavity by an amount that is inversely proportional to Q. For instance, a typical diode will cause a temperature frequency coefficient of –1,000kHz/°C in an X-band cavity with a Q of 10. However, for a Q of 100 the drift is reduced to –100kHz/°C. If the cavity's Q is maintained in the 100 to 1,000 region, the diode's contribution to the oscillator drift will be insignificant.

In many applications, a high degree of frequency stability with temperature is necessary. A technique called "temperature compensation" allows Gunn sources to achieve a stability approaching that of a quartz crystal.

Temperature compensation turns metal expansion to advantage for cancelling out the basic causes of drift. This is done by mounting the dielectric tuning rod inside a metal shaft which expands with temperature. If the tuner and the shaft are only connected at the one place (top of shaft), the expanding shaft will withdraw the tuner as the temperature rises. This withdrawal tunes the frequency upward while cavity expansion is tuning the frequency downward. If everything is right, one effect just cancels the other and there is no net drift. This never happens in practice, but drift under 50kHz/°C is not difficult to achieve.

6.7.8 Heatsinking

Referring again to Fig 6.48, it can be seen that heatsinking from the chip is specifically from one end. Fig 6.55 shows the outline dimensions of a typical low-power diode. With such devices, heatsinking presents no major problems. Diodes may therefore be used either way up to suit the polarity of the rest of the equipment, although the thermal stability will be improved if the heatsink end is connected to the body of the cavity rather

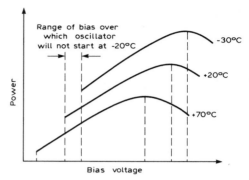

Fig 6.54. Effect of temperature on the swept response of a Gunn oscillator

than the mounting post. To improve heatsinking, the heatsink end of the diode should be a firm fit in its mount and the contact area should be maximised by removing burrs. A tiny drop of heatsink compound may be applied to this joint. Although the encapsulation is quite strong in pure compression, shear forces should be kept very small. The flanged end of the diode may therefore be a loose mechanical fit in its post to allow for any misalignment.

With high-power devices, heatsinking is crucial since several tens of watts are to be dissipated. The heat-extraction end of the diode is usually mounted in a collet arrangement, and heatsink compound used to minimise the thermal resistance of the joint. Unfortunately this joint cannot be soldered, since this would damage the diode (though soldering can be used to solve the same problem with high-power varactor diodes). Since a mounting post would be incapable of conducting the heat away fast enough, the heatsink end of the diode and its mounting collet are up against the broad face of the waveguide cavity, with suitable cooling fins on the waveguide outer surface. The usual rule with power semiconductors applies: "if it is too hot to hold, the heatsinking is inadequate". Overheating degrades the stability of the oscillator and reduces the life of the diode.

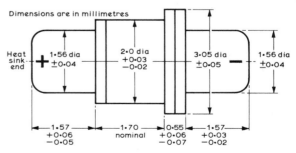

Fig 6.55. The outline dimensions of a typical low-power Gunn diode encapsulation

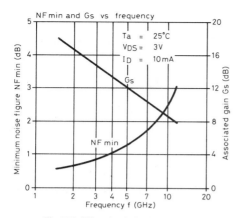

Fig 6.56. NF and gain for MGF1402 fet

6.8 AMPLIFIERS

Amplifiers can be generally classed as either small-signal or power amplifiers. Low-noise types invariably use semiconductors nowadays, the most common being the GaAsfet. Valves are still the only means of generating really high powers, though at the lower frequencies semiconductors can now produce medium powers.

6.8.1 Low-noise amplifiers

In most terrestrial microwave systems, thermal noise from the earth or lossy components in circuitry limit the sensitivity of receivers to a noise figure of around 3dB. For applications where antennas point out into space, benefits can be had from using receivers with still-lower noise figures. The term "low noise" generally refers to amplifiers with a noise figure comparable with these limits; ie under about 10dB, and usually around 3dB or better.

In order to obtain the optimum noise performance from a low-noise device, its operating conditions must be set up fairly accurately. Often, the results do not come up to expectation because one or more of the following basic requirements have not been met.

(a) The device must have a low inherent noise figure.
(b) The device must be biased to the correct operating point.
(c) The input matching must transform the source to the correct impedance at the device terminals.
(d) The input matching circuitry must have sufficiently low losses.
(e) The amplifier must be well screened to prevent variations in its surroundings either detuning it or introducing noise.
(f) The amplifier is stable.

In general, the matching conditions for optimum noise figure are not the same as those for maximum gain. Both gain and noise matching conditions are usually

quoted in the manufacturer's data sheets for the higher-performance devices.

Vacuum devices such as travelling-wave tubes can have noise figures down to about 8dB, but they cannot compete with the solidstate devices.

Transistors can provide quite low noise figures of around 1dB up to a few gigahertz, while GaAsfets can provide noise figures of small fractions of a decibel up to a few gigahertz, and 1–2dB at 10GHz. Associated gains for both devices are about 10–15dB in their appropriate frequency ranges. Fig 6.56 shows the variation of noise figure and gain for a typical fet, the MGF1402. FETs are becoming available for 10–20GHz and the progress upward in frequency is still continuing. All these devices obtain their good high frequency response by extremely small electrode geometries and spacing – because of this they are fairly delicate devices. Circuits for various bands are given in the appropriate chapters in Volume 3.

The fet can be mounted on microstrip on either glassfibre- or ptfe-loaded pcb, but these materials are quite lossy and line lengths must be minimised. The level of loss depends on the application. For ultimate low-noise figures, eg 30–50K around 1GHz, the device has to be mounted in the lowest-loss circuitry possible. All input matching circuitry should be air line. At 10GHz it is possible to mount the whole device and its circuitry in the waveguide, and this could give very low losses. However, it is a little more likely to be unstable as the waveguide cannot provide any defined impedances outside its normal operating range. One technique is to build an amplifier with very short input and output matching lines on a pcb mounted on the outside of the broad face of the guide, and use probes to couple through into the guide, as in Fig 6.57.

6.8.2 Reflection amplifiers

These rely on devices which exhibit negative resistance to provide gain. When signals are sent down a line which is terminated by a device which shows negative resistance, the power reflected from the device is larger than the incident power. This can be seen if negative values are used in the expressions for reflection coefficient.

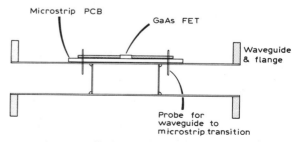

Fig 6.57. GaAsfet amplifier

The only problem is to separate the incident and reflected waves. This is usually done using a circulator, as shown in Fig 6.58. The input signals enter port 1 of the circulator, and leave at port 2 to go to the negative-resistance device, which may be a Gunn or avalanche diode. The reflected power then enters port 2 and leaves via port 3. The maximum gain is limited by the isolation of the circulator and the source and load matches, as power reflected from the load can get back to the input from port 3 to port 1.

6.8.3 Parametric amplifiers

A parametric amplifier produces gain by altering the parameters of a circuit at a frequency of many times that of the one to be amplified. This type of amplifier is capable of extremely low noise figures, eg 3K, if cooled to a low temperature, eg with liquid helium. They are used where the ultimate in low noise figure is required, such as in radio telescopes. A typical arrangement is shown in Fig 6.59. The low noise figure is mainly due to the diode being a pure reactance; it has few losses which would contribute thermal noise to the signal.

They operate by transferring energy from the high-frequency pump signal to the lower frequency to be amplified. In practice this is usually done using voltage-variable capacitors across a tuned circuit, in the form of variable-capacitance diodes. The operation of the circuit can be more easily explained if the variable capacitance were made by mechanically varying the spacing of the capacitor plates.

The tuned circuit is fed with a constant-amplitude sine wave, and the value of the capacitance can be varied either mechanically, by moving the plates apart, or electrically. When V is a maximum the capacitance is reduced, eg by separating the plates. The charge on the plates does not change so, since $Q = C \times V$, the voltage will increase. The capacitance is increased to its original value when the voltage is at zero. The plates will have been pulled apart against an attractive force, requiring work to be done: they are moved together against no force as there is no voltage across the plates. Thus there has been a net input of energy to the circuit, as illustrated in Fig 6.60.

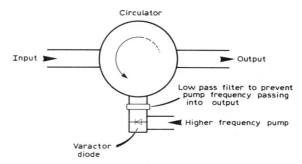

Fig 6.59. Parametric amplifier

6.8.4 Power amplifiers

At the lower microwave frequencies transistors can provide some tens of watts at fairly low gains per stage, but vacuum devices are still the best choice for higher powers, whether for amplifiers or oscillators. Powers of many hundreds of watts are possible, together with many tens of decibels of gain. Designs are given in the appropriate band chapters in Volume 3.

At higher frequencies, eg 10GHz, GaAsfets give output powers of several watts, with gains of 5 to 10dB per stage. For more power, valves must be used; more information is given later in the section on valves.

6.8.5 Distributed amplifiers

This technique is a means of combining many devices in parallel to give increased output power, or to produce very broadband amplifiers.

Capacitance from input and output terminals to earth in the device sets an upper limit to the high-frequency response by reducing the input and output impedances. The effects of this capacitance are usually removed by tuning them out with a parallel inductance, giving the familiar tuned amplifier configuration, Fig 6.61. The disadvantage of this method is that the Q required from the tuned circuit becomes very large at high frequencies, and the bandwidth is consequently very narrow. A point is finally reached where the losses in the tuned circuits become unacceptable.

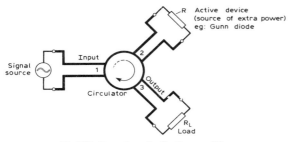

Fig 6.58. Operation of reflection amplifier

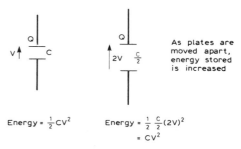

Fig 6.60. Operation of parametric amplifier

A distributed amplifier can provide a constant gain from dc to the same upper frequency limit, but this time with a completely broadband, flat response. The circuit is shown in Fig 6.62. It consists of a number of similar devices effectively connected in parallel, but used in such a way as to produce a lumped-constant transmission line using the input and output capacitances.

The load impedance presented to each device is the characteristic impedance of the transmission line,

$$Z = \sqrt{\left(\frac{L}{C}\right)}$$

The upper frequency limit is determined by the resonant frequency of the L and C combination, which forms a multi-element, low-pass filter.

The effect is to produce a wave travelling along past each device in turn, which at the same time produces an amplified version in the output line. The phase of the output signals is such that they combine to produce a wave travelling in the same direction in the output line.

One advantage of operating devices in parallel is that it reduces the output resistance, so that less matching has to be done in tuned circuits.

6.9 SWITCHES AND VARIABLE ATTENUATORS

Switches and attenuators referred to here are electrically controlled switches and attenuators; they usually consist of pin diodes (see earlier). They use the ability of the diode to change its resistance under control of the dc bias. Devices which are operated from the rf level passing through them are known as "limiters", or "t-r cells", and are made from either pin diodes or gas-discharge tubes.

6.9.1 PIN diode switches

Switches can be designed simply to reflect the incident power back to the source when in the "off" state – very little power is then dissipated in the diodes. This is the simplest design, but often signal sources do not like the reflected power, and so more frequently switches,

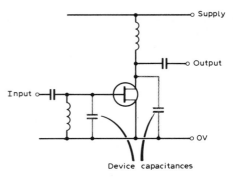

Fig 6.61. Simple fet amplifier

attenuators and modulators are designed to present constant impedances to the source and loads. This may be done using a π or T network of diodes, or using a circulator or isolator. In these cases, the unwanted power is either absorbed in the diodes or routed to some other load by the circulator or isolator. PIN diodes are capable of controlling microwave power from microwatts to kilowatts, in either pulsed or cw operation.

Examples of the diode used as a series and shunt element in a switch are shown in Fig 6.63. For the switch to be "on", the series diode must be of low resistance, and the shunt diode of high impedance. In the "off" state, these two change over. To obtain the best compromise of low insertion loss and high isolation, the values of the "on" and "off" resistances must be chosen to be suitably distributed either side of the impedance of the transmission line in which they are used.

Consider the diode in the circuit shown in Fig 6.64, mounted in a 50Ω line and used at 1GHz. The transmission loss is given by:

$$\text{Loss} = 10 \times \log(R^2 + X^2/(4 \times Z_o^2) + R/Z_o + 1)$$

When forward biased at 50mA, R_f is 1Ω, so $R = R_f + R_s = 2Ω$, and $X_l = 2 \pi \times f \times L = 2.5Ω$. In this case C_p can be ignored compared to X_l. This gives an insertion loss of 0.2dB. When reverse biased, $R_f = 10kΩ$ and,

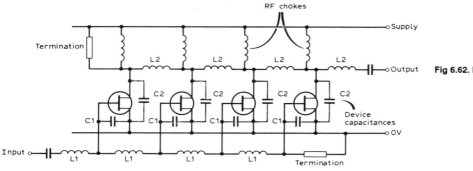

Fig 6.62. Distributed fet amplifier

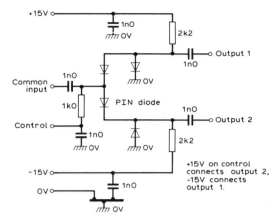

Fig 6.63. PIN diode two-way switch

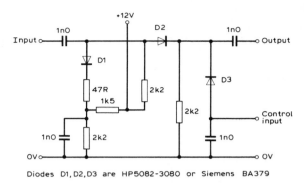

Diodes D1, D2, D3 are HP5082-3080 or Siemens BA379

Fig 6.65. Typical pin diode attenuator at uhf

ignoring C_p, the attenuation is about 24dB. The junction capacitance degrades the isolation by shunting R_r: without it the isolation would be about 40dB and independent of frequency. In reality both the insertion loss and isolation degrade as the frequency is increased. The performance can be improved for narrowband operation by adding external reactances to cancel out the diode reactances: C_p and L_p should be parallel-resonant at forward bias, and C_i and L_p in series resonance at reverse bias. The tuned switch might typically have a bandwidth of 5 per cent. Higher isolation can be obtained by cascading these circuits, at the expense of higher insertion loss and lower bandwidth.

6.9.2 PIN diode attenuators

The same circuits can be used as variable attenuators by varying the dc bias smoothly between the extremes used for switching. They are particularly useful as modulators and agc stages. Another application is to control rf levels remotely, so that the rf does not have to leave the circuit board and travel to the panel control. If

designed correctly, they are unlikely to introduce any significant intermodulation distortion – amplifier and mixer stages will usually be the limiting factor.

A pi attenuator constructed from pin diodes is shown in Fig 6.65. A simple waveguide attenuator is shown in Fig 6.66. The waveguide impedance is matched to the diode impedance by the taper. The diode is placed in a position of maximum electric field and absorbs energy from the passing wave in the waveguide. How much energy it absorbs and dissipates as heat is determined by the resistance of the diode, which is in turn determined by the bias.

6.9.3 Limiters and t-r cells

PIN diodes can be used to limit the level of rf power that they pass to protect receiver front ends, for example. They can do this automatically without bias. When a signal of sufficiently high power appears, it will saturate the intrinsic region with charge when it forward biases it, but will not be able to remove it when the voltage reverse biases it. The average current increases and the diode impedance drops, shorting the line and reflecting most of the incident power. Effectively the diode rectifies the incident power which then biases itself "on". The response time is several times the carrier lifetime, so a very short pulse of the incident power will still get through before limiting takes place; typically this time is 100ns. The diode can however cope with quite high powers – up to several kilowatts.

T-R cells perform a very similar function, and are used to protect a receiver from the transmitter output during transmit. They were originally developed for radars which required very rapid receive-transmit

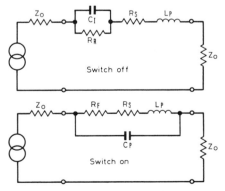

Fig 6.64. PIN diode mounted in 50 Ohm line

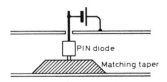

Fig 6.66. Waveguide pin diode attenuator

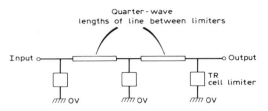

Quarter-wave lengths of line between limiters

Fig 6.67. Cascading t-r cells

changeover switching, typically under a microsecond. It is not possible to perform such changeovers mechanically, and so a purely electronic means of changeover and protection was developed. They are basically gas-discharge tubes, rather like neon bulbs, mounted across the waveguide or coaxial line. When the transmit power appears in the line, the tube strikes, and becomes a very low impedance which reflects most of the power, protecting the receiver. Special mixtures of gases and electrode geometries are used to minimise the time the tube takes to strike. Radioactive sources are sometimes included to lower the threshold.

An arrangement of quarter-wave lengths of line are used to maximise the isolation on transmit, as shown in Fig 6.67.

6.9.4 Phase shifters

PIN diodes can be used to produce phase shifts by using them to switch in extra lengths of transmission line. This has many applications in phased-array antennas and modulators. A circuit to do this using a "rat race" (hybrid combiner) is shown in Fig 6.68, omitting the biasing details for the diodes. Without the diodes and stub lines, power entering the combiner at arm 1 splits equally between arms 2 and 4, and none appears at arm 3, as can be verified by summing the path lengths around the coupler.

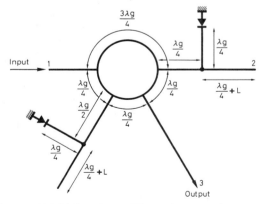

Fig 6.68. Hybrid-ring phase shifter makes use of directional properties of the coupler and used pin diodes to switch reactive lengths of line in and out of circuit

When both diodes are of low impedance, this is transformed up to a high impedance at the end of the quarter-wave lines where they join the ring. When the diodes are biased off, and of high impedance, the length of each stub is increased by the length L. Switching the diodes changes the phase of the output by $180+2\times L\times360/\lambda_g$ degrees. By suitable choice of L, any phase shift between 0 and 360° can be produced.

6.10 DEVICE PACKAGING

Packaging is one of the major factors which limits the high-frequency performance of devices. At vhf it is normal practice to keep lead lengths short compared with the wavelength, but still to use conventional packages. At microwave frequencies the wavelengths are so small that the leads within a conventional package are too long. Thus special techniques are often used; these include naked chips on stripline and integrating the mechanical mounting with the electrical matching.

6.10.1 Naked chips

In professional circuitry, such as hybrids, naked chip devices can be mounted directly on the ceramic substrate and connections made by very short (1/1,000in diameter) bond wires. This technique gives the shortest lead length of all, but requires special assembly techniques.

6.10.2 Surface-mounted devices

In coaxial or microstrip circuitry, packages use the minimum lead length possible.

Beam-lead packages have thin tape-type leads on the bottom of the package, and are intended for mounting directly on microstrip (see Fig 6.69). They are the semiconductor equivalent of chip capacitors and resistors. They can be soldered or stuck down in place using conductive epoxy adhesive and are easier to use than naked chips. Professionally, ceramic substrates are used for the microstrip but ptfe pcb can be used instead (see chapter 5).

At lower microwave frequencies wire-ended components can be mounted on stripline in a similar manner to proper surface-mounting components. Indeed, some devices are intended to be used in this way, eg transistors such as BFR91 and BFR96, which have the dimensions shown in Fig 6.70.

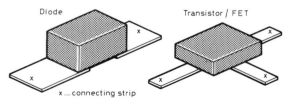

Fig 6.69. Beam-lead devices

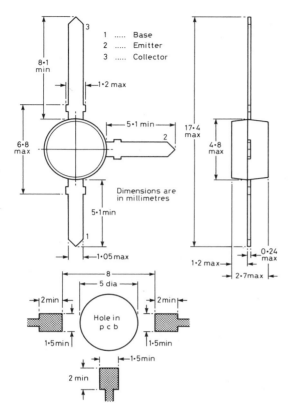

Fig 6.70. BFR91 package and recommended mounting hole

6.10.3 Cartridge mounts

The cartridge type of mount is shown in Fig 6.71 and is intended for use in coaxial line only. It operates over similar frequency ranges to the waveguide-mounted type and is often used mounted on top of a waveguide-to-coaxial transition. Common examples are the CS10B used on 10GHz and the 1N26 for 24GHz.

6.10.4 Waveguide mounts

Waveguide-mounted diodes are usually mounted in cylindrical ceramic packages. Several types are shown in Fig 6.72.

The larger package was the one originally used for microwave diodes, but is still fairly popular up to X-band as the package just fits across the waveguide. Some common types are the point-contact mixers 1N21 (for 3GHz) and 1N23 (for 10GHz). The suffixes (eg 1N23C) indicate the noise figure; later suffixes have a better performance.

A variety of smaller packages are used for Gunn diodes and more recent varactor, mixer and detector diodes. They can be used at much higher frequencies because of their lower package parasitics.

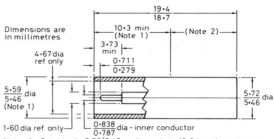

Fig 6.71. Cartridge diode (1N26 type)

Mixer diodes using these packages are often used in coaxial mounts as broadband detectors. With careful design, one mount can operate from hf up to tens of gigahertz.

6.11 MICROWAVE TUBES

The conventional valve still has a useful role to play where power is required at the lower microwave frequencies. The ubiquitous 2C39 and its many variants are capable of outputs of tens of watts at these frequencies.

At higher frequencies, travelling-wave tubes can provide high broadband gain with a high output power; klystrons and magnetrons can provide higher powers but are narrowband. These devices are most common at frequencies from a few gigahertz to 10GHz or so, although they are available at frequencies from uhf to several tens of gigahertz.

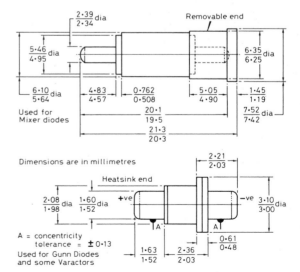

Fig 6.72. Diodes packaged for waveguide mounting

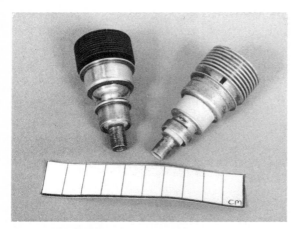

Fig 6.73. The 2C39 triode, showing glass version (left) and ceramic version (right). The anode cooling fins on the ceramic version are removable, clamped in place with Allen bolts

6.11.1 Valves

The most common microwave valve is the 2C39 triode (see Fig 6.73). It has very small electrode spacings to minimise the transit-time delays and the structure is designed so that direct, low-inductance connections can be made to all the electrodes. In fact, at these frequencies it is essential to make the valve structure part of the resonant cavity, so that the valve actually sits with its cathode in one cavity, the grid forming a screen common to both, and the anode forms the inner line of the output cavity. This makes grounded grid the natural mode of operation.

One problem with the 2C39 is that of cooling – the anode fins that are supplied with it are very difficult to force air through and it needs some structure around it to force the air to go through the fins. The alternative is to make a more suitable structure; this is often quite easy since the anode either unscrews or unclamps on some variants of the tube. The anode cavities operate at

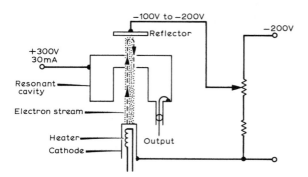

Fig 6.74. Configuration of a simple form of klystron

a high Q, and tuning drift as the valve warms up is often a problem; this is because the anode-to-grid capacitance is the only capacitance across the cavity. The only solution to this is to cool the valve adequately so the anode temperature does not change significantly, possibly using water instead of air.

6.11.2 Klystrons

A klystron is a valve-like device which usually has the necessary frequency-determining components built in, so that merely applying the appropriate working voltages is all that is required to produce rf power. The output may be via a coaxial connector, a coaxial line terminating in a waveguide probe, or via waveguide. The overall operating efficiency of a klystron is typically a few per cent.

The construction of a simple form of reflex klystron is shown schematically in Fig 6.74. A fairly conventional heater/cathode assembly is used to produce a focused electron beam which is directed at a second electrode called a "resonator". This consists of a cavity which is resonant at the design frequency of the klystron and is operated at normal valve anode voltages and currents. Built into many klystrons is a mechanism by which the dimensions of the cavity can be altered so its resonant frequency can be changed. The resonator has two central holes through which part of the electron stream can pass. Beyond the resonator is a third electrode which is biased a few hundred volts negative with respect to the cathode. Electrons approaching this electrode are repulsed and return either to the resonator body or back through the holes in the resonator. For obvious reasons, this third electrode is called a "reflector" or "repeller".

The mode of operation of a klystron is as follows. Electrons emitted by the cathode have a wide range of velocities. If the klystron is assumed to be oscillating, then the rf field existing in the holes in the resonator will affect the velocity of the electrons passing through, slower-moving electrons being retarded and faster electrons being accelerated. In other words, the electron stream is velocity-modulated at the frequency of oscillation of the klystron. Because of their higher velocity, the faster electrons travel further into the resonator/reflector space and therefore cover a relatively long path before returning into the vicinity of the resonator. However, slower electrons travel a shorter path, albeit at low velocity. The overall effect is that the time of flight of the electrons tends to be the same irrespective of initial velocity, so that electrons which enter the resonator/reflector space in a random manner return in bunches.

If these bunches pass back through the holes in the resonator at a point in the oscillation cycle such that the electrons are slowed by the rf field, then they will deliver power to the resonator and the klystron will oscillate. This oscillation will be strongest when the time of flight of the electrons in the resonator/repeller space corresponds to (n + 3/4) cycles of the resonator frequency, where n is an integer. If the bunches pass through the resonator when the field is trying to accelerate them, then energy will be removed from the resonator and oscillation will be suppressed.

The time of flight of the electrons is dependent on the reflector voltage, and therefore oscillation will occur only when the voltage is set to a number of particular voltages. This is illustrated in Fig 6.75. The reflector voltage which produces the highest peak is normally selected. Note that if the resonator cavity is tuned to a different frequency, then the reflector voltage will also have to be altered to maintain output.

Changes of the order of a few volts to the reflector voltage when the klystron is oscillating have two effects: the output power varies from zero to a maximum, and the frequency of oscillation varies in a fairly linear manner as shown by Fig 6.75. The frequency range of this electronic tuning is of the order of 10MHz before the output power falls to half its maximum value. These characteristics may be used in modulating the device by the appropriate choice of reflector voltage and modulating voltage as the following examples show.

(a) If the reflector voltage is set for maximum power output, ie operating point A in Fig 6.75, then a small modulating voltage will generate fm with little a.m. This is the operating condition usually used in amateur practice.

(b) If the reflector voltage is set midway between A and B, or A and C, then an additional modulating voltage will produce mixed a.m/fm output.

(c) If the reflector voltage is set at or just below B, and pulse modulation is applied with a peak voltage sufficient to reach point A, then a pulse/fm output will be obtained. Alternatively the reflector may be set at or just above point C.

Adjustment of the reflector voltage can also be used as a fine tuning control of limited range. This may be done either manually or by an afc voltage. The latter technique may be used to lock the oscillator on to an incoming signal or on to a local frequency standard. Because of the dependence of frequency on reflector voltage, and to a lesser extent on reflector voltage, the dc supplies should be stable and hum-free.

6.11.3 Magnetrons

Magnetrons are high-power oscillator tubes developed during the second world war, and widely used in radars and (more recently) in microwave ovens.

Physically, a typical magnetron consists of a central cylindrical cathode and a concentric cylindrical anode, the latter comprising a solid copper block with a number of cavities resonant at the frequency of operation. Fig 6.76 shows a section through the magnetron.

The device is operated with a strong axial magnetic field provided by a permanent magnet, and a potential

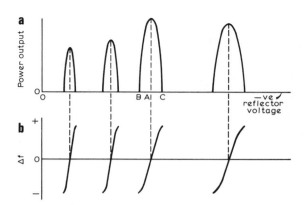

Fig 6.75. The relationship between reflector voltage of a klystron and (a) power output, (b) frequency of oscillation

of 10 to 50kV on the anode. An electron on its way from the cathode to the anode experiences a magnetic force perpendicular to its direction of motion, and an electric force radially towards the anode. Thus under normal conditions of operation, but in the absence of oscillation, an electron would travel approximately in a circle such that its farthest point from the cathode is about half-way across the cathode-anode space. However, if at this point the electron is retarded by the rf magnetic field associated with one of the cavities, it gives up some of its energy and moves in a path which brings it closer to the anode (where the rf field is stronger) than it would be in the absence of the rf field. If it arrives opposite another cavity at the moment when it is again retarded, it again gives up energy to the rf field and moves still closer to the anode.

Hence, if the right phase relationship can be maintained, some of the electrons will give up energy to several cavities in succession. Equally, of course, some

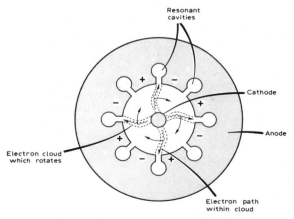

Fig 6.76. Cross section through a magnetron

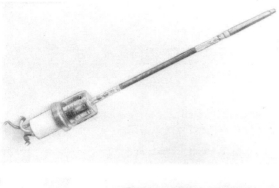

Fig 6.77. A 10W output X-band twt by STC (upper) and the same tube in its mount (lower). Note the controls for adjusting the focusing and the waveguide input and output

electrons will be accelerated by the rf field and will return to the cathode, but on balance the latter take much less energy from the rf field than the former give to it, and the net transfer of energy maintains oscillation. The power is extracted by means of a coupling loop or through a waveguide slit in one of the cavities.

Radar magnetrons are operated in pulsed mode, in pulses of the order of 1s duration at a pulse repetition frequency of the order of 1ms. High efficiency (up to 70 per cent) is obtained in this mode of operation. Since the frequency of operation is determined by the resonant frequency of the anode cavities, magnetrons are fixed-frequency devices.

While radar magnetrons are unlikely to be of use to amateurs, microwave oven magnetrons are cw devices, working at frequencies around 2.4GHz (the top end of the 13cm band) and delivering powers of the order of 1kW. In principle it should be possible to phase- or injection-lock such a tube, which would give a high-power narrowband transmitter of considerable potency.

6.11.4 Travelling-wave tube amplifiers (twts)

The history of the twt goes back to the second world war, when research into radar devices and techniques was at a particularly intense level. The twt was invented in the Nuffield Laboratory Physics Department, Birmingham University, by Rudolf Kompfner. He was seeking an alternative to the klystron with better noise performance, and in a 1946 paper he explained his reasoning:

> "One of the main reasons for the lack of sensitivity of the klystron as an amplifier is the inevitable energy exchange between the electron beam and the electric field in the rhumbatrons (resonators). It was therefore a very inviting thought to use the signal in the form of a travelling electric field (instead of a stationary one) and utilise the energy exchange between the travelling field and electrons which travel at about the same velocity."

In December 1943 the first tube gave a gain of about 8dB at a 9.1cm wavelength, with a 13dB noise figure. The work was later transferred to the Clarendon Laboratory, Oxford. Much of the mathematical theory of twt operation was developed by John R Pierce, of Bell Labs, and in 1947 Kompfner joined Pierce to continue twt research.

Nowadays, twts are by far the most widely used microwave tubes, and are employed extensively in communication and radar systems. They are especially suited to airborne applications, where their small size and light weight are valuable. Satellite communication systems are another extremely important application for the same reasons.

Practical travelling-wave tube amplifiers (twtas) have applications in both receiver and transmitter systems, and come in all shapes and sizes, but they all consist of three basic parts – the tube, the tube mount (which includes the beam focusing magnets) and the power supply.

When used as receiver rf amplifiers, they are characterised by high gain, low noise figure and wide bandwidth, and are known as twt "lnas" (low-noise amplifiers). These usually come with tube, mount and power supply in one integral unit, with no external adjustments to make – just input socket, output socket and mains-supply connections. A typical twt lna would have an octave bandwidth (eg 2 to 4GHz), 30dB gain, 8dB noise, and a saturated power output of 10mW, within a volume of 2 by 2 by 10in (see Fig 6.77).

Transmitter twtas are naturally somewhat bulkier, and often have the power supplies as a separate unit. Medium-power tubes have power outputs of up to about 10W, while high-power tubes deliver several hundred watts. The major manufacturers of twts are EMI-Varian, Ferranti, EEV, Hughes, STC, Litton, Raytheon, Siemens, Watkins-Johnson and Thomson-CSF.

Construction

The features of a typical twt are shown in Fig 6.78. The electron beam is provided by an electron gun which is

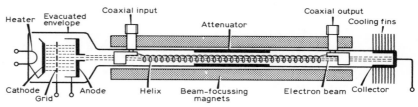

Fig 6.78. Essential features of a typical travelling wave tube

very similar to those used in crts, though the beam current is much larger. Electrons from a heated cathode are accelerated towards the anode, which is held at a high potential with respect to the cathode, and a proportion pass through a hole in the anode to produce the beam. Some tubes have a grid between the cathode, at a few tens of volts (adjustable) and negative with respect to the cathode, to control the beam current. The electron beam travels down the tube, inside the helix, to the collector, which is maintained at a high voltage with respect to the cathode. The helix is also held at a high potential but the helix current is low because of the beam focusing.

As is shown in Fig 6.79, this focusing is achieved by a magnet (either a solenoid electromagnet or permanent magnets) round the outside of the tube. An electron with a component of velocity perpendicular to the magnetic field lines experiences a restoring force tending to bring its direction parallel to the field lines.

A very large magnetic field is required to achieve good focusing by this method, which can mean a bulky, heavy magnet. However, the arrangement usually employed is called "periodic permanent magnet" (ppm) focusing, in which a number of toroidal permanent magnets of alternating polarity is arranged along the tube, as is shown in Fig 6.80; this figure also shows the contour of the beam. This arrangement greatly reduces the weight of the magnet (under ideal conditions by a factor $1/N^2$, where N is the number of magnets used). The alternative method, solenoid focusing, is generally only used in high-power, earth-station twts where size and weight are unimportant.

The input to, and output from, the helix are via coaxial connectors or occasionally via waveguide. In practice, it is impossible to provide a perfect match at these transitions, especially over a wide bandwidth, so an attenuator is used to prevent the energy reflected back down the helix causing instability. This usually takes the form of a resistive coating on the outside of the tube, though a physical discontinuity in the helix is also used in some cases. The attenuator reduces the rf

input signal, as well as the reflected signal, to nearly zero but the electron bunches set up by the signal are unaffected.

The helix itself is a delicate structure and must be provided with adequate thermal dissipation to prevent damage. In medium-power tubes the helix is often supported in between three beryllia or alumina rods, but for high-power twts alternative slow-wave structures are employed (eg coupled cavities), though usually at the expense of bandwidth. In this form, the twt resembles a klystron amplifier.

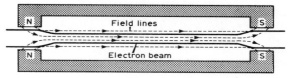

Fig 6.79. The focusing of the electron beam by the magnetic field

Theory

The essential principle of operation of a twt lies in the interaction between an electron beam and an rf signal. The velocity v of an electron beam is given by:

$$v = \sqrt{(2e \times V_a / m)}$$

where V_a is the accelerating anode voltage; e is the electron charge (1.6×10^{-19} coulomb); and m is the electron mass (9.1×10^{-31} kg).

An anode voltage of 5kV gives an electron velocity of 4×10^7 m/s. The signal would normally travel at c, the velocity of light (3×10^8 m/s), which is much faster than any "reasonable" electron beam (relativistic effects mean that the electron mass actually increases as its velocity approaches c, so that achieving electron velocities approaching c is a complicated business). If, however, the signal can be slowed down to the same velocity as the electron beam, it is possible to obtain

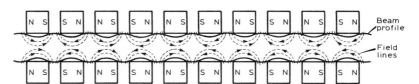

Fig 6.80. Periodic permanent-magnet focusing

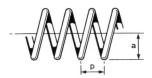

Fig 6.81. The geometry of the helix

amplification of the signal by virtue of its interaction with the beam. This is usually achieved using the helix electrode, which is simply a spiral of wire around the electron beam.

Without the helix, the signal would travel at a velocity c. With the helix, the axial signal velocity is approximately:

$$c \times \frac{p}{2\pi \times a}$$

where c is the velocity of light, and a and p are as shown in Fig 6.81, so the signal is slowed by the factor $p/(2\pi \times a)$. Note that this is independent of the signal frequency. The signal travelling along the helix is known as a "slow wave", and the helix is referred to as a "slow-wave structure". The condition for equal slow-wave and signal velocities is therefore approximately:

$$\frac{c \times p}{2\pi \times a} = \sqrt{\left(\frac{2 \times e \times V_a}{m}\right)}$$

The interaction between the beam and the slow wave takes the form of "velocity modulation" of the beam (ie some electrons are accelerated and some retarded) forming electron bunches within the beam, as with the klystron. The beam current therefore becomes modulated by the rf signal, and the bunches react with the rf

field associated with the slow wave travelling down the helix, resulting in a net transfer from the beam to the signal and consequent amplification. Since there are no resonant structures involved in this interaction, amplification is obtained over a wide bandwidth. In fact the principal factors which limit bandwidth are the input and output coupling arrangements.

Operation

A schematic circuit for a power supply for a typical twt is shown in Fig 6.82. The voltages and currents given are for a 10W output tube, but the alignment details apply to most tubes. The manufacturers' data regarding electrode voltages should be referred to before running up a particular tube. It is important that a matched load be connected to the output of the amplifier, as the power reflected from any mismatch is dissipated in the helix and can burn it out.

The beam current is controlled by the grid-cathode voltage. In modern twts, the magnetic-beam focusing is preset and no adjustment is necessary, but if the focusing is adjustable the tube should be run initially at a low beam (collector) current, and the beam-focusing magnets adjusted for minimum helix current. The helix voltage should also be set for minimum helix current.

With the tube running at its specified collector current, rf drive can be applied. The collector current will hardly change, but the helix voltage should be set for maximum output consistent with not exceeding the tube voltage or helix current ratings. If the focusing is adjustable, this should be re-adjusted for minimum helix current since the rf drive will defocus the beam slightly.

As the helix is fragile and will not dissipate more than a certain power without damage, the helix current should be metered and a current trip incorporated to cut the power supplies to the tube if it becomes excessive. The eht supplies to the tube, especially the helix, should be well smoothed since the ripple will phase-modulate the output and give a rough note.

If the collector dissipates more than about 100W it may be necessary to use a blower to cool the collector

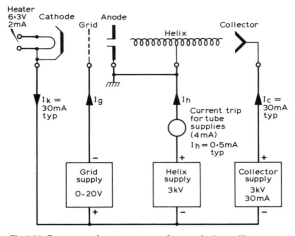

Fig 6.82. Power supply arrangements for a typical travelling-wave tube amplifier

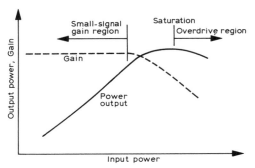

Fig 6.83. The transfer characteristic of a travelling-wave tube amplifier

end of the tube. Typical efficiency of the twta is about 10 per cent, though some modern tubes may reach 40 per cent. The transfer characteristic is essentially linear (see Fig 6.83), which permits the tube to be used to amplify ssb – one of its great advantages in an amateur context. However, as the input is increased the amplifier saturates. There is no harm to the tube in operating at saturated output power, though amplification is no longer linear, but if appreciable harmonic power is generated this may be reflected at the output transition and damage the helix through over-dissipation.

6.11.5 Backward-wave oscillators (bwos)

Analysis of wave propagation along a slow-wave structure shows that, as well as the forward wave used in the twt, there is the possibility of propagation of a so-called backward wave, whose energy travels in the reverse direction. In mathematical terms, the phase and group velocities of the forward wave are both in the positive direction while, for the backward wave, the phase velocity is in the positive direction and the group velocity is in the negative direction. (Phase velocity = w/k, group velocity = dw/dk, where w = $2\pi f$, k = $2\pi/\lambda$.) This type of device is called a "backward-wave oscillator" (bwo).

As long as the phase velocity of the wave and the electron beam velocity are synchronised, energy transfer from the beam to the wave can occur. Although for a given beam velocity there will be a number of backward-wave modes capable of interaction with the beam, in practice only one is generated. The oscillator is tuned by varying the electron beam velocity, which is achieved simply by varying the beam accelerating voltage.

In common with twts, the primary advantage of bwos is their wide bandwidth, since a precisely tunable output can be obtained over a full waveguide band (for example 8 to 12GHz) or more. BWOs have been extensively used in swept-frequency sources (sweepers), which is where the amateur is most likely to encounter them, but they are nowadays increasingly being replaced in this application by solidstate sources.

6.12 REFERENCES AND FURTHER READING

[1] *Introduction to Microwave Electronics*, T C Edwards, Edward Arnold, 1984. A good introduction to microwave semiconductors and valves.

[2] "Optimum design for high-frequency communications receivers", U L Rohde, DJ2LR, *Ham Radio* October 1976, pp10–25. Contains some fet mixer circuits.

[3] "Performance capability of active mixers", U L Rohde, DJ2LR, *Ham Radio* March 1982, pp30–35 and April 1982, pp38–43.

[4] "Design ehf mixers with minimal guesswork", S A Maas, *Microwaves* August 1979, pp66–70.

[5] "Diode applications in frequency multipliers for the microwave range", H Fleckner, DC8UG, *VHF Communications* 3/1978, pp145–153.

[6] "Harmonic generation using step-recovery diodes and srd modules", Hewlett Packard Application Note 920.

[7] "High dynamic range transistor amplifiers lossless feedback", D E Norton, *Microwave Journal* May 1976, pp53–57.

[8] "Low-noise cooled GaAsfet amplifiers", S Weinreb, *IEEE Transactions on Microwave Theory and Techniques*, Vol MTT-28, No 10, October 1980, pp1041–1054.

[9] "L-band cryogenically cooled GaAsfet amplifier", D R Williams and S Weinreb, *Microwave Journal* October 1980, pp73–76. Explains use of source inductance for gain and noise matching.

[10] *GaAs FET Principles and Technology*, ed J V DiLorenzo and D D Khandelwal, Artech House, 1982.

[11] *Microwave Diode Control Devices*, R V Garver, Artech House, 1976.

Catalogues

The following manufacturers publish catalogues containing useful applications notes: Anzac, Avantek, Minicircuits, Watkins Johnson, Alpha Industries, Microwave Associates (MA), Hewlett Packard, Mullard.

Index

Some other RSGB publications...

PRACTICAL WIRE ANTENNAS
Wire antennas offer one of the most cost-effective ways to put out a good signal on the HF bands, and this practical guide to their construction has something to interest every amateur on a budget. Theory has been kept to a minimum – instead, the author has shared his years of experience in this field.

HF ANTENNAS FOR ALL LOCATIONS
This book explains the ''why'' as well as ''how'' of hf antennas, and takes a critical look at existing designs in the light of latest developments.

AMATEUR RADIO AWARDS (third edition)
This new edition of Amateur Radio Awards gives details of major radio amateur awards throughout the world. Each award is listed in an easy to understand format giving all the information on how to achieve the award. An innovation for this edition is the provision of checklists so that the amateur can keep a record of progress. This book is essential reading for the avid award hunter and the dx chaser alike.

AMATEUR RADIO OPERATING MANUAL
Covers the essential operating techniques required for most aspects of amateur radio including station organisation, and features a comprehensive set of operating aids.

RADIO COMMUNICATION HANDBOOK
First published in 1938 and a favourite ever since, this large and comprehensive guide to the theory and practice of amateur radio takes the reader from first principles right through to such specialised fields as radio teleprinters, slow-scan television and amateur satellite communication.

WORLD PREFIX MAP
This is a superb multi-coloured wall map measuring approximately 1200mm by 830mm. It shows amateur radio country prefixes worldwide, world time zones, IARU locator grid squares, and much more. A must for the shack wall of every radio amateur.

RADIO SOCIETY OF GREAT BRITAIN
Lambda House, Cranborne, Road, Potters Bar, Herts. EN6 3JE

Notes